15 00/1

10633084

Yu. I. Khol'kin

# CHROMATOGRAPHY IN WOOD CHEMISTRY

Editor Professor V. I. Sharkov

Translated from Russian
by J. Schmorak

Israel Program for Scientific Translations
Jerusalem 1969

UNIVERSITY OF VICTORIA
LIBRARY
Victoria, B. C.

© 1969 Israel Program for Scientific Translations Ltd.

This book is a translation of

KHROMATOGRAFIYA V KHIMII DREVESINY

Izdatel'stvo "Lesnaya Promyshlennost'"
Moskva 1968

UDC 543.544 : 634.0.813



IPST Cat. No. 2212



Printed and Bound in Israel
Printed in Jerusalem by Keter Press
Binding: Wiener Bindery Ltd., Jerusalem

UNIVERSITY OF VICTORIA
LIBRARY
Victoria, B. C.

TABLE OF CONTENTS

Page

iii

## FOREWORD

The woody tissue consists of a large number of substances formed as a result of biosynthetic processes taking place in the growing tree. The structure and composition of many of these substances is very complex, and the components are highly reactive and undergo substantial changes during their separation and isolation.

The intensified study of the composition and properties of these substances, during the past few years, is due to a large extent to the application of chromatographic techniques. Thus, the development of quantitative methods of analysis of mixtures of sugars by paper chromatography and, most recently, gas-liquid chromatography, is responsible for the great advances in the structural chemistry of natural polysaccharides and their derivatives.

No less important are chromatographic methods in the study of processes which take place during the chemical treatment of the vegetal raw material and in the qualitative and quantitative analysis of semiproducts and finished industrial products of complex composition.

The reasons for the popularity of chromatographic methods are that with their aid multi-component mixtures can be identified and their component concentrations determined without a preliminary separation; the methods are rapid and highly sensitive; individual components can be isolated pure in preparative amounts; automatic chromatographs ensure continuous control of industrial processes as pick-up units in automatic production control. Purification of substances and separation of complex mixtures are now performed increasingly often by adsorption, ion exchange and chromatographic methods.

The scientific literature now includes several thousand publications on the development and application of chromatographic methods in chemistry and chemical technology of woody material and its components. Hundreds of new studies are published every year in the "Journal of Chromatography" and in other periodicals.

This book is the first attempt at a systematization and survey of the work published on the subject. In compilation, the abundant available material had to be accommodated within the limited volume of the book; accordingly, the bibliography quoted could not be made exhaustive and the reader is referred to the reviews quoted at the beginning of each chapter for an account of the early work. The lists of references include mainly work published during the last decade; publications which appeared in 1966 have been quoted only in part.

Only the most commonly used and the most recent experimental procedures have been given in detail; most experimental methods have received only a brief mention. The descriptions of chromatographic techniques in Chapter II in conjunction with the brief data given in each chapter will enable the reader in most cases to perform the analysis without recourse to the original paper, the reference to which is, however, invariably given.

The arrangement of the subject matter by chapters follows the chemical composition and structure of the components of woody tissue and the different industrial methods of chemical processing of wood.

It is my pleasant duty to acknowledge the valuable assistance of Professor V. I. Sharkov and of many Soviet and foreign workers who sent me the copies of their publications and descriptions of experimental methods.

Any comments on the book will be gratefully received.

## INTRODUCTION

### HISTORICAL

In 1903 Mikhail Semenovich Tsvet* first published /5/ an account of his new method of separation of multi-component mixtures of organic compounds which he referred to as "chromatographic." He could not have foreseen at that time that 60 years later a chromatograph would be designed /6/ by means of which trace amounts of compounds with boiling points between −182 and +72°C would be detected and determined on the surface of the Moon, neither could he have suspected that this method would result in major discoveries in many fields of natural science and would find extensive analytical and technological applications in various branches of industry.

At first, Tsvet's method was simply neglected. His contemporaries were incapable of realizing its vast potentialities despite the fact that Tsvet himself gave a detailed description of the analytical procedure and pointed out its application to the study of the multi-component mixture of organic compounds which constitute chlorophyll /7/.

As a rule, a long time elapses between the statement of the fundamental principle of a new discovery and the completion of its exhaustiv study. It is therefore particularly striking that Tsvet not merely proposed, but also developed in detail the different variants of chromatographic analysis, pointed the way to its future development and applied it to the study of extremely complex organic compounds.

The principles and potentialities of chromatography were clearly stated by Tsvet in his very first publication /5/, in which he also reported large-scale experimental analysis of chlorophyll by this method. He wrote: "The various components of the pigment mixture are distributed in the calcium carbonate column like light rays in a spectrum, so that they can be qualitatively and quantitatively analyzed" /8/. Tsvet's experiments were mostly carried out on colored substances, but he pointed out at the same time that "... these adsorption effects are not given by chlorophyll pigments alone; it is clear that the same laws are also obeyed by many other colored and colorless compounds" /8/. The extensive applications of chromatographic methods to the analysis of both colored and colorless compounds are ample confirmation of this statement.

The next step in the development of the method was Kuhn and Lederer's /9/ preparative scale separation of carotenes and xanthophylls on calcium carbonate and aluminum carbonate columns. Chromatographic adsorption analysis of colorless compounds was first realized in 1938 by Steiger and Reichstein /10/, who developed the technique of liquid chromatography. The

---

* For biography of Tsvet and history of development of the chromatographic method, see /1−4/.

transport of the separated components to the filtrate, which is the principle of liquid chromatography, had also been mentioned by Tsvet /11/:
"...substances which form strongly dissociated compounds with the powder employed move slowly downwards as rings and may be separately collected at the bottom of the tube."

Frontal development and displacement development, which are variants of chromatographic adsorption analysis, were proposed by Tiselius /12/ and developed by Claesson /13/.

Thin layer chromatography, which has been widely studied during the past 5—6 years, was proposed in 1938 by Izmailov and Shraiber /14/. A full account of the subsequent development of this method will be found in the book by Stahl /15/.

The development of the ion exchange technique must be credited to Schwab /16/, whose first publications appeared in 1937—1940.

The development of the chromatographic techniques which are at present most widely employed began with the discovery of partition chromatography by Martin and Synge /17/ in 1947; these workers applied the method to the study of the amino acid composition of proteins. Their discovery of partition chromatography and its practical applications was crowned in 1952 by the Nobel Prize /18/.

Gordon, Martin and Synge /19/ in 1943, and Consden, Gordon and Martin /20/ in 1944 described a new variant of partition chromatography in which the mixture is separated on a strip of filter paper rather than in a column. This was the beginning of paper chromatography /21/, which has been developing rapidly ever since.

The first study on gas-liquid chromatography was published by James and Martin /22/ in 1952. These workers separated volatile fatty acids from formic to dodecanoic by this method. At present the technique is developing at a fast rate and has found use in various branches of science and technology.

It will be seen that, despite being of relatively recent date, chromatographic methods occupy a very important place in analytical chemistry and have found extensive application in various fields of knowledge, including the chemistry and chemical technology of wood.

## GENERAL DESCRIPTION AND CLASSIFICATION OF CHROMATOGRAPHIC METHODS

**Definition of chromatography.** As chromatographic methods continued to develop, many different general definitions of chromatography were proposed /23, 24/, which then proved inadequate owing to subsequent discoveries of altogether new variants of the method. Other definitions /25, 26/ were so general that they would include any method for mixture separation, including rectification, fractional precipitation, etc. Most definitions, even the most satisfactory /27/, consider chromatography as a physical method of mixture separation, even though several of its variants are based on chemosorptional processes.

In our own view /31/, the following definition is sufficiently general and at the same time sufficiently specific: chromatography is a method for the separation of a mixture of substances based on the different sorptional distributions of the components between a mobile and a stationary phase.

**Classification of chromatographic methods.** One of the first classifications of chromatographic methods /29/ was based on the nature of the interaction between the substances to be separated and the sorbent. This principle was also adopted by other authors /21, 28, 30/. Other classification systems /26, 27/ are based on the state of aggregation of the phases between which the components to be separated are distributed.

A more complete classification of chromatographic methods must take into account /31/:

1. Nature of processes responsible for the separation of the components of the mixture.

2. State of aggregation of the phases.

3. Analytical technique of chromatographic analysis.

Depending on the nature of the atomic and molecular interaction of the components of the mixture with the stationary phase, the following types of chromatography may be distinguished:

1. Adsorption chromatography. The separation of the components is based on their different capacities to be sorbed on a sorbent with a highly developed active surface.

2. Partition chromatography. The components being separated have different coefficients of partition (absorption) between a mobile phase and a stationary liquid phase on the surface of an inert solid support.

3. Ion exchange chromatography. The separation of the components is based on the different exchange sorption of ions on ion-exchanging materials.

4. Chemosorptive chromatography is based on the chemical reactions between the components of the mixture and the stationary phase.

5. Molecular sieve distribution of the components. The separation is based on the different permeabilities of stationary porous phases to molecules of different sizes. A particular case of this method is gel filtration in which the stationary phase is constituted by a high-molecular substance with a given distance between the cross-linked macromolecules in the swollen state.

This classification of chromatographic methods is arbitrary, since in most cases encountered in practice the separation of the components is due to the simultaneous effect of different kinds of forces.

In accordance with the state of aggregation of the mobile and stationary phases, chromatographic methods may be classified as shown in Table 1.

TABLE 1. Chromatographic methods classified by the state of aggregation of the phases

| Stationary phase | Mobile phase | Chromatographic method |
|---|---|---|
| Solid | Liquid | Liquid adsorption chromatography. Ion exchange chromatography |
| Solid | Gas | Gas adsorption chromatography |
| Gel | Liquid | Gel filtration |
| Liquid | Liquid | Liquid partition chromatography |
| Liquid | Gas | Gas-liquid partition chromatography |

Table 1 includes only the most important chromatographic methods, which are extensively employed to separate mixtures of organic compounds.

Depending on the analytical technique, the following types of chromatography may be distinguished:

1. Column chromatography. The mobile phase, which contains the components to be separated, is passed through a layer of the stationary phase in a column. Adsorbents, ion exchangers, solid carriers with a stationary liquid layer, etc., may be used as the stationary phase. Thus, all five types of chromatographic analysis listed above may be performed by the technique of column chromatography.

Depending on the state of aggregation of the mobile phase, we distinguish:

a) liquid column chromatography (liquid as the mobile phase);

b) gas chromatography (gas as the mobile phase).

Gas chromatography, which includes gas adsorption and gas-liquid chromatography, involves extensive use of complicated automatic instruments — chromatographs — which are designed on a principle different from that of the instruments used in liquid column chromatography. Accordingly, gas chromatography is an independent method of chromatographic analysis as far as the experimental technique is concerned.

2. Paper chromatography is a particular case of partition chromatography. The stationary phase is constituted by a liquid layer on the surface of a solid support, which is chromatographic grade paper; the mobile liquid moves through the paper downwards (descending technique) or upwards (ascending technique). The distribution of the components between the two liquid phases may be accompanied by sorptional processes on the surface of the cellulose fibers in the paper.

3. Thin layer chromatography. The stationary phase, which consists of a thin sorbent layer, is applied to the surface of a plate (most often a glass plate) and the liquid phase is passed through by the ascending or descending technique. Depending on the nature of the sorbent, adsorption, partition and other types of chromatographic separation may be performed.

As has been pointed out above, chromatographic separation may involve the simultaneous effects of different processes on the components to be separated, so that it is difficult to assign a given technique to a given type of chromatography. An example of such difficulties is the separation of mixtures on cellulose and cellulose derivatives, in particular diethylaminoethylcellulose which acts as ion exchanger. In this case the component separation is the result of ion exchange, partition and sorptional processes /15/ at the same time.

Accordingly, our description of the experimental techniques and special chapters on the analysis of the components of wood and the products of its chemical processing will be based on the classification by different experimental techniques. The treatment of theoretical problems is based on the nature of the interaction of the components to be separated with the stationary phase.


GENERAL SCHEME OF CHROMATOGRAPHIC
ANALYSIS OF WOOD

At present the study of almost all components of wood and nonwoody plants can be performed by chromatographic methods. Chromatographic methods can also be applied to the analysis of any product of chemical processing of wood. Advanced studies in the chemistry of wood can no longer be carried out without using chromatographic methods; in the near future, chromatographic methods will be generally employed in routine control of industrial production based on the chemical technology of wood.

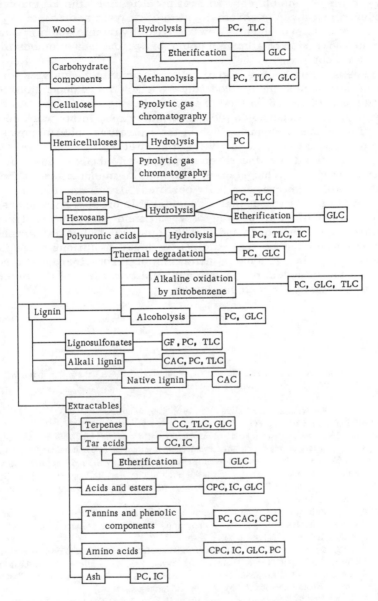

FIGURE 1. General scheme for chromatographic analysis of wood:

CAC − column adsorption chromatography; CPC − column partition chromatography PC − paper chromatography; TLC − thin layer chromatography; GLC − gas–liquid chromatography; GF − gel filtration; IC − ion exchange chromatography; CC − column chromatography.

Figure 1 illustrates the possibilities offered by chromatographic methods in the study of the composition and structure of the components of wood. Only a few of the methods — those most frequently employed in wood chemistry — have been shown in the figure.

As distinct from conventional analytical procedures, which can be employed for dozens of years without modification, the experimental procedures employed in chromatographic analysis are constantly modified with a view to improvement. New analytical variants and new analytical techniques give rise to a large number of various new methods of analysis of the same component.

In general, this book will give several variants of analysis for each group of compounds; the method actually chosen will depend on the technical facilities available and on the purpose of the determination. As a rule, a research worker about to employ chromatography in his work does not simply follow the procedure given in the literature, but improves it by choosing the most suitable analytical parameters.

The classification of the chromatographic methods of analysis of industrial products is based on the methods of manufacture of these products, with allowance for their chemical structure.

It should be pointed out that a considerable proportion of industrial products of chemical processing of wood cannot as yet be analyzed by chromatographic methods, and that the number of chromatographic techniques which can be applied directly under conditions of industrial production are few. Extensive utilization of chromatography in routine control of technological processes and quality control of the finished products are tasks for the near future.

BIBLIOGRAPHY

1. RIKHTER, A. A. and T. A. KRASNOSEL'SKAYA. — In: Sbornik "M. S. Tsvet, Khromatograficheskii analiz," pp. 215—228; 229—231. Izd. AN SSSR. 1946.
2. DHÈRÈ, C. — Candollea (Genève), Vol. 10: 23—73. 1943.
3. WEIL, H. and T. I. WILLIAMS. — Nature, Vol. 166: 1000. 1950; Vol. 167: 906. 1951.
4. ZECHMEISTER, L. — Nature, Vol. 167: 405. 1951.
5. TSVET, M. S. O novoi kategorii adsorbtsionnykh yavlenii i o primenenii ikh k biokhimicheskomu analizu (A New Category of Adsorption Effects and Their Application to Biochemical Analysis). — Trudy Varshavskogo Obshchestva Estestvovedeniya, Otdel Biologii, Vol. 14: 20—30. 1903. Quoted from sbornik: "M. S. Tsvet. Khromatograficheskii adsorbtsionnyi analiz," pp. 9—29. Izd. AN SSSR. 1946.
6. WILHITE, W. F. and M. R. BURNELL. "Analys. Instrumentat. 1963." — Pittsburgh, Pa, Instrum. Soc. America, pp. 113—130. 1963.
7. TSVET, M. S. Khlorofilly v rastitel'nom i zhivotnom mire (Chlorophylls in the Vegetal and Animal Kingdom). Varshava. 1910. Quoted from sbornik: "M. S. Tsvet. Khromatograficheskii adsorbtsionnyi analiz," p. 150. — Izd. AN SSSR. 1946.
8. TSVET, M. S. Fiziko-khimicheskie issledovaniya khlorofilla. Adsorbtsiya (Physicochemical Studies on Chlorophyll. Adsorption). — In: Sbornik "M. S. Tsvet. Khromatograficheskii adsorbtsionnyi analiz." Izbrannye raboty, Izd. AN SSSR, Leningrad. 1946. [Also contained in the German "Michael Tswett's erste chromatografische Schrift" by M. Woelm. Eschwege. 1954.]
9. KUHN, R. and E. LEDERER. — Naturwissenschaften, Vol. 19: 306. 1931; Ber., Vol. 64: 1349. 1931.
10. STEIGER, M. and T. REICHSTEIN. — Helv. Chim. Acta, Vol. 21: 546. 1938.
11. TSVET, M. S. Adsorbtsionnyi analiz i khromatograficheskii method (Adsorption Analysis and Chromatographic Method). — In: Sbornik "M. S. Tsvet. Khromatograficheskii adsorbtsionnyi analiz." Izbrannye raboty, Izd. AN SSSR, Leningrad. 1946. [Also contained in the German "Berichte," Vol. 24: 384—393. 1906.]

12. TISELIUS, A. − Arkiv Kemi., Mineral., Geol., Vol. 14B, No. 22. 1940; Vol. 14B, No. 32. 1941; Vol. 15B, No. 6. 1941.
13. CLAESSON, S. Studies on Adsorption and Adsorption Analysis. − Almquist. 1946.
14. IZMAILOV, N. A. and M. S. SHRAIBER. − Farmatsiya, No. 3:1. 1938.
15. STAHL, B., editor. Dünnschicht-Chromatographie, ein Laboratoriumshandbuch. − Berlin. 1962. [Russian translation from the German. 1965.]
16. SCHWAB, G. − Angew. Chem., Vol. 50:546. 1937; Vol. 50:691. 1937; Vol. 51:709. 1938; Vol. 52:666. 1939; Vol. 53:39. 1949.
17. MARTIN, A. J. P. and R. L. M. SYNGE. − Biochem. J., Vol. 35:1358. 1941.
18. Discovery, 14(I):2−3. 1953.
19. GORDON, A. H., A. J. P. MARTIN, and R. L. M. SYNGE. − Biochem. J. Vol. 37:86. 1943.
20. CONSDEN, R., A. H. GORDON, and A. J. P. MARTIN. − Biochem. J., Vol. 38:224. 1944.
21. HAIS, I. M. and K. MACEK, editors. Paper Chromatography [Russian translation from the Czech. 1962.]
22. JAMES, A. T. and A. J. P. MARTIN. − Biochem. J., Vol. 50:679−690. 1952.
23. RACHINSKII, V. V. − Trudy Komissii po Analiticheskoi Khimii, 6(9):21−29. 1955.
24. SHEMYAKIN, F. M. − In: Sbornik "Khromatografiya, ee teoriya i primenenie," pp. 17−20. Izd. AN SSSR. 1960.
25. MOKRUSHIN, S. G. − Kolloidnyi Zhurnal, 19(6):759−760. 1957.
26. BAYER, E. Gas Chromatography. [Russian translation from the German. − Elsevier. 1961.]
27. SHINGLYAR, M. Gazovaya khromatografiya v praktike (The Practice of Gas Chromatography), p. 9. − Izdatel'stvo Khimiya. 1964.
28. RACHINSKII, V. V. Vvedenie v obshchuyu teoriyu dinamiki sorbtsii i khromatografii (Introduction to the General Theory of Sorption and Chromatography), p. 16. − Izdatel'stvo Nauka. 1964.
29. GAPON, E. N. and T. B. GAPON. − Doklady AN SSSR, Vol. 59:921. 1948; Vol. 60:817. 1948; Uspekhi Khimii, Vol. 17:452. 1948.
30. RACHINSKII, V. V. and T. B. GAPON. Khromatografiya v biologii (Chromatography in Biology). − Izd. AN SSSR. 1953.
31. KHOL'KIN, Yu. I. − Obshchaya i Prikladnaya Khimiya, Vol. 1, No. 2. 1968.

*Chapter I*

## THEORETICAL PRINCIPLES OF CHROMATOGRAPHY

### 1. ADSORPTION CHROMATOGRAPHY

Since this book is mainly concerned with problems of practical significance, only enough theory will be given to enable the reader to understand the relationships governing the separation of mixtures by the different chromatographic techniques.

In adsorption chromatography component separation takes place as a result of different sorbabilities of different components on the active surface. The accumulation of the substances from the mobile phase (solution) on the active adsorbent is the result of intermolecular adsorptional forces.

At constant temperature and pressure, the amount of the substance adsorbed (adsorbate) will depend only on its nature and on the nature and structure of the adsorbent surface.

In classical adsorption chromatography, the components to be separated are in a liquid solvent (liquid chromatography); in the recent technique of gas adsorption chromatography the mixture is separated as a vapor in the medium of a carrier gas.

The equilibrium state of adsorption (static state) may be described by means of adsorption isotherms. These isotherms are a graphic representation of the adsorption as a function of the concentration of the solution (or the partial pressure of the gas) at constant temperature.

Monomolecular adsorption is most often described with the aid of Langmuir's equation, developed on the assumption that the molecules of the adsorbate cannot freely move along the surface and do not interact with one another:

$$A = \frac{Kp}{1 + Kp}, \tag{1}$$

where $A = \frac{a}{a_m}$ is the proportion of the occupied surface ( $a$ is the magnitude of the adsorption per unit weight of adsorbent and $a_m$ is the limiting adsorption in a continuous monolayer); $p$ is the pressure of the adsorbate and $K$ is the equilibrium constant of the interaction between the adsorbent and the adsorbate.

If the molecules of the adsorbate interact with one another, the equation becomes more complicated. The simplest expression is that of Kiselev /1/:

$$p = \frac{A}{K_I (1 - A)(1 + K_{II} A)}, \tag{2}$$

where $K_I$ and $K_{II}$ are constants which approximately represent the attraction between adsorbate and adsorbent and between adsorbate and adsorbate.

These equations describe the equilibrium state of adsorption. In chromatography, a more important factor is the kinetics and dynamics of the adsorption.

The adsorption kinetics, i. e., the rate of adsorption of the adsorbate, are determined by the diffusion of the adsorbate molecules from the bulk of the phase to the interphase boundary (external diffusion), by the motion of the adsorbate along the surface (surface diffusion) and by the diffusion within the pores (internal diffusion). The adsorption rate is determined by the equation

$$u = \frac{p\delta}{2\pi kTm}(1 - A),\qquad (3)$$

where $u$ is the rate of physical adsorption, $\delta$ is the probability that an impact on the surface will result in adsorption, $m$ is the mass of the gas molecule, $k$ is the Boltzmann constant and $(1 - A)$ is the vacant surface of the adsorbent.

The equation leaves out the rate of diffusion of the adsorbate molecules to the surface.

Chromatographic separation of mixture components is greatly affected by the streaming rate and by the pore size of the adsorbent which determines the rate of penetration of the molecules into the grains of the adsorbent. For a detailed mathematical description of the dynamics of these processes see /2/.

Chromatographic analysis on columns usually comprises three variants of the method: frontal, elution and displacement. In the frontal analysis, the mixture is passed through the column with the sorbent. The elution of frontal analysis contains a number of zones, the least strongly sorbed component constituting the first zone; in each subsequent zone the number of components in the filtrate increases. In elution chromatography, the mixture to be separated is introduced into the column and the pure solvent is then passed through the column, whereby the mixture components become separated into individual zones. Displacement analysis consists in displacing the components of the mixture from the column by the introduction of a new substance which is sorbed more strongly than some or all the components of the mixture. All three variants are widely employed in column adsorption and partition chromatography.


## 2. PARTITION CHROMATOGRAPHY

In partition chromatography component separation is based on their differing solubilities in the stationary liquid phase on the surface of an inert solid support.

In practice, it is quite difficult to select a perfectly inert carrier, so that separation by partition chromatography takes place not only by partition but also by adsorption and ion exchange. In theoretical treatment these secondary processes are neglected /3 — 5/.

Partition chromatography includes the most important analytical techniques: column chromatography on sorbents such as silica gel, starch, etc., paper chromatography, gas-liquid chromatography and thin layer chromatography on certain sorbents. In the first two cases the components are distributed between two liquid phases, while in gas-liquid chromatography the gas is the mobile phase while the liquid is the stationary phase.

The distribution of the material between the two phases is described by the following equation which is generally valid for all types of partition chromatography:

$$K = \frac{C_s}{C_m},$$

(1)

where $K$ is the distribution coefficient and $C_s$ and $C_m$ are the concentrations of the component in the stationary and the mobile phases, expressed in the same units.

## Partition chromatography on columns

In the theoretical treatment of partition chromatography it is usually assumed that the substance is instantaneously distributed between the two phases, that it does not diffuse along the column and that the time of formation of the mobile phase front tends to zero. If the effect of all these factors on the chromatographic analysis is allowed for, the resulting equations become much more complex /5/; for a more rigid mathematical analysis of the dynamics of sorption and chromatography, see /2/.

In partition chromatography on columns the length of the column zone $l$ occupied by each component and the rate of motion of the zone front are of importance. The shorter the zone length of each component, and the larger the differences between the rate of motion of the fronts of individual zones, the better will be the separation.

When a given volume $V$ of the solution of the mixture to be separated is introduced in the top of the column, an equilibrium distribution of the component to be determined between the mobile and the stationary solvents is established. In the top layer of the column the concentration of the material in the mobile solvent $C_m$ will be equal to its initial concentration $C_0$, while in the lower layers it will decrease to zero. The length of the zone with solution of the concentration $C_0$ will be $l$. The concentration of the component in the stationary solvent $C_s$ in this zone will be

$$C_s = KC_0.$$

(2)

The length of the zone of this component is found from the material balance equation:

$$VC_0 = A_m l C_m + A_s l C_s,$$

(3)

where $A_m$ and $A_s$ are cross-sectional areas of the column occupied by mobile and stationary solvents, respectively, $VC_0$ is the amount of the component introduced into the column, $A_m l C_m$ is the amount of the component in the mobile solvent and $A_s l C_s$ is its amount in the stationary solvent.

13

Substituting $C_m = C_0$ and $C_s = KC_0$ (equation (2)) into equation (3), we obtain

$$V = A_m l + A_s l K,$$ (4)

whence

$$l = \frac{V}{A_m + KA_s}.$$ (5)

Experimental determination of $A_m$ and $A_s$ is difficult; accordingly it is more common to use the volumes of the mobile and stationary solvents $V_m$ and $V_s$ contained in 1 ml of the column. Equation (5) then assumes the form

$$l = \frac{V}{A (V_m + KV_s)},$$ (6)

where $A$ is the cross section of the column.

The rate of motion of the zone front on passing through a volume $V$ of the solution is determined by the equation:

$$\frac{l}{V} = \frac{1}{A (V_m + KV_s)}.$$ (7)

in the frontal analysis technique.

When using the elution technique, the zone displacement $x$ is given by the equation

$$x = \frac{V'}{A_m + KA_s},$$ (8)

where $V'$ is the volume of the pure solvent.

The zone displacement per unit volume of solvent (rate of shift of the zone) is given by

$$\frac{x}{V'} = \frac{1}{A_m + KA_s}.$$ (9)

The zone displacement may also be expressed through a dimensionless coefficient $R$, equal to the ratio between the zone displacement $x$ and the volume of the pure solvent passed through:

$$R = \frac{xA}{V'}.$$ (10)

Substituting the value of $\frac{x}{V'}$ from (9) we find

$$R = \frac{A}{A_m + KA_s}$$ (11)

or

$$R = \frac{1}{V_m + KV_s}.$$ (12)

Thus, the mobility of each component is a function of the distribution coefficient $K$ only and is independent of the concentration of the component and the presence of other components in the mixture. The zone of each component will move at its own constant rate given by

$$\frac{x}{V'} = \frac{1}{A_m + KA_s} = \frac{R}{A}.$$ (13)

The larger the difference in the values of $K$ between the components to be separated, the larger the difference in the values of $x$ and the better the separation, i.e., $x = f(K)$.

Complete separation between two components is achieved if

$$x_2 - x_1 \geqslant l_1,$$ (14)

where $x_1$ and $x_2$ are the zone displacements of the two components.

In order for these components to be fully separated, a volume $V'$ of the pure solvent equal to

$$V' = \frac{R_1 V}{R_2 - R_1}.$$ (15)

must be passed through the column.

The second condition for a complete separation of the components is a minimum length $H$ of the column. This will be achieved if $x_2 \geqslant x_1 + l_1$. Then $H \geqslant x_2$.

From equation (13) we have $x_2 = \frac{R_2 V'}{A}$, i.e., $H \geqslant \frac{R_2 V'}{A}$. Substituting the value of $R$ from equation (15), we find

$$H \geqslant \frac{R_2 R_1}{R_2 - R_1} \cdot \frac{V}{A}.$$ (16)

Figure 2 shows an example of an ideal separation of two components with respective zone lengths $l_1$ and $l_2$ and zone displacements $x_1$ and $x_2$ when the column is washed with the solvent.

In experimental practice, longitudinal diffusion results in the blurring of the head and tail boundaries of the zones, so that the elution curves of chromatographic analysis have the form of peaks. Symmetrical peaks are to be aimed at for a quantitative evaluation of the chromatogram, but the blurring of the boundaries may sometimes be unequal and asymmetric peaks may occasionally be obtained. Blurring of the tail boundary is most frequently encountered owing to the adsorption effects given by many solid carriers, and also to association and dissociation of the substances to be separated.

## Partition chromatography on paper

In paper chromatography the shift of the component to be analyzed is expressed as the coefficient $R_f$, which is analogous to the coefficient       in partition chromatography on columns (equation (11)). The coefficient $R_f$

is experimentally determined by dividing the displacement $x$ of the zone of the substance (or, rather, the position of the maximum substance concentration in the spot) by the displacement $x_f$ of the solvent front

$$R_f = \frac{x}{x_f}. \qquad (17)$$

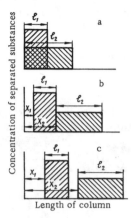

FIGURE 2. Situation of zones in partition chromatography:

a – primary chromatogram; b and c – eluted chromatograms.

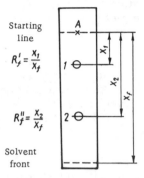

FIGURE 3. Experimental determination of $R_f$ on paper chromatogram:

$x_1$, $x_2$, $x_f$ – displacements of component I, component II and solvent respectively; $R_f'$ and $R_f''$ – distribution coefficients of components I and II respectively.

From equation (13) we have $x = \dfrac{RV'}{A}$ ; $x_f = \dfrac{V'}{A_m}$. . Substituting in (17), we obtain

$$R_f = \frac{RV'A_m}{AV'} = \frac{RA_m}{A}. \qquad (18)$$

Substituting the value of $R$ given by (11) we have

$$R_f = \frac{A}{A_m + KA_s}, \qquad (19)$$

where $A_m$ and $A_s$ are the fractions of the cross section of the chromatographic paper occupied by the mobile and stationary phases, respectively.

Since $R_f$ values can be readily determined by experiment, the following equation is most often used in the determination of the distribution coefficient /6/:

$$K = \frac{A_m}{A_s}\left(\frac{1}{R_f} - 1\right). \qquad (20)$$

16

It follows from equation (20) that the constant $R_f$ is constant for any given substance if $A_m/A_s$ is constant. The $R_f$-value can be altered by other processes including adsorption and ion exchange, their effects depending on the properties of the paper employed. The $R_f$-value may also be affected by the experimental technique.

Figure 3 shows an example of the determination of $R_f$-values from the displacement values $x_1$ and $x_2$ of the components of the mixture /5/.

Occasionally, the coefficient $R_p$ is calculated rather than $R_f$. It is obtained by dividing the displacement $x$ of the zone center of the substance to be analyzed by the displacement of a standard substance $x_p$:

$$R_p = \frac{x}{x_p} . \qquad (21)$$

The standard (etalon), which is introduced into the mixture, is a substance of a structure similar to that of the compounds being analyzed, but not originally present in the mixture.

These relationships are also valid for thin layer partition chromatography.

**Gas-liquid partition chromatography**

The characteristic feature of gas-liquid chromatography (GLC) is that the mobile phase is a gas, while the stationary phase is a liquid.

The behavior of a substance in the chromatographic column is commonly described by the theory of theoretical plates, adapted to gas-liquid chromatography by James and Martin /7/. It is assumed that the solid carrier exerts no sorptional effects and that the gas phase is not compressible.

The separation of components by GLC is described in terms of two main parameters: extraction coefficient $k$ and distribution coefficient $K$ /8/. The extraction coefficient $k$ is determined as the quotient of the fraction of the substance $P$ in the liquid phase and the fraction of the substance $q$ in the gas phase in any part of the column:

$$k = \frac{P}{q} . \qquad (22)$$

Since $P+q = 1$, we may write

$$\frac{k}{k+1} + \frac{1}{k+1} = 1. \qquad (23)$$

The distribution coefficient is defined as the ratio of the concentration of the substance in the liquid phase to its concentration in the gas phase in the theoretical plate:

$$K = \frac{C_s}{C_m} ,$$

i.e., the general equation (1), which describes the distribution of the components between two phases, also applies to GLC.

17

The distribution coefficient $K$ is connected with the extraction coefficient $k$ by the equation

$$K = \frac{kV_m}{V_s} = k\beta, \qquad \beta = \frac{V_m}{V_s}: \qquad (24)$$

where $V_m$ and $V_s$ are the volumes of mobile and stationary phases in the column.

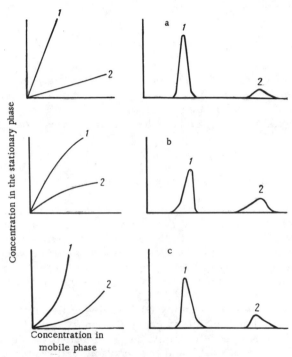

FIGURE 4. Chromatograms of various isotherms:

a — gas–liquid chromatography; b and c — gas–adsorption chromatography. 1 and 2 — components being separated.

In partition chromatography, the distribution coefficient is independent of the concentration of the component, so that the distribution isotherm is linear. The formation of asymmetric peaks in GLC is usually due to the adsorption effect exerted by the solid carrier, i. e., to a combination of gas-liquid partition chromatography with gas-adsorption chromatography. Adsorption isotherms are, as a rule, curvilinear, as a result of which gas-adsorption chromatography usually yields asymmetric peaks. Figure 4 shows an example of the connection between the shapes of isotherms and the shapes of the peaks in the adsorption chromatography of the respective components /9/.

Let us consider the processes which take place in the chromatographic column in terms of the theory of theoretical plates. A theoretical plate corresponds to that part of the column in which the elementary act of distribution of the component between the two phases takes place, in accordance with the corresponding partition isotherm. The main parameter of a theoretical plate is its height, which depends on the structure of the components, i. e., on their distribution coefficients.

Van Deemter et al. /10/ proposed the following expression for the height $H$ of the theoretical plate:

$$H = 2\lambda d_p + 2\frac{\gamma D_g}{u} + \frac{8}{\pi^2}\frac{k'}{(1+k')^2}\frac{d_f^2 u}{D_1}, \qquad (25)$$

where $k' = \frac{KA_1}{A_g}$

The meanings of the symbols are as follows:

$\lambda$ — static heterogeneity of packing;

$d_p$ — particle diameter of solid support;

$\gamma$ — coefficient of curvature of pore channels;

$D_g$, $D_1$ — coefficients of molecular diffusion in gas and liquid phase respectively;

$u$ — linear velocity of carrier gas;

$d_f$ — average thickness of the liquid film;

$A_g$ and $A_1$ — proportions of column cross section occupied by gas and liquid phases, respectively.

Equation (25) is frequently written in the simplified form

$$H = A + \frac{B}{u} + Cu, \qquad (26)$$

where $A$ is a term representing the effect of turbulent diffusion of the component, $B$ is a term representing the effect of molecular diffusion of the vapor of the component along the column and $C$ is the resistance of the packing in the column to the mass transfer of the component.

Thus, the widening of the peak, as measured by the height of the theoretical plate, depends on the diffusion of the substance to be determined, dissolved in the stationary liquid phase, on certain physical parameters of the column and on the velocity of the carrier gas which determines the residence time of the sample in the column.

Basing himself on the kinetic theory of chromatography, Zhukhovitskii /11/ proposed the following formula for the calculation of $H$:

$$H = A + \frac{B}{u} + M_c u^{\frac{1}{2}} + Cu, \qquad (27)$$

where $M_c$ is the coefficient of external diffusion mass transfer.

It is not possible to determine experimentally all the data which are required to perform the calculations according to the above equations. Accordingly, the plate height is obtained in practice by dividing the length of the column by the number of theoretical plates.

The number of plates $n$ is readily found from the equation

$$y = \frac{4(V_R - V_0)}{\sqrt{n}}. \qquad (28)$$

where $y$ is the width of the peak corresponding to the intercepts made by the tangents at the inflection points with the zero line; $V_R$ is the held volume of the component and $V_0$ is the held volume of air.

It is interesting to compare the theoretical limits of separating powers of gas and liquid chromatography. The selectivity of the separation, which is connected with the distribution coefficient, will depend on the molecular structure of the substances to be separated, and in this respect the differenc between gas and liquid chromatography is inconsiderable /12/. In principle, however, liquid chromatography can ensure 100 — 1000 times more theoretical plates than can gas chromatography.

In actual practice, gas chromatography has been recently used more frequently due to the convenience in handling, the availability of high-efficiency selective liquid stationary phases, rapidity and other advantages offered by this technique.

In principle, it is very difficult to give a comparative evaluation of the different chromatographic techniques. The choice will be dictated in each case by the task in hand.

## 3. FUNDAMENTAL PRINCIPLES OF ION EXCHANGE AND ION EXCHANGE CHROMATOGRAPHY

For theoretical principles of ion exchange see the monograph /13/, books /5, 14, 15 — 17/ and papers /18 — 21/.

**Static ion exchange.** Ion exchange takes place between the solution and a solid phase-ion exchanger, which absorbs a certain species of ions from solution and releases an equivalent amount of other ions into solution. The ion exchanger can absorb cations or anions by exchange sorption, so that all ion exchangers are cation exchangers or anion exchangers. Ion exchange is a reversible process.

The mechanism of ion exchange may be described by the following general scheme /19/:

$$\dot{Z}_2 R_{Z_1} m_1 + Z_1 m_2^{\pm Z_1} \rightleftarrows Z_1 R_{Z_2} m_2 + Z_2 m_1^{\pm Z_1}, \tag{1}$$

where $m_1$, $m_2$ are the ions being exchanged, $R$ is the organic part of the ion exchanger and $Z$ are the valencies of the respective ions. The ion exchange equilibrium will then be described by the equation:

$$\left| \frac{A_1^{\frac{1}{Z_1}}}{A_2^{\frac{1}{Z_2}}} = K_{1,2} \frac{a_1^{\frac{1}{Z_1}}}{a_2^{\frac{1}{Z_2}}} \right., \tag{2}$$

where $|A_1$ and $|A_2$ are the activities of the ions sorbed in the exchanger, $|a_1$ and $|a_2$ are the activities of the ions sorbed in the liquid phase, $|Z_1$ and $|Z_2$ are the charges on the ions being exchanged, and $|K_{1,2}$ is the ion exchange constant, which is the thermodynamic characteristic of ion exchange equilibrium.

This equation is valid in the absence of molecular sorption and of the interaction between the ions and the organic matrix of the ion exchanger. The pore size of the exchanger should not interfere with the penetration of the ions into the bulk of the exchanger.

Experimentally, the ion exchange constant $K$ is determined from the volume of the solution $V_{max}$ (in ml), which must be passed through the column with the exchanger to obtain a maximum on the elution curve /5/:

$$K = \frac{V_{max}[H^+]^z}{a^z V},$$ (3)

where $[H^+]$ is the hydrogen ion concentration in the wash solution of the acid, g-eq/ml; $Z$ is the charge on the ion being displaced, $a$ is the full capacity of the exchanger, meq/ml, and $V$ is the volume of the exchanger, ml.

A somewhat different expression for the description of the statics of ion exchange has been deduced from Donnan's theory. The selectivity coefficient $k$ is found from the formula /13/:

$$k = \frac{[M_1]_n^{Z_2}[M_2]^{Z_1}}{[M_2]_n^{Z_1}[M_1]^{Z_2}},$$ (4)

where $[M]$ and $[M]_n$ are the concentrations of the exchanged ions 1 and 2 in solution and in the exchanger phase.

Equations (2) and (4) are based on the Law of Mass Action and are valid for both cation and anion exchange.

The selectivity constant $k$ differs from the ion exchange constant $K$ in that the concentrations rather than the activities of the ions are employed in formula (4).

An important property of ion exchange equilibrium is the distribution coefficient, which is the ratio between the equilibrium concentration of the ion in the exchanger and its equilibrium concentration in solution.

The separation coefficient, which is equal to the ratio between the distribution coefficients of two ions, determined under the same conditions, shows the relative sorbabilities of two ions under the given conditions. This index is very important in choosing the experimental conditions for separation of mixtures of ions by ion exchange.

Ion separation is significantly affected not only by the size of the ionic charge, but also by the ionic structure. Organic cations, carrying equal charges, can be arranged in the following affinity sequence of the values of selectivity coefficients when sorbed on phenolsulfonate exchanger with a low degree of cross-linking /22/:

$$NH_4^+ < (CH_3)_4 N^+ < (C_2H_5)_4 N^+ < (CH_3)_3 (h - C_5H_{11}) N^+ <$$
$$< C_6H_5 (CH_3)_2 (C_2H_2N^+) < C_6H_5 (C_6H_5CH_2) (CH_3)_2 N^+.$$

In addition to the size of the charge and the ionic structure, the ion exchange process is strongly affected by the properties of the exchanger, concentration of the ions in the solution, tendency of the ions to complex formation, experimental temperature and other factors /13/. The most important of these is the identity of the ion exchanger, which may be a strongly acid or a weakly acid cation exchanger or a strongly basic or a weakly basic anion exchanger.

**Ion exchange kinetics and ion exchange chromatography.** The considerations given above concerned the equilibrium state of ion exchange. In actual practice, however, mixture separation by ion exchange chromatography will be strongly affected by diffusion processes. On the whole, ion transfer by ion exchange may be said to comprise three stages:

1) ion transport from the bulk of the solution to the surface of the exchanger;

2) ion transport inside the exchanger (diffusion in the grains of the exchanger);

3) ion exchange proper.

Similar stages of mass transport from the mobile to the stationary phase, diffusion of components within the stationary phase and the binding of the components by the stationary phase are typical of all chromatographic processes.

The rate of diffusional processes depends on the difference in ion concentrations between the solution and the exchanger phase, structure of the exchanger matrix, nature of solvent, temperature and other factors. In strongly swollen polystyrene ion exchangers, in which the ions have free access to the exchangeable groups of the exchanger, the equilibrium is established within a few seconds. On the other hand, in sulfonated phenol resins with a compact structure it takes as long as 90 minutes for the equilibrium to become established /13/.

Ion exchange proper takes place, as a rule, very rapidly, so that the overall rate of the process is determined by diffusion factors.

Ion exchange chromatography involves in practice only one kind of chromatographic technique — elution analysis. This comprises two stages— absorption of the components to be separated and the stage of the elution (regeneration of the exchanger).

**Sorption of organic compounds.** The sorption of numerous organic compounds and of dissociating high-molecular compounds (polyelectrolytes) takes place not only by polar ion sorption, but also by other types of binding. For this reason the laws of ion exchange which have just been discussed and which have been established for inorganic ions, will frequently not be valid in the case of the sorption of dissociating organic compounds.

In the chemistry of wood the technique of ion exchange is used for both inorganic ions (e. g., in the purification of hydrolyzates of polysaccharides) and in the separation of organic ions and polyelectrolytes (isolation and separation of uronic acids, oligosaccharides, etc.).

BIBLIOGRAPHY

1. KISELEV, A. V. — Vestnik AN SSSR, No. 10 : 43. 1957; Kolloidnyi Zhurnal, 20(3) : 338. 1958.
2. RACHINSKII, V. V. Vvedenie v obshchuyu teoriyu dinamiki sorbtsii i khromatografii (Introduction to the General Theory of Sorption Dynamics and Chromatography). — Izdatel'stvo Nauka. 1964.
3. MARTIN, A. I. P. and R. L. M. SYNGE. — Biochem. J., Vol. 35 : 1358. 1941.
4. FUKS, N. A. — Uspekhi Khimii, Vol. 17 : 45. 1948.
5. OL'SHANOVA, K. M. et al. Rukovodstvo po ionoobmennoi i osadochnoi khromatografii (Textbook of Ion Exchange and Precipitation Chromatography). — Izdatel'stvo Khimiya. 1965.
6. HAIS, I. M. and K. MACEK, editors. Paper Chromatography. [Russian translation from the Czech. 1962.]
7. JAMES, A. T. and A. J. P. MARTIN. — Biochem. J., Vol. 50 : 679. 1952.
8. NOGARE, S. D. and R. S. JUVET. Theory and Practice of Gas-Liquid Chromatography. [Russian translation. 1966.]
9. SHINGLYAR, M. Gazovaya khromatografiya v praktike (The Practice of Gas Chromatography), p. 15. — Izdatel'stvo Khimiya. 1964.
10. DEEMTER, van J. J., F. J. ZUIDERWEG, and A. KLINKENBERG. — Chem. Eng. Sci., Vol. 5 : 271. 1956.

11.  ZHUKHOVITSKII, A. A. — Uspekhi Khimii, Vol. 28 : 1201. 1959.

12.  GIDDINGS, J. C. — Analyt. Chem., 36(10) : 1890 −1892. 1964; 37(1) : 60 −63. 1965.

13.  SAMUELSON, O. Ion Exchange Separation in Analytical Chemistry. — Wiley. 1963.

14.  SAMSONOV, G. V. Sorbtsiya i khromatografiya antibiotikov (Sorption and Chromatography of Antibiotics). — Izd. AN SSSR. 1960.

15.  SALDADZE, K. M., A. B. PASHKOV, and V. S. TITOV. Ionoobmennye vysokomolekulyarnye soedineniya (High-Molecular Ion Exchangers). Moskva. 1960.

16.  HELFFERICH, F. Ion Exchangers. [Russian translation from the German. 1962.]

17.  DORFNER, K. Ionenaustausch–Chromatographie. — Berlin, Akad. Verb. 1963.

18.  TUNITSKII, N. N. Teoriya ionoobmennykh protsessov (Theory of Ion Exchange Processes). — In: Sbornik "Materialy soveshchaniya po primeneniyu ionnogo obmena v tsvetnoi metalurgii." 1957.

19.  NIKOL'SKII, B. P. and V. I. PARAMONOVA. — Uspekhi Khimii, 8(10) : 1535−1567. 1939.

20.  GAPON, E. N., T. B. GAPON, and E. S. ZHUPAKHINA. Teoriya ionoobmennoi khromatografii (Theory of Ion Exchange Chromatography). — In: Sbornik "Issledovaniya v oblasti khromatografii," pp. 5 −29. Izd. AN SSSR. 1952.

21.  RACHINSKII, V. V. — In: Sbornik "Issledovaniya v oblasti ionoobmennoi khromatografii," pp. 5 −37. Izd. AN SSSR.

22.  KRESSMAN, T. R. E. and J. A. KITCHENER. — Chem. Soc., pp. 1190, 1201, 1208, 1211. 1949.

*Chapter II*

## TECHNIQUE OF CHROMATOGRAPHIC ANALYSIS

The chromatographic techniques are extremely numerous; this chapter will accordingly deal only with the most important chromatographic experimental techniques which are employed in the chemistry and chemical technology of wood.

## 1. COLUMN CHROMATOGRAPHY

Column chromatography is a classical variant of chromatographic analysis, which was used by M. S. Tsvet.

A diagram of the apparatus used in column chromatographic analysis is shown in Figure 5. Eluate fractions are now frequently collected in automatic fraction collectors of different designs.

Sorbents which are mostly employed in adsorption, partition and ion exchange chromatography on columns include alumina, activated carbon, silica gel and different ion exchange materials. They have been described in numerous monographs and textbooks /1 — 3, etc./.

Nonpolar and weakly polar substances in polar solvents (e. g., in aqueous solutions) are mostly separated on activated carbons of different brands. The following brands are at present available on the market: BAU — activated birchwood charcoal, comminuted, particle size 1 — 5 mm; SKT — granulated peat charcoal, 1.5 — 2.7 mm; AR-3 — granulated recovered charcoal, 2 — 5 mm; KAD — iodine active; KAD — ground charcoal; AG-3 — granulated, for gas chromatography, 1.5 — 2.7 mm; OU — clarifying charcoal powder including brand A (dry, alkaline) and brand B (moist, acid); AGN — ground pellets 0.5 — 10.0 mm, and AG-5 — fine granulated for gas chromatography, 1.0 — 1.5 mm.

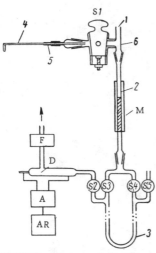

FIGURE 5. Diagram of chromato-graphic apparatus with a micro-reactor:

1 — inlet of carrier gas; 2 — quartz tube; 3 — chromatographic column; 4 — glass rod; 5 — rubber gasket; 6 — T-tube; S1—S5 - stopcocks; M — microreactor; D — dosimeter; F — flowmeter; A — amplifier; AR — automatic recorder.

Before filling the columns, active charcoal or other sorbent is ground, sieved into fractions, and the filled column washed with the pure solvent for a long time in order to extract the soluble matter from the sorbent.

The activity of hydrophilic sorbents used in the extraction and separation of polar substances in nonpolar solvents is greatly affected by the water content in the sorbent. The widely employed active alumina has five degrees of activity, corresponding to its water content.

Brockmann activities of alumina

| Degree of activity | I | II | III | IV | V |
|---|---|---|---|---|---|
| Water content, % | 0 | 3 | 6 | 10 | 15 |

The water content is also a major factor in the activity of silica gel.

In order to prevent changes in the activity of the sorbents, they must be kept in airtight vessels.

**Ion exchange chromatography.** The most frequently used ion exchangers are polystyrene-divinylbenzene resins with introduced structurally bound exchangeable groups /4/. In these copolymers divinylbenzene forms the cross links between the polystyrene chains. The contents of divinylbenzene in the resin may vary. The degree of cross linking is expressed as percent divinylbenzene added during copolymerization, marked as the number following a multiplication sign in the brand names of certain ion exchangers. For example, Dowex-50(×8) means that the sulfonated Dowex-50 resin contains 8% divinylbenzene.

TABLE 2. Approximate exchange capacities of Dowex-50 and Dowex-50W cation exchangers

| Exchange capacity | Degree of cross linking, % divinylbenzene | | | | | |
|---|---|---|---|---|---|---|
| | 1 | 2 | 4 | 8 | 12 | 16 |
| Meq/g of dry ion exchanger | 5.2 | 5.2 | 5.2 | 5.1 | 5.0 | 4.9 |
| Meq/ml of ion exchanger | 0.4 | 0.7 | 1.1 | 1.8 | 2.3 | 2.5 |

The effect of the degree of cross linking on the exchange capacity of cation exchangers Dowex-50 and Dowex-50W in the $H^+$-form is shown in Table 2.

Cation exchangers are usually prepared by sulfonating copolymers of styrene and divinylbenzene or phenolic polymers; in order to impart anion-exchanging properties to the resin, quaternary ammonium salt groups are introduced.

A general description of a number of ion exchangers manufactured in the Soviet Union /5/ is shown in Table 3.

These ion exchange materials are obtained from different synthetic resins.

Different sorbents made of cellulose, in particular ion-exchanging varieties of cellulose, have been increasingly frequently used in chromatographic work during the past few years /6/. Different kinds of natural celluloses and technical cellulose preparations are weak ion exchangers /7/. The exchange capacity of cellulose is enhanced by replacing the hydroxyls by ionogenic groups such as $-COOH, -SO_3H, -PO_3H_2$ etc. The capacity of cellulose could be increased by a factor of 10—15 in this way.

TABLE 3. Properties of a number of ion exchangers manufactured in the Soviet Union

| Brand | Main functional groups | Specific volume of swollen ion exchanger, ml/gram | Exchange capacity, meq/liter |
|-------|------------------------|---------------------------------------------------|------------------------------|
| Cation exchangers | | | |
| KU-1 | $-SO_3H$, OH | 3.0 | 4.5−5.1 |
| KU-2 | $-SO_3H$ | 2.5 | 4.9−5.1 |
| SDV | $-SO_3H$ | 3.2 | 4.2 |
| SBS | $-SO_3H$ | 2.5 | 3.0 |
| KB-4 | $-COOH$ | − | 10.0 |
| Anion exchangers | | | |
| AV-17 | $-\overset{+}{N}(CH_3)_3$ | − | 4.3 |
| EDE-10P | $=NH$, $\equiv N$, $\overset{+}{N}(CH_3)_3$ | 3.4 | 8.5−9.0 |
| AN-2F | $=NH$, $\equiv N$ | 2.5−2.8 | 10.6 |
| N−0 | $=NH$, $\equiv N$ | − | 4.1 |
| AN-1 | $-NH_2$, $=NH$ | 2.2−2.5 | 4.0 |

The ion-exchanging celluloses described in Table 4 /6/ are most often employed in chromatographic and sorptional work.

A cellulose ether /8/ with $\alpha$-pyridinecarbinol with a low degree of substitution ($\gamma$ about 10), which is a typical weakly basic anion exchanger with a maximum capacity of about 0.5 meq/g, has been prepared and is used in chromatographic separation of viruses.

Wood chemistry makes extensive use of DEAE-cellulose, several examples of the application of which are given in the following chapters.

The technique of utilization of ion-exchange cellulose has the following special features. It has been said above that most ion exchangers are used in column chromatography, but ion-exchanger celluloses can also be used in paper and in thin layer chromatography.

All kinds of ion-exchanger celluloses which have been reduced to powder are employed in c o l u m n  c h r o m a t o g r a p h y. Displacement and elution methods are used with these sorbents. Buffer solutions are used as eluents and solvents, owing to the amphoteric nature of dissociated organic compounds, whose ionogenic groups differ in their degree of dissociation.

The separation efficiency of components on ion-exchanger celluloses is strongly affected by the pH of the eluent and its content of salts and other dissolved substances. A frequently employed technique is gradient displacement analysis in which the pH and the electrolyte composition of the eluent is made to vary continuously or stepwise. In gradient analysis the blurring of the zones of the separated substances is prevented.

In addition to ion-exchanger cellulose powders, ion-exchanger chromatographic paper for analytical purposes is also available on the market.

Buffer solutions are also employed in ion-exchanger p a p e r c h r o m a t o g r a p h y.

Ion-exchanger cellulose powders to be used in t h i n  l a y e r c h r o m a t o g r a p h y have also recently appeared on the market. The plates are prepared in the usual way.

26

TABLE 4. Types of ion-exchanger cellulose

| Brand symbol | Full name | Ionogenic group | Acidic or basic | Full absorption capacity,* meq/g |
|---|---|---|---|---|
| | | Cation exchangers | | |
| SE | Sulfoethylcellulose | $-C_2H_4 \cdot SO_3H$ | Strongly acid | 0.4 |
| P | Phosphorylated cellulose | $-PO_3H_2$ | " " | 0.8 |
| CE | Carboxyethylcellulose | $-C_2H_4COOH$ | Medium acid | 0.7 |
| CM | Carboxymethylcellulose | $-CH_2COOH$ | Weakly acid | 0.7 |
| C | Carboxycellulose (oxycellulose) | $-COOH$ | " " | 0.7 |
| | | Anion exchangers | | |
| PAB | p-Aminobenzylcellulose | $-CH_2 \cdot C_6H_4NH_2$ | Weakly basic | 0.6 |
| ECTEOLA | Reaction product of ethylchlorohydrin and triethylamine with cellulose | Structure of ionogenic group not established | " " | 0.5 |
| AE | Aminoethylcellulose | $-C_2H_4NH_2$ | " " | 0.7 |
| TEAE | Reaction product of ethyl bromide with DEAE-cellulose | Structure of ionogenic group not established | Medium basic | |
| DEAE | Diethylaminoethyl-cellulose | $-C_2H_4N(C_2H_5)_2$ | " " | 1.0 |
| CE | Guanidoethylcellulose | $-C_2H_4NHC - NH_2NH_2OH$ | " " | 0.7 |

\* Approximate values of absorptive capacity.

Ion-exchanger cellulose chromatography is used in the analysis of products obtained from wood, e.g., in the separation of gluconic and glucuronic acids /9/. Thin layer chromatography on ion-exchanger cellulose has been reviewed in detail /10/.

## 2. PAPER CHROMATOGRAPHY

The technique of chromatographic analysis on paper has been discussed in detail /11/. The quality of the chromatographic separation is affected to a major extent by the quality of the chromatographic paper, properties of the solvent and the analytical technique.

**Chromatographic paper.** The paper used for chromatographic and electrophoretic separations must meet the following specifications /12/: a uniform structure, a large imbibition capacity, adequate wet strength, chemical purity, absence of bivalent cations (copper and iron), absence of reducing compounds, aromatic compounds, carboxylated compounds and other substances interfering with the identification of the components to be separated by their color reactions.

In the Soviet Union, chromatographic grade paper is produced in two brands — slow brand M and fast brand B. Technical parameters /13/ of new types of chromatographic and electrophoretic grade paper have been laid down in order to permit a better control of the elution rate of the components.

27

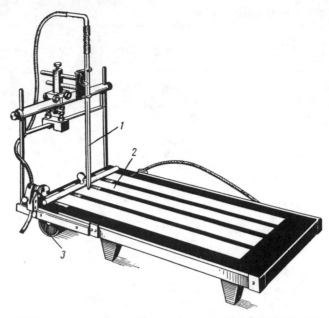

FIGURE 6. Chromatographic table for the application of samples to paper.

**Analytical technique.** The accuracy and the reproducibility of chromatographic analysis on paper are strongly affected by the technique of application of the samples to be separated to the paper and the subsequent separation technique. A convenient set of paper chromatographic appliances "Chropa" (German Democratic Republic) is now available on the market.

The sample is applied to the strips of chromatographic paper on the chromatographic table in Figure 6. The mixture is applied to paper strips 2 with the aid of a micropipet 1. In order to accelerate the evaporation of the solvent, a section of the paper strips is warmed by an electric bulb 3.

Different automatic instruments have been proposed /14/ for use in the application of the mixture to the paper, in which the duration of contact between the micropipet and the paper can be adjusted and the desired spot diameters and time intervals between applications necessary for the sample to dry thus ensured.

Figure 7 gives a diagram of airtight chambers for descending (a) and ascending (b) chromatographic analysis. The paper strips 1 with the samples of the mixtures to be separated are placed in airtight chambers 2 and covered with lids 3. In the descending technique of elution the solvent system is placed in the top trough 4, into which the top ends of the paper strips are dipped and are held in place by the glass insert 5. In ascending chromatography the solvent is placed in the lower trough 6 into which the lower ends of the paper strips are immersed. The solvent system is fed into the troughs from funnel 7.

The separated substances are revealed by spraying or wetting the paper strips with special reagents, after which the chromatograms are dried in an oven.

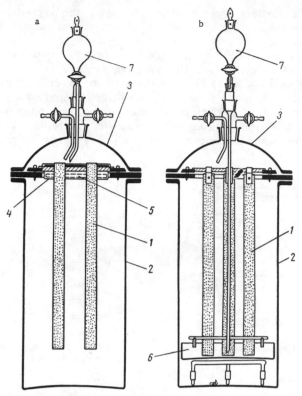

FIGURE 7. Apparatus used in paper chromatography:

a – descending technique; b – ascending technique.

**Electrophoretic chromatography.** One variety of chromatography is paper electrophoresis. A constant potential difference of a few hundred volts is applied to the ends of the moist paper sheet, when the mixtures are separated in the resulting electric field in accordance with the charges they carry. In this method buffer solutions with definite pH values serve as the stationary phase.

## 3. THIN LAYER CHROMATOGRAPHY

For a detailed review of thin layer chromatographic techniques, see Stahl /15/ and other publications /2/.

Sorbents used in thin layer chromatography are those employed in column chromatography. The finely ground sorbent (particle size $0.07 - 0.10$ mm) is applied in a thin layer ($250 - 300\,\mu$) onto the surface of a square-shaped or rectangular glass plate. In order to obtain a uniform, solid layer, the sorbent is first mixed with plaster in the amount of about 5% of its own weight. Water is added to the mixture, when a paste is obtained, which is brought onto the plate with the aid of special instruments. After drying and simultaneous thermal activation the plate is ready for use.

A nonbound sorbent layer may also be used; the dry sorbent powder is uniformly spread over the glass plate. The layer thickness in this technique is 0.5 — 1 mm.

Figure 8 represents the simplest device for the preparation of a nonbound sorbent layer. Glass rod 1, with short segments of rubber tubing 2 at both ends, is used as a roller to even up the sorbent layer 3 on glass plate 4.

Mixtures of substances to be separated are applied onto plates prepared in this manner, placed in airtight chambers and developed by the ascending or descending technique, using various solvent systems. The analytical technique is the same as that employed in paper chromatography.

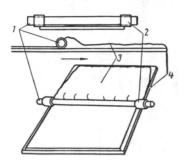

FIGURE 8. Preparation of nonbound thin sorbent layer.

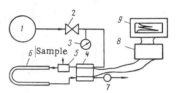

FIGURE 9. Principal diagram of a gas chromatograph.

## 4. GAS CHROMATOGRAPHY

The most sophisticated apparatus is employed in gas chromatography /16 — 23/. Several dozen chromatographs are now on the market and are used for analytical and preparative purposes and for automatic control of technological processes. Despite some differences in design, all chromatographs have the same basic units, which are schematically represented in Figure 9.

The carrier gas is stored under pressure in tank 1, from which it is led through reducing valve 2 to the comparison cell of detector 4 and block 5 of the sample inlet. During analysis the pressure must be constant; this is controlled with the aid of manometer 3 mounted on a carrier gas line. A liquid or gaseous sample of the mixture to be analyzed is fed into block 5. The temperature in the block should be higher than the boiling points of the liquid components to ensure their rapid vaporization. The vapor mixture of the substances to be analyzed is entrained with the carrier gas into column 6, which is filled with the adsorbent (gas adsorption chromatography) or with an inert solid support covered with a layer of a liquid stationary phase (gas-liquid chromatography). The components in the column are separated into zones as a result of sorption or partition processes. The carrier gas issuing from the column, which contains the separated components of the mixture, enters the measuring cell of detector 4, and thence through the gas flowmeter 7 into the atmosphere.

TABLE 5. General description of laboratory type chromatographs produced in the Soviet Union

| Brand of instrument | Manufacturer | Detectors | Type of columns | Working temperature of columns, °C | Accessory units |
|---|---|---|---|---|---|
| KhL-3 | SKB ANN Mosneftekip | Katharometer with thermistors | Packed | 20-120 | |
| KhL-4 | The same | Katharometer with threads and thermistors | " | 20-170 | |
| KhL-7, pyrolytic | " " | Katharometer | " | Up to 150 | Pyrolysis block |
| KhT-2MU | VNIIKA-neftegaz | Thermochemical | " | Up to 200 | Temperature programming up to 200°C. Furnace for eluate conversion |
| KhT-63 | The same | Katharometer, densimeter, triode ionization, flame ionization, thermochemical | " | 30-300 (KhT-63-I) | Temperature programming up to 450°C (KhT-63-P) |
| KhT-8K | " " | Heat conductance | Adsorption | Room temperature | Instrument serves to analyze constant gas flows |
| KhT-7 | " " | Heat conductance, density, flame ionization, argon, ionization-discharge | | 35-500 | Stepwise and exponential programming of column temperature |
| LKhM-7a | SKB IOKh AN SSSR | Katharometer, flame ionization | Packed capillary | 40-300 | Programming of column temperature |
| Tsvet-1-64 | Dzerzhinskii Branch of OKBA | Flame ionization katharometer | Packed and capillary | Up to 300 | |
| Tsvet-2-65 | Dzerzhinskii Branch of OKBA | Differential flame ionization | Packed capillary micro-packed | Up to 400 | Programmed rise in temperature |
| Preparative chromatograph | Dzerzhinskii Branch of OKBA | Flame ionization | Preparative packed | 40-250 | Preparative fraction collector |
| UKh-1 | Vyrusskii Gas Analyzer Plant | Heat conductance | Preparative packed | | Two columns operating by different mechanisms |
| Khromass MKh1307 | | Mass analyzer | Capillary | Positive and negative | |
| Khromass-1 MKh5301 | SKB AP AN SSSR | The same | The same | | Cinematographic and photographic recording of mass spectra |
| KhG-1301 | SKB AP | Ionization | Capillary | Up to 200 | |
| KhG-1302 | | Heat conductance, argon triode, coaxial and microdetector, electron capture | U-shaped | 30-300 | Programming of column temperature; sampler |
| PAKhV-02 preparative | SKB INKhS AN SSSR | Katharometer | Preparative | 50-350 | Sampler |

TABLE 6. Industrial chromatographs

| Brand of instrument | Manufacturer | Detectors | Type of columns | Working temperature of columns, °C | Accessory units |
|---|---|---|---|---|---|
| RKh-1 | Dzerzhinskii Branch of OKBA | Flame ionization | U-shaped, packed | Up to 80 | |
| RKh-5 | The same | The same | The same | Up to 180 | |
| KhTP-2b industrial chroma-thermograph | VNIIKA-neftegaz | | | | Automatic operation |
| KhTP-2 | The same | | | | Analysis of pyrolytic gases |
| KhTP-63 | Mosneftekip | Heat conductance, density, argon | Packed | 40–250 | Automatic operation |

The measuring and the comparison cells of the detector are connected in a bridge circuit which is put out of balance only if the carrier gas passing through the detector contains a component of the mixture. The signal is sent from the detector to amplifier 8 and is picked up by an automatic recorder 9 which usually consists of different kinds of electronic potentiometers.

Table 5 gives a general description of a number of laboratory chromatographs manufactured in the Soviet Union on an industrial scale. It will be seen that there is a large selection of instruments of different types, with the aid of which very different analytical tasks may be performed. Improved new models of these instruments appear every year.

In the past few years chromatographs for industrial use have also become available. These are used for routine production control, consisting as a rule of the analysis of gaseous samples. These chromatograms are provided with units for automatic sample withdrawal from the production line and their introduction into the chromatograph in accordance with a preset program. Table 6 shows the general characteristics of a number of industrial chromatographs produced in the Soviet Union.

The separating power is determined in the first instance by the working parameters of the chromatographic column; the nature and the granulometric composition of the adsorbent or the solid carrier, properties and content of the stationary liquid phase, temperature and rate of flow of the carrier gas. The minimum number of components which can be determined depends on the design of the detector, which is the second most important part of any chromatograph.

We shall now discuss the design features of the main units of a gas chromatograph and their working parameters.

**Chromatographic column**

The columns are made of stainless steel, copper or glass. U-shaped, W-shaped and coil-shaped columns are most frequently used. In order to facilitate packing, the column often consist of individual sections connected in series. The column is thermostated at the working temperature in special thermostats to within ± (0.05 — 1.0)°. Air thermostats with forced (fan) air circulation are most often used.

Chromatographs designed during the past few years ensure a programmed increase in the temperature of the column during chromatographic separation. The maximum working temperature of most commercially available chromatographs is 220 — 300°; high-temperature chromatographs work up to 450 — 500°, but at such high temperatures it is difficult to select a suitable liquid stationary phase.

In addition to packed columns, capillary columns are extensively used in gas-liquid chromatography. The liquid phase is applied directly onto the walls of thin (0.3 — 3.0 mm) but very long (30 — 100 meters) chromatographic columns.

Gas chromatography on packed capillary columns may be used /24/ to determine trace impurities in the major component and in rapid analyses of gaseous hydrocarbons.

In gas-adsorption chromatography the chromatographic column is filled with adsorbents, usually activated carbons, different kinds of graphitized carbon black, silica gel and porous glass, zeolites of types A and X, Teflon and certain other porous polymers /25/.

In gas-liquid chromatography the separation will be mainly determined by the properties of the liquid stationary phase held on the inert support.

Stationary liquid phases consist of different high-boiling compounds, some of which are described in Table 7.

One important specification such phases must meet is a low volatility at the temperatures of mixture separations.

Gerrard et al. /26/ studied the effect of temperature on the stability and volatility of a number of stationary phases used in gas chromatography. They showed that practically all stationary phases are to a certain extent volatile and many of them are decomposed at relatively low temperatures.

Table 8 shows the decomposition temperatures of some stationary phases.

The effective service life of a chromatographic column will depend not only on the temperature but also on other factors. It has been shown, in particular /27/, that if the phase surface is contaminated by surface-active substances, the effective operation of the column is greatly decreased.

The separation effect of mixtures by gas-liquid chromatography is also affected by the properties of the solid support. Most such supports are prepared by subjecting kieselguhr to a special treatment.

Solid supports "chromosorb" of different brands, marketed by Johns-Manville Co., are widely employed in gas-liquid chromatography.

Chromosorb P is ignited diatomaceous earth; it has the largest specific surface of all chromosorbs, and strongly adsorbs polar compounds on the surface.

Chromosorb W is ignited diatomaceous earth with a specific surface 4 times smaller than Chromosorb P.

Chromosorb G is diatomaceous earth with the highest separating power; the adsorption surface is weakly developed; suitable for separation of polar substances. It is hard and its bulk density is low; it is enough to add 5% of stationary liquid phase.

Chromosorb A is diatomaceous earth with a modified surface, suitable for the application of a large amount of the liquid phase.

TABLE 7. Description of liquid stationary phases most commonly employed is gas–liquid chromatography

| Name | Molecular weight | Density at 20°C, g/cm³ | Maximum working temperature, °C | Recommended solvents |
|---|---|---|---|---|
| Apiezones: | | | | |
| N | – | – | 270 | |
| K | – | – | 285 | Methylene chloride, hexane, toluene, diethyl ether |
| M | – | – | 300 | |
| O | – | – | 300 | |
| L | – | – | 350 | |
| Benzyldiphenyl | 244.34 | – | 120 | Hexane, toluene |
| Vaseline | – | 0.875 – 0.890 | 130 | Hexane, diethyl ether petroleum ether |
| Dibutyl phthalate | 278.36 | 1.045 | 120 | Methylene chloride, acetone, chloroform |
| Dioctyl phthalate | 390.56 | 0.978 – 0.985 | 140 | The same |
| Dinonyl phthalate | 418.62 | 0.967 – 0.972 | 150 | "     " |
| Di-(2-ethylhexyl) sebacate | 426.6 | 0.913 | 175 | "     " |
| Diglycerol | 166.18 | 1.27 | 150 | Chloroform, methanol |
| β,β'–Dicyanodiethyl ether (β,β'–Oxydipropionitrile) | 124.15 | 1.05 | 90 | Methylene chloride, acetone |
| β,β'–Dicyanodiethyl sulfide (β,β'–Thiodipropionitrile) | 140.22 | 1.111 | 70 | Methylene chloride, acetone |
| Polyethylene glycols (carbowaxes): | | (at 25°) | | |
| 300 | 300 | – | 100 | |
| 400 | 400 | – | 100 | |
| 600 | 600 | – | 125 | |
| 1000 | 1000 | – | 160 | Methylene chloride, acetone; chloroform, methanol |
| 1500 | 1500 | – | 175 | |
| 2000 | 2000 | – | 180 | |
| 4000 | 4000 | – | 200 | |
| 6000 | 6000 | – | 225 | |
| 20M | 20000 | – | 250 | |
| Polypropylene glycol (Ukon-LB 550-X) | 550 | – | 225 | Chloroform, methanol |
| Polyethylene glycol adipate (Rheoplex 400) | – | – | 225 | Chloroform |
| DS-200 (polymethylsiloxane) | – | 1.06 – 1.07 (at 25°) | 225 | Methylene chloride, diethyl ether |
| DS-550 (polyphenylmethyl-siloxane) | – | – | 225 | The same |
| DS-710 (polyphenylmethyl siloxane) | – | 1.10 (at 25°) | 225 | Methylene chloride, diethyl ether |
| Silicone elastomers: | | | | |
| SE-30 | – | – | 375 | Chloroform, toluene |
| E-301 | – | – | 300 | The same |
| Silicone grease | – | – | 330 | Methylene chloride |
| Squalane (2,6,10,15,19, 23-hexamethyltetracosane) | 422.83 | 0.805 – 0.810 | 160 | Acetone, methylene chloride |
| Tween-60 and Tween-80 (polyoxy-ethylenesorbitol monooleate) | – | – | 180 | Chloroform |
| Tricresyl phosphate (tritolyl phosphate) | 368.37 | 1.179 (at 25°) | 170 | Acetone |
| Triethylene glycol | 150.17 | 1.118 – 1.125 | 100 | Methanol, ethanol |
| Triethylene glycol dibutyrate | 290.34 | 1.037 – 1.038 | 110 | Acetone |

TABLE 8. Conditions for decomposition of stationary phases

| Phase | Temperature, °C | Substances evolved |
|---|---|---|
| Polypropylene glycol sebacate | 150 | Water |
| Polyethylene glycol adipate | 150 | Water |
| Dinonyl phthalate | 150 | Water, phthalic anhydride |
| Benzyldiphenyl | 140 | Benzyldiphenyl |
| Squalane | 150 | Squalane |
| Silicone oil | 300 | Silicone oil |
| Saccharose acetate isobutyrate | 150 | Odor of caramel and butyric acid |

Chromosorb T is prepared from high-molecular polytetrafluoroethylene (Teflon G). It is a highly inert support.

All chromosorb brands (except Chromosorb T) are available: 1) untreated; 2) after preliminary washing with acid; 3) treated with hexamethyldisilazane or washed with acid or treated with dimethylchlorosilane.

Solid supports commonly used in gas-liquid chromatography are listed in Table 9.

TABLE 9. Solid supports mainly used in gas-liquid chromatography

| Supports | Specific surface, $m^2/g$ | Retains liquid phase, % | Sorptional power |
|---|---|---|---|
| April brick . . . . . . . . . . . | 42 | > 30 | Strong |
| Insen brick . . . . . . . . . . . | 4 – 8 | > 30 | Medium |
| Refractory brick (chamotte) C-22 . . . . . . . . . . . . . . | 4.1 | 25 | Medium |
| Celite 545 . . . . . . . . . . . | 0.45 – 1.1 | 30 | Weak |
| Kieselguhr . . . . . . . . . . . | 1 – 3 | 30 | Weak |
| Resorb . . . . . . . . . . . . . | 6.8 – 8.3 | – | – |
| Glass beads (0.1 – 0.2 mm) . . . . | Less than 1 | 1 – 3 | Weak |
| Teflon . . . . . . . . . . . . . | 0.23 | 3 – 16 | None |

It has been shown in the previous chapter that the shape of chromatographic peaks is strongly affected by the residual adsorptive capacity of the solid support, which should be allowed for in choosing the experimental conditions for the analysis.

A detailed study of the effect of a number of commonly employed solid supports on the efficiency of the columns was performed by Saha and Giddings /28/. These workers compared the efficiences of various columns filled with supports of different particle sizes, at different temperatures, different contents of liquid phase and other parameters. Chromosorb P proved to be the best, while Chromosorbs W and G and Gasochrom S gave an inferior performance.

Kiselev et al. /29/ gave an exhaustive survey of the applications of granulated zeolites of the molecular sieve type in gas chromatography.

Turkel'taub et al. /30/ discussed the part played by sorbents in gas-adsorption chromatography and by solid supports in gas-liquid chromatography, as well as the quality specifications these materials must satisfy.

35

They concluded that the assortment of the marketed sorbents for use in gas chromatography must be considerably extended.

## Detectors

The carrier gas emerging from the chromatographic column contains single zones of the separated substances. Each such zone is a binary system containing the carrier gas and one of the components of the mixture. The presence of the component in the carrier gas alters its properties such as density, thermal conductivity, ability to ionize, etc. In detecting, the difference between a given property of the pure carrier gas and the carrier gas containing the mixture components is measured.

Detectors most often used in chromatography work on the principle of thermal conductivity (katharometers) and ionization. Densimeters, electron-capture, thermochemical and other types of detectors are more rarely employed. The general characteristics of a number of detector types are shown in Table 10.

TABLE 10. Description of detectors

| Type of detector | Limiting sensitivity | Upper linearity limit, % | Time constant, secs |
|---|---|---|---|
| Katharometer . . . . . . . . . | $10^{-3}-10^{-5}$ kg/ml | 15 | 1-2 |
| Flame ionization . . . . . . . . | $10^{-9}-10^{-12}$ mg/sec | 0.5 | $2 \cdot 10^{-2}$ |
| Direct ionization . . . . . . . | $10^{-4}-10^{-5}$ mg/ml ($10^{-2}$ %) | - | 1-2 |
| Argon . . . . . . . . . . . . . | $4 \cdot 10^{-8}$ mg/sec | 0.5 | 1-2 |
| Argon microdetector . . . . . . | $4 \cdot 10^{-10}$ mg/sec | 0.2 | $2 \cdot 10^{-3}$ |
| Densimeter . . . . . . . . . . | $10^{-4}-10^{-5}$ mg/ml | - | 1-2 |
| Electron capture . . . . . . . . | $3 \cdot 10^{-11}$ mg/sec ($10^{-11}$ vol. % $CCl_4$) | - | - |
| Mass analyzer . . . . . . . . | $10^{-4}$ vol.% | - | - |

## Introduction of samples into the chromatograph

In quantitative analysis of mixtures by gas-liquid chromatography, the samples are introduced into the chromatograph with the aid of syringes or micropipets. According to the data obtained in eight laboratories /31/ on chromatographs of different brands, it is preferable to use syringes, as in this way the results are more reproducible, especially as concerns mixtures of low-boiling compounds.

## Withdrawal of samples of components after separation

The collection of samples of the separated components for their subsequent identification is an important stage in gas chromatography.

In preparative chromatography a manifold connected to individual sample collectors is employed. The collectors are actuated in succession, so that a known amount of the separated components can be collected. In analytical chromatography this procedure is difficult to employ, since the very small samples of the separated substances are lost in the manifold and in the stopcock system.

Khol'kin et al. /32/ proposed a simple and convenient design of a sample collector, which may be employed in both preparative and analytical gas chromatography. Figure 10 represents three variants of this design.

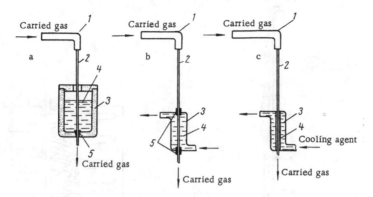

FIGURE 10. Sample collector in gas chromatography.

After separation in the chromatographic column the mixture components enter a glass capillary 2 together with the stream of carrier gas, through rubber tube 1. The capillary passes through vessel 3 with cooling agent 4. The cooling agent may be liquid nitrogen, mixtures with solid $CO_2$, liquid cooling mixtures. The cooling agent is poured into a vessel (e.g., a Dewar vessel made of plastic foam) or is passed through the system. The gaskets 5 prevent losses of the coolant. One component of the mixture is condensed in the cooled part of the capillary, after which the capillary is pulled down, the zone with the solid or liquid sample is cut off and sealed on both sides. The succeeding components are collected in a similar manner. The beginning and end of passage of each component is controlled on the potentiometer of the chromatograph.

This method was applied to samples of various volatile compounds separated on chromatograph KhL-4.

The capillary tube zone was cooled with liquid nitrogen, the components were identified by their IR-spectra taken on a UR-20 spectrometer.

An interesting combination of gas-liquid chromatography with two-dimensional glass-plate chromatography of submicroscopic amounts of components emerging from the gas chromatograph was proposed by Janak /33/. The method is suitable for the identification of nanogram and picogram amounts of compounds after separation by gas-liquid chroma-tography.

## Technique of pyrolytic chromatography

Since the method of pyrolytic chromatography is only of recent date, the design of a pyrolysis apparatus ensuring quantitative reproducible results has not yet been finally established. The rule is for each worker to construct his own pyrolysis reactor as a modification to a standard chromatograph, or else to design a specially constructed chromatograph which includes a pyrolysis block. Industrial type pyrolysis reactors have appeared on the market only very recently.

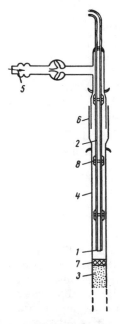

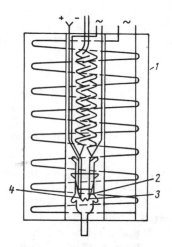

FIGURE 11. Glass cell for pyrolysis:

1 – nichrome spiral; 2 – tungsten electrodes; 3 – sorbent; 4 – column; 5 – inlet of carrier gas; 6 – ground glass joint; 7 – layer of glass wool; 8 – gaskets.

FIGURE 12. Pyrolytic accessory unit to gas chromatograph:

1 – furnace; 2 – pyrolytic cell; 3 – platinum spiral; 4 – thermocouple.

The advantages and disadvantages of various pyrolytic methods have been discussed in detail /34/.

The main type of reactor used in pyrolytic chromatography of high polymers, is a furnace made of a thin-walled quartz tube heated with a platinum heating spiral.

Groten /35/ modified a Perkin-Elmer 154 chromatograph by adding a pyrolysis furnace and a supplementary six-way gas valve. The reactor is equipped with a quartz capillary (d = 2 mm) with a platinum wire coil; about 1 mg of the polymer to be analyzed is placed in the middle part of the capillary. The polymer is ashed in the flame at 700 — 900° for one minute. The author used this apparatus in his study of numerous high polymers and showed that more than 150 polymers may be qualitatively analyzed under the same conditions of pyrolysis and analysis; he also developed a quantitative analytical procedure for the determination of cellulose ethers.

The different setups for pyrolytic gas chromatography are shown in Figures 11 and 12.

## Parameters of chromatographic peak and quantitative interpretation of gas chromatograms

If the shape of the peak is not altered by adsorptional effects, the elution curve shows symmetrical peaks, each of which corresponds to a separated mixture component. Figure 13 shows a number of principal parameters of the chromatographic peak, used in calculating its surface area /36/.

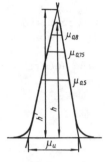

FIGURE 13. Chromatographic peak parameters.

The height of the chromatographic peak is directly proportional to the concentration of the component in the sample. Accordingly, this parameter is determined in quantitative analysis. This method is particularly convenient in the case of components with a short retention time, when the peak width is small. In order to obtain sufficiently accurate results, the parameters of chromatographic analysis must be strictly standardized, the column must not be overloaded with the sample and the analysis must be performed within the linearity range of the detector and the recording system.

More accurate quantitative data are obtained by measuring the surface areas of chromatographic peaks. This may be done by different methods: planimetry, excision and weighing of the parts of the paper bounded by the peak, constructing tangents to the curve at the inflection points and determination of the area of the resulting triangle, utilization of integrating instruments.

The surface area of chromatographic peaks is most often found by multiplying the peak height $h$ by the peak width at mid-height $\mu_{0.5}$.

$$S = \mu_{0.5} \cdot h.$$

However, this method can only be applied to symmetrical, fully separated peaks. Areas of nonsymmetrical or imperfectly separated peaks may be determined if certain assumptions are made /36/, but the accuracy of the determination is then lower.

Three main variants of analytical technique are employed in quantitative chromatographic analysis: absolute calibration, internal normalization, and internal standard methods.

The most convenient and most accurate is the method of a b s o l u t e   c a l i b r a t i o n, in which the relationship between the height or the surface area of the peak and the amount of the component introduced into the chromatograph is determined. The calibration is effected by introducing into the instrument definite sample volumes containing accurately known amounts of components. The results are used to plot calibration graphs giving the relationship between the height or area of the peak and the concentration or the amount of the substance introduced.

In the internal normalization method the surface area of all peaks on the chromatographic curve is taken as 100%, when the surface area of a peak will give the proportional content of the component in the mixture. The method will determine the mutual proportions of the components only and is applicable if all the components of the sample have been fully eluted. Since most detectors are not equally sensitive to substances of different structures, suitable correction factors must be applied when using the method. The method is unsuitable for the determination of trace amounts of components in mixtures.

In the internal standard method, a given amount of an etalon substance, of a structure similar to that of the sample components, but not originally present in the mixture, is introduced. The content of the mixture components to be determined is found by comparing the surface areas of their peaks with the surface area of the peak of the standard substance. This method may be used to find both macro amounts and traces of various substances.

A correct choice of the analytical method will enhance the accuracy of the results.

BIBLIOGRAPHY

1. SHEMYAKIN, F. M., E. S. MITSELOVSKII, and D. V. ROMANOV. Khromatograficheskii analiz (Chromatographic Analysis). − Goskhimizdat. 1955.
2. AKHREM, A. A. and A. I. KUZNETSOVA. Tonkosloinaya khromatografiya (Thin Layer Chromatography).− Izdatel'stvo Nauka. 1964.*
3. OL'SHANOVA, K. M. et al. Rukovodstvo po ionoobmennoi, raspredelitel'noi i osadochnoi khromatografii (Textbook of Ion Exchange, Partition and Precipitation Chromatography). − Izdatel'stvo Khimiya. 1965.
4. SAMUELSON, O. Ion Exchange Separations in Analytical Chemistry.— Wiley. 1963.
5. SALDADZE, K. M., A. B. PASHKOV, and V. S. TITOVA. Ionoobmennye vysokomolekulyarnye soedineniya (Ion-Exchanging High Molecular Compounds). − Goskhimizdat. 1960.
6. KHAVIDOVA, E. G. and V. V. RACHINSKII. − Uspekhi Khimii, 34(2): 253−275. 1965.
7. NIKITIN, N. I. Khimiya drevesiny i tsellyulozy (Chemistry of Cellulose and Wood). − Izd. AN SSSR. 1962.**
8. GOL'BRAIKH, L. S. et al. − In: Sbornik "Tsellyuloza i ee proizvodnye," pp. 8−11. Izd. AN SSSR. 1963.
9. MYHRE, D. V. and F. SMITH. − J. Org. Chem., Vol. 23: 1229. 1958.
10. RANDERATH, R. − Angew. Chem., Vol. 74: 48. 1962.
11. HAIS, I. M. and K. MACEK, editors. Paper Chromatography. [Russian translation from the Czech. 1962.]
12. RYUKHIN, N. V., N. A. AFONCHIKOV, and V. M. KHANINA. − In: Sbornik "Novye vidy bumagi i ikh primenenie," pp. 62−77. Izd. TsINTI bumdrevproma. 1961.
13. RYUKHIN, N. V., V. M. KHANINA, and O. K. IVINA. − Bumazhnaya Promyshlennost', No. 3: 26−28. 1963.
14. ZAALISHVILI, M. M. and F. O. SHRAIBMAN. − Biokhimiya, 25(3): 570−572. 1960.
15. STAHL, E. editor. Dünnschicht-Chromatographie, ein Laboratoriumshandbuch. Berlin. 1962. [Russian translation from the German. 1965.]
16. PHILLIPS, C. G. S. Gas Chromatography. [Russian translation. 1958.]
17. BAYER, E. Gas Chromatography. − Elsevier. 1961.
18. ZHUKHOVITSKII, A. A. and N. M. TURKEL'TAUB. Gazovaya khromatografiya (Gas Chromatography). − Gostoptekhizdat. 1962.
19. LITVINOVA, E. M. Gazovaya Khromatografiya (Gas Chromatography). − Bibliographical Index of Soviet and Foreign Literature, 1952−1960. Izd. AN SSSR. 1962.

----------------

* [Available in English translation as IPST No. 2174.]
** [Available in English translation as IPST No. 2172.]

20. SHINGLYAR, M. Gazovaya khromatografiya v praktike (The Practice of Gas Chromatography). — Izdatel'-stvo Khimiya. 1964.
21. NOGARE, S. D. and R. S. JUVET. Gas—Liquid Chromatography. [Russian translation. 1966.]
22. GOL'BERT, K. A. and M. S. VINDERGANZ. Kurs gazovoi khromatografii (A Course in Gas Chromatography). — Izdatel'stvo "Khimiya." 1967.
23. BIRCHFIELD, H. and E. STORRS. Biochemical Applications of Gas Chromatography. — Academic Press. 1962.
24. SVYATOSHENKO, A. T. and V. G. BEREZKIN. — Neftekhimiya, 4(6): 934—942. 1964.
25. KISELEV, A. V. and Ya. I. YASHIN. Gazo—adsorbtsionnaya khromatografiya (Gas Adsorption Chromatography). — Izdatel'stvo Nauka. 1967.
26. GERRARD, W., S. HAWKES, and E. MOONEY. In: Proceedings of Third International Symposium on Gas Chromatography, Edinburgh. 1960. [Russian translation. 1964.]
27. GIDDINGS, J. C., M. R. JAMES, and H. EYRING. — Analyt. Chem., 37(4): 612. 1965.
28. SAHA, N. C. and J. C. GIDDINGS. — Analyt. Chem., 37(7): 830—835. 1965.
29. KISELEV, A. V., Yu. L. CHERPEN'KOVA, and Ya. I. YASHIN. — Neftekhimiya, 5(1): 141—148. 1965.
30. TURKEL'TAUB, N. M., A. A. ZHUKHOVITSKII, and V. P. SHVARTSMAN. — In: Sbornik "Prirodnye mineral'nye sorbenty," pp. 78—87. Izd. AN UkrSSR, Kiev. 1960.
31. CRANT, D. W. and L. KNOTT. — Analyst, 89(1065): 801. 1964.
32. KHOL'KIN, Yu. I., A. K. POTAPOVICH, and G. A. GRIDYUSHKO. — Zavodskaya Laboratoriya. (In press.)
33. JANAK, J. J. — Chromatogr., 16(3): 494—501. 1964.
34. BEREZKIN, V. G. Analiticheskaya reaktsionnaya gazovaya khromatografiya (Analytical Reaction Gas Chromatography). — Izdatel'stvo Nauka. 1966.
35. GROTEN, B. — Analyt. Chem., Vol. 36: 1206—1212. 1964.
36. ANDREEV, L. V., M. I. AFANAS'EV, O. G. CHABROVA, and M. S. VIGDERGAUZ. — Uspekhi Khimii, 34(5): 920—942. 1965.

41

*Chapter III*

## CHROMATOGRAPHY OF CARBOHYDRATES

Carbohydrates are a major component of wood and other vegetable material. Processes involving the isolation of carbohydrates and their chemical treatment form the base of all major industrial chemical processing of wood.

Carbohydrates are present in the extractable substances of wood as monosaccharides, water-soluble oligo- and polysaccharides or glycosides; cellulose and a complex of hemicellulosic polysaccharides form part of the cell wall. During chemical processing the polysaccharides are hydrolyzed to varying extents, yielding monosaccharides, which are then sent to biochemical or chemical treatment. Thus, analyses of mixtures of monosaccharides, oligosaccharides and polysaccharides, as well as various derivatives of carbohydrates all have to be performed in practice.

The first section of the present chapter deals with the general methods of chromatographic analysis of monosaccharides and their derivatives, and also of some low-polymerized oligosaccharides. The second section deals with the chromatography of polysaccharides and their derivatives. The analysis of carbohydrates in industrial products will be discussed in Chapter VI.

Each section of this chapter is provided with a list of references. No attempt has been made to present an exhaustive list of publications on the chromatography of carbohydrates, as such a list would have to include several thousand items.

As has been pointed out above, it is more convenient to deal with the chromatographic methods by individual techniques, rather than by the nature of the separation processes involved.


## A. CHROMATOGRAPHY OF MONOSACCHARIDES AND THEIR DERIVATIVES

### 1. Column chromatography of carbohydrates

Tsvet's classical adsorption chromatography on columns used to be widely employed in both analytical and preparative chemistry of carbohydrates, but owing to the great advances made in paper chromatography, and then in thin layer and gas-liquid chromatography, this technique has assumed a secondary importance. The method is at present used in the laboratory mainly for purification and clarification of different products, in rough fractionations of mixtures for preparative and for certain analytical purposes.

This section will deal with adsorption chromatography (on activated charcoals), partition chromatography (on cellulose and cellulose derivative columns) and ion exchange chromatography (ion exchanger columns) of monosaccharides, oligosaccharides, substituted sugars and their derivatives.

## Monosaccharides and oligosaccharides

Carbohydrates are polyhydroxy compounds with a large number of hydrophilic hydroxyl groups. Accordingly, sugar molecules are distinctly polar and are thus readily adsorbed from aqueous solutions on hydrophobic nonpolar adsorbents.

Reviews are available of the early work on the column chromatography of sugars and their derivatives /1/, chromatographic separation of sugars on activated charcoal columns /2,3/, and chromatographic separation and identification of oligosaccharides /4/.

**Chromatography on activated charcoal.** The capacity of monosaccharides to become adsorbed on activated charcoal, which is a typically hydrophobic adsorbent, has been utilized for a long time for analytical and technical purposes. Of the early studies, we may mention the work of Claesson /5, 6/, who utilized the results of his studies on the adsorption chromatography of sugars, oligosaccharides, fatty acids, alcohols and other compounds to develop a fairly stringent mathematical method for the calculation of the results of frontal, elution and displacement analysis /7/. His findings have remained perfectly valid up to the present day /8/.

The adsorption of sugars on wood charcoal obeys Freundlich's equation /9/ and the general theory of chromatography /10/. The equations deduced for the migration of the solvent front along the column are a faithful description of the experimental results. The sorption isotherm or the concentration of the sorbed substance in solution may be calculated from the results of a single experiment.

Improvements have been repeatedly introduced /11, 12/ into the separation technique of sugars on activated charcoal columns.

A recent technique in chromatography on columns /15/ is to separate and purify sugars on columns filled with a mixture of charcoal and celite in a ratio of 1:1. This method is also used in the studies of the chemistry of wood and its carbohydrate components. Gradient elution of sugars with a water-alcohol mixture is employed, the concentration of alcohol being gradually increased /18/. The usual technique is to elute with water, 5% and 15% solutions of ethanol in succession. The method was employed /16/ in quantitative analysis of mixtures of mono- and disaccharides, the disaccharides remaining on the column while the monosaccharides pass into solution.

The separation of sugars on charcoal-celite mixtures is largely affected by the pH of the mixtures /19/. The narrowest and most symmetrical peaks of glucose and other monosaccharides are obtained as a result of gradient elution analysis at a pH of about 3; 0.01 N solution of acetic acid in a water-alcohol mixture is employed as eluent. Figure 14 shows the chromatogram of a preparative separation of the oligosaccharides formed during the hydrolysis of dextran. An $88 \times 7.5$ cm column was filled with a mixture of 750 g active charcoal and 750 g celite 535.* The oligosacchardies were satisfactorily separated and were isolated in their pure form. The presence of acid in the eluent did not produce hydrolysis of oligosaccharides. The pH of the eluate had no effect on the elution curve of galacturonic acid and glucose-1-phosphate.

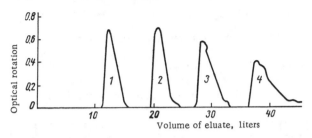

FIGURE 14. Chromatogram of dextran hydrolyzate on column with activated charcoal and celite:

1 – isomaltose; 2 – isomaltotriose; 3 – isomaltotetraose; 4 – isomalto-pentaose.

This method was applied /20/ in studying the composition of the hydrolyzate of different starch fractions. A mixture of No. 3761 carbon powder with celite (1:1) was employed. The mixture glucose-saccharose-raffinose was separated by gradient development (stepwise and continuous); the components were successively eluted with water, 5% and 15% aqueous alcohol. In the analysis of the hydrolyzate of dextran the following fractions were isolated: (composition of solvent during development indicated in parentheses): glucose (water and 1.5% alcohol); isomaltose + glucose (5% alcohol); isomaltotriose + isomaltose (8% alcohol); isomalto-tetraose + higher oligosaccharides (15% alcohol); from the hydrolyzate of amylose: maltose (5 and 8% alcohol); maltotriose (15% alcohol); malto-tetraose (25% alcohol); maltopentaose (30% alcohol). The column separation is conveniently followed by paper chromatography in the system butanol:pyridine:water = 6:4:3; the zones are revealed with a mixture of 2% alcoholic diphenylamine, 2% alcoholic aniline and concentrated $H_3PO_4$ (10:10:1.5).

In order to facilitate the filtration of the solutions through the charcoal layer, silicic acid may be added /21/ to the charcoal as a filter aid. When the ratio of these components in the solid phase was 1:1, glucose, saccharose and raffinose could be satisfactorily separated. The elution was conducted with water, and then with 5 and 15% ethanol. The completeness of component separation was checked by paper chromatography using the system butanol:pyridine:water = 6:4:3.

A mixture of carbon and alumina was employed /22/ in a separation of mono-, di- and trisaccharides. Celite columns were also employed /23/ in a preparative separation of sugars.

* A description of the sorbents mentioned in this book is given in Chapter II.

Activated charcoal columns yield pure maltose /14/. This adsorbent also produces a satisfactory separation of oligosaccharides /17/, the separation of which is improved in the presence of borates /13/.

Thus, sugar chromatography on activated carbon or carbon-celite columns is mainly employed for preparative purposes and yields chromatographically pure preparations of simple sugars and oligosaccharides.

**Separation of sugars on polysaccharide sorbents.** Sugar separation of cellulose, starch, etc. columns mainly involves partition rather than adsorption.

A method for the separation and quantitative determination of mono-saccharides on a starch column has been described /24/. Examination on wet starch columns was employed /25/ to separate and estimate the relative molecular sizes of numerous organic compounds including sugars.

A powdered hydrocellulose column was employed /26/ to separate both sugars and their methyl ethers. A mixture of four sugars was separated /27/ by column chromatography on Sephadex G-25, swollen in the solvent system butanol: acetic acid: water = 62:15:25, used for the development. Sephadex filtration was also employed /28/ to separate mineral matter and saccharose. A method of chromatographic separation of disaccharides on a column at an elevated temperature has been described /29/.

In preparative work polysaccharide sorbents are used to a smaller extent than activated carbon or ion exchangers.

**Separation of sugars on ion exchange resins.** Column chromatography of sugars on ion exchange resins has been recently used with increasing frequency, mainly in preparative separation of substances of differing structures. Ion exchange column separations of free sugars mainly proceed by partition effects; sugars may also be complexed with inorganic compounds, as a result of which they are separated by typical ion exchange processes.

Two- and three-component mixtures of sugars have been separated /30/ on columns with Dowex-1 ($\times$8) in the $SO_4^{2-}$-form. If 65% aqueous ethanol is used as the developing system, glucose may be separated from verbascose, glucose from stachyose, glucose from raffinose and from stachyose; 74% alcohol will separate glucose from raffinose and xylose from maltose. It will be seen that the solvent is particularly suitable in the separation of mono- and disaccharide mixtures.

More complex mixtures are separated /31, 32/ by partition chromato-graphy on porous anion exchanger Dowex-21K in the $SO_4^{2-}$-form, particle diameter $15-40\ \mu$. Development with 65% alcohol will separate mixtures of glucose, stachyose and raffinose; 70% ethanol will separate a mixture of rhamnose, glucose, and melibiose; 74% ethanol will separate mixtures of 2-deoxy-D-glucose, arabinose and glucose; saccharose, melicitose and raffinose; rhamnose, ribose, sorbose, galactose, maltose, melibiose, raffinose and stachyose. A mixture of arabinose, xylose, mannose, galactose and glucose may be developed by eluting with 88% ethanol.

Monosaccharides obtained by hydrolysis of wood may be separated /33/ by passing the solution through a column filled with a mixture of finely ground Dowex-21K ion-exchange resin (particle size $1-40\ \mu$, exchange capacity 4.2 meq/g) or of another resin with celite 545. The experimental conditions are the same as in /32/. Aqueous 88% ethanol is used as eluent. The eluate is subjected to continuous automatic analysis with the aid of a photocolorimetric analyzer. Arabinose, xylose, mannose, galactose and glucose can be separated by this method. In order to enhance the rate of diffusion of the sugars inside the grains of the ion exchanger, it is recommended to raise the temperature of the column.

The automatic separation of monosaccharides on Dowex-21K ion exchange resin /34/ is based on this principle. Also, a determination of as little as 4 $\gamma$ of individual sugars in a mixture may be effected by ion exchange chromatography with gradient elution on Dowex-1 ($\times$8) column /40/. The identification of the sugars in the fractions is effected by paper chromatography.

The anion exchanger Dowex-1 ($\times$8) may also be employed /36/ in the separation and isolation of uronic acids from hemicelluloses precipitated from sulfite lyes /36/. Sugars have also been separated /37/ on Dowex-50W Oligosaccharides can be separated /38/ on the neutral cation exchanger Dowex-50W ($\times$2) in the Li-form, while monosaccharides can be separated /39/ on this resin in the Ba-form.

Sugars have been separated /41/ on the anion exchanger Deacidite SRA 68 with 3.5% cross links, finer than 200 mesh, in a 100$\times$2 cm column. The anion exchanger was in the $Cl^-$-, $CO_3^-$- and $HCO_3^-$-forms, and the elution was effected with water. Under these conditions D-glucose, saccharose and raffinose are eluted in the decreasing sequence of their molecular size.

Ion exchange resins are used in the separation of lactones and reducing sugars /42/. Sugars in the form of their borate complexes can be separated on Dowex-2 ($\times$8) /43/. Equilibrium separation of glucose, galacturonic acid and sulfuric acid on strongly basic anion exchange resins has been recently described /44/. Sugars may also be separated on other styrene-divinylbenzene resins /35/.

In practical chemical work on wood, paper chromatography is very successfully used for analytical purposes. Ion exchange chromatography is mainly of interest as a means of preliminary purification of hydrolyzates and spent lyes and for group fractionation of the components of various industrial products. These problems will be discussed in detail in Chapter VI.

Uronic and aldonic acids

Uronic acids occur widely in natural polysaccharides, as components of mixed polysaccharides or as more or less homogeneous polyuronic acids. They are found in the products of hydrolysis of wood in mixtures with sugars; the methods for their analysis together with monosaccharides have been mentioned in the preceding section /44/. This section will also deal with the analysis of the products of oxidation of sugars — aldonic acids.

The chromatographic method is suitable /45/ for preparative separation and isolation of mono-, di- and trigalacturonic acids from unpurified hydrolyzate of pectic acids.

Owing to the fact that they contain carboxyl groups, uronic acids are readily separated on anion exchangers. A satisfactory separation of glucuronic and galacturonic acids was achieved by eluting with solutions of acetic acid /46/. Uronic acids may be eluted with both acetic /47/ and formic /48/ acids. Glucuronic acids and glucuronides may be determined /49/ with the aid of ion exchange resins.

Uronic acids in alginate hydrolyzates were separated and quantitatively determined /50/ on the anion exchanger Dowex-1 ($\times$8) in the acetate form in an organic glass column (20$\times$2 cm).

Gaponenkov and Protsenko /51/ developed a method of preparation of galacturonic acid from pectin by the ion exchange method. The pectin, which had been obtained from sugar beet bagasse and sunflower husks, was hydrolyzed with 0.5 N sulfuric acid on a boiling water bath for 6 hours, the resulting precipitate filtered off, the filtrate neutralized at 55 — 60° with BaCO₃ and the solution was again filtered. The filtrate, which contained D-galacturonic acid, was passed through a column with EDE-10 anion exchanger in the OH-form at the rate of 20 — 25 drops per minute. The completeness of the absorption of the acids from the filtrate was verified by measuring the pH of the solution or by the use of an indicator. The absorbed D-galacturonic acid was eluted from the column with a 0.25 N solution of NaOH. In order to remove the cations, the solution was passed through a column of KU-1 cation exchanger. The filtrate was then evaporated in vacuo and crystallized at − 5°. When D-galacturonic acid solutions were evaporated under atmospheric pressure, the yield of the acid did not exceed 8 — 10% of the theoretical. Pectin may also be hydrolyzed by the use of pectinase produced by the fungus Aspergillus niger.

A convenient method for the separation of uronic acids was developed by Samuelson and Wictorin /52/ who utilized the strongly basic anion exchanger Dowex-1 ($\times$8) in the acetate form.

The resin with a grain size of 40 — 60 $\mu$ is placed in a 9$\times$920 mm column and treated with the solvent to produce preliminary swelling. The solution of uronic acids is neutralized with a solution of KOH and held at pH 8 in order to open the lactone rings. The solution of the acids to be analyzed is introduced into the top part of the column and eluted with sodium acetate solutions of different concentrations at a rate of 1.2 cm²/min. The eluent may be fed in and the eluate fractions collected by means of an automatic device. The eluate was analyzed on an autoanalyzer /53/ by oxidizing the fractions with chromic acid.

Figure 15 shows that a satisfactory separation of uronic acids by this method can be achieved if the eluent is a 0.08 M solution of sodium acetate; aldobiuronic acids are eluted with 0.02 M sodium acetate. If 0.15 M sodium acetate is employed, $\alpha$-methyl-D-mannuronoside can be separated from glucuronic acid.

It is preferable to use sodium acetate rather than formic or acetic acids as eluents. If calibration graphs are plotted, uronic acids can be determined to within 3%.

Uronic acids are eluted in the sequence of decreasing molecular weight (Figure 15); this has also been noted for different hydroxyacids /54/, in particular aldobiuronic and aldonic acids /55/.

Hexuronic acids have been separated /56/ under conditions resembling those just described.

In the studies of wood chemistry several techniques of chromatographic analysis are used simultaneously for analytical and preparative purposes. Thus, for instance, the structure of polysaccharides is investigated /57/ by a combined procedure, involving the clarification of the polysaccharide hydrolyzate on a column of Amberlite IR-120, absorption of its acid components on a column of Dowex-1 ($\times$4) in the acetate form, elution of uronic acids by formic acid and their separation by preparative paper chromatography. The combination of ion exchange and chromatography on paper resulted in the separation of an aldobiuronic acid /58/ from the hydrolyzate of pinewood.

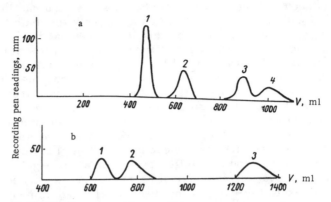

FIGURE 15. Chromatographic separation:

a – of uronic acids: 1 – 4-o-methyl-D-glucuronic acid; 2 – D-galac-turonic acid; 3 – D-glucuronic acid; 4 – D-mannuronic acid; b – of aldobiuronic acids: 1 – 2-o-(4-o-methyl-α-D-glucopyranosyl)-D-xylose; 2 – 6-o-(β-D-glucopyranosyl)-D-galactose; 3 – 2-o-(α-D-glucopyranosyl)-D-xylose.

Procedures for the separation of aldobionic and aldonic acids on anion exchangers have also been described /55, 59/. Aldonic acids — gluconic and arabonic — may be quantitatively extracted from aqueous alcohol solutions passed through a column of Dowex-1 (×8) anion exchanger in the sulfate form, and may then be fully desorbed by washing the column with water /60/. The feasibility of this process is due to the inhomogeneous distribution of alcohol between the resin and the solution: the lower concentration of the alcohol in the resin favors the passage of the aldonic acids into this phase. If the resin is totally present in the $SO_4^{2-}$-form, some of the acids are absorbed by conventional ion-exchange mechanism and may be eluted only with 0.05 M sulfuric acid. This is prevented by a partial conversion of the resin into the bisulfite form by treatment with 0.01 M sulfuric acid. This procedure makes it possible to achieve quantitative separation of aldonic acids both from the exchanged anions (e.g., from anions of toluenesulfonic acid) and from the nonadsorbed soluble substances.

The sections which follow give a few examples of the application of chromatographic methods to the study of polyuronic acids and polyuronides.


Polyhydric alcohols

Frontal adsorption analysis on activated charcoal columns has been employed /61/ in a quantitative determination of the composition of glycerol and ethylene glycol mixtures in aqueous solutions. Glycerol in the presence of saccharose can be determined /62/ on a cellulose column, using butanol, saturated with 1% aqueous ammonia as eluent.


Carbohydrate derivatives and substituted sugars

Column chromatography of sugar derivatives is employed in studying the structure and reactions of carbohydrates. A procedure /63/ for the separation of methylated methylglycosides is extensively employed. Methylglucosides, tri- and tetramethylglucoses are readily separated when their mixture is passed through a 15×2 cm column. If the eluent employed is a mixture of ether with petroleum ether (bp 60— 80°) (2:1 by volume), tetramethylmethyl-glucoside is eluted, while the methylglucoside of trimethylglucose is partly eluted at a later stage and is fully eluted with methanol. The amount of trisubstituted methylglucoside may be 20 times higher than that of tetramethyl-methylglucoside, the yield of the latter being 94% under these conditions. The method can also be used to separate $\alpha$- and $\beta$-methylglucosides, the $\beta$-form being less strongly adsorbed.

Methylated sugars can also be separated on a charcoal column /64/; this applies particularly to methylglucosides /65/. Methylated and unsubstituted sugars were separated on a powdered hydrocellulose column /66/.

A relationship was found /67/ between the adsorptive capacity of a mixture of magnesol (hydrated acid magnesium silicate) and celite 535 (5:1) and the conformational structure of methylglycosides and pentose and hexose acetates. A 200:1 or 300:1 mixture of benzene with ethanol was used as eluent.

The chromatographic behavior of anomeric methylglycosides has been studied /68/ from the point of view of steric hindrances. The well-known rule, according to which the most sterically hindered isomer is the first to be eluted in chromatographic operations, also applies to methylglycosides. The methylglycosides which can be chromatographically separated are those which have a large difference in the $O_{(1)} - O_{(2)}$ distance and in the projected valency angles, i. e., those which display large differences in the capacity of formation of hydrogen bonds between the $CH_3O$- groups of methylglycosides and the OH-groups of cellulose, due to the different extents of screening of the $CH_3O$-group at $C_{(1)}$ by the OH-group at $C_{(2)}$. Accordingly, isomeric methylglucofuranosides, methylglucopyranosides of D-mannose, L-rhamnose, D-galactose and D-ribose can be separated. The rate of acid hydrolysis of methylglycosides is usually proportional to their rate of migration on the chromatogram.

Chromatography on silica gel column has been used /69/ to separate saccharose mono-, di- and polyethers. The eluents were mixtures of chloroform with methanol in different proportions; unsubstituted saccharose was eluted with dimethylformamide.

Anomeric glucosides have been separated /70/ on a cellulose column.

Column chromatography is used in the purification of sugar sulfates. Cellulose column /71/ was used to separate sugar monosulfates, disulfates and sugars. Monosaccharide sulfates were separated from inorganic salts on a charcoal column /72/. After sulfonating 1, 2- 5, 6-diisopropylidene-D-glucose, the neutralized reaction mixture is evaporated and passed through a 10×3.4 cm charcoal-kieselguhr (1:1) column. Washing the column with water removes $BaCl_2$, while glucose sulfate is eluted with 25% alcohol solution. Under these conditions glucose is partly separated from glucose-6-phosphate, the former being eluted more rapidly.

These methods of separation of sugar derivatives, in particular their methylation products, are very important techniques in the studies of structural chemistry of polysaccharides.

Separation of sugar derivatives on ion exchange resins takes place much more readily than the separation of free sugars, owing to the presence of functional groups participating in the ion exchange.

A rapid and effective separation of mixtures of isomeric glucosides was performed /73/ by chromatography on strongly basic ion exchange resins of the type of Dowex-1, Dowex-2 and the permutite Deacidite FF in the OH-form. Compounds which have been separated on these resins include 2-o-$\alpha$- and 2-o-$\beta$-D-glucosylglycerols, methyl-$\alpha$- and methyl-$\beta$-glucosami- dines, methyl-$\alpha$-D-glucopyranoside and methyl-$\alpha$-D-galactopyranoside. The resin used was Dowex-1 (2% cross linking). The spent resins were regenerated by washing with 1 N HCl and then with water until neutral.

Ion exchange resins were also employed in the separation of mixtures of partly methylated sugars /74/. Sugar phosphates are separated on a Dowex-1 ($\times$4) column in the borate form /75/. Ion exchange chromatography was also employed to separate glucosamines of oligosaccharides /76/.

Ion exchange chromatography was successfully employed in the separation of epimeric aldonic acids, viz., D-gluconic and D-mannonic acids /77/. Satisfactory separation /78/ of $\alpha$- and $\beta$-glucometasaccharic acids, formed by the cleavage of 3-o-methylglucose with alkali, was achieved on a 33.2$\times$3.3 cm column of Dowex-1 ($\times$8) (400 mesh) in the borate form. The eluent was 0.07 M solution of borax, and the filtration rate was 0.3 ml $\cdot$ cm$^{-2}$ $\cdot$ min$^{-1}$.

These examples of applications of ion exchange chromatography in the chemistry of sugars and sugar derivatives are by no means exhaustive. The use of Soviet-made ion exchangers, described in Chapter II, is of great help in the studies of the chemistry of wood.

Alteration of carbohydrates on sorbents and ion exchangers

During their chromatographic separation, carbohydrates may enter secondary reactions owing to the presence of active sites on the surface of surface-active materials and ion exchangers. A number of sorbents and ion exchangers are used as catalysts in the reactions given by carbo- hydrates — polymerization, oxidation, hydrolysis, etc.

Sugars react particularly vigorously with ion exchange resins /79/, in particular with anion exchangers /80, 81/. It has been noted /82/ that sugars are cleaved on IRA-400 column in the OH-form. Quaternary ammonium base type anion exchange resins produce epimerization and cleavage of glucose /83/. When D-glucose is heated with Amberlite at 130° for 10 minutes, the sugar becomes partly polymerized; the reaction products have been separated on charcoal-cellite (1:1) column, and eluted with water and with 2 — 10% aqueous alcohol /84/.

In experimental work, the possible alteration of carbohydrates under conditions of chromatographic analysis must be taken into account. Strongly basic ion exchangers are particularly dangerous in this respect. If they are intended to be used for purification of solutions of carbohydrates or for similar purposes, the analyst must first ensure that the carbohydrates are stable under the experimental conditions employed.

BIBLIOGRAPHY

1. BINKLEY, W. W. — Advances in Carbohydrate Chemistry, Vol. 10:55—94. 1955.
2. INANO, MATUDA. — J. Japan Chem., Vol. 11(5):24—29. 1957.
3. LEDERER, E. and M. LEDERER. Chromatography. A Review of Principles and Application, pp. 153—158. — Elsevier Publ. Comp., New York. 1953.
4. LEDERER, M. Chromatographic Reviews, Vol. 4. — Elsevier Publ. Co., New York. 1962.
5. CLAESSON, S. — Arkiv Kemi, Mineral., Geol., 23A(1):1—133. 1964.
6. CLAESSON, S. — In Sbornik: "Khromatografiya." [Russian translation. 1949.]
7. CLAESSON, S. Adsorption Analysis of Mixtures. [Russian translation. 1950.]
8. RACHINSKII, V. V. Vvedenie v obshchuyu teoriyu dinamiki sorbtsii i khromatografii (Introduction to the General Theory of Adsorption and Chromatography). — Izdatel'stvo Nauka. 1964.
9. WALKER, E. A. and P. MORTON. — Analyst, 89(1061):512—519. 1964.
10. WILSON, I. N. — J. Am. Chem. Soc., Vol. 62:1583. 1940.
11. WHISTLER, R. L. — Science, 120(3126):899—900. 1954.
12. ANDREWS, P., L. HOUGH, and D. B. POWELL. — Chem. and Ind., No. 26:658. 1956.
13. BARKER, S. A., E. J. BOURNE, and O. J. THEANDER. — Chem. Soc., Dec., pp. 4276—4280. 1955.
14. TÄUFEL, K. and H. RUTTLOFF. — Ernährungsforschung, 6(5):579—583. 1961.
15. WHISTLER, R. L. and D. F. DURSO. — J. Am. Chem. Soc., Vol. 72:677. 1950.
16. CORBETT, W. M. — Chem. and Ind., No. 48:1285. 1953.
17. BARKER, S. A., E. J. BOURNE, and D. M. O'MANT. — Chem. and Ind., No. 16:425. 1955.
18. ALM, R. S. — Acta Chem. Scand., Vol. 6:1186. 1952.
19. TAYLOR, P. M. and W. J. WHEALAN. — Chem. and Ind., No. 1:44—45. 1962.
20. RUTTLOFF, H. — Ernährungsforschung, 7(4):540—560. 1963.
21. RUTTLOFF, H., A. TÄUFEL, and W. HUNZ. — J. Prakt. Chem., 20(3—4):142—150. 1963.
22. STEFANOVIĆ, V. D. — J. Chromatogr., 5(5):453—454. 1962.
23. LEMIEUX, R. U., C. T. BISHOP, and G. E. PELLETIER. — Can. J. Chem., 34(10):1365—1371. 1956.
24. GARDELL, S. — Acta Chem. Scand., 7(1):201—206. 1953.
25. LATHE, G. H. and C. R. RUTHVEN. — Biochem. J., 62(4):665—674. 1956.
26. GEERDES, J. D. et al. — Analyt. Chem., 26(2):264—266. 1954.
27. ZELEZNICK, L. D. — J. Chromatogr., 14(1):139—141. 1964.
28. ČÍŽ, K. — Listy Cukrovarn., 80(12):316—319. 1964.
29. TU CHEN-CHUAN, and K. WARD. — J. Am. Chem. Soc., 77(18):4938—4939. 1955.
30. SAMUELSON, O. and B. SWENSON. — Acta Chem. Scand., 16(8):2056—2058. 1962.
31. DAHLBERG, J. and O. SAMUELSON. — Svensk Kem. Tidskr., 75(4):178—183. 1963.
32. DAHLBERG, J. and O. SAMUELSON. — Acta Chem. Scand., 17(7):2136—2138. 1963.
33. ARWIDI, B. and O. SAMUELSON. — Analyt. Chim. Acta, 31(5):462—466. 1964.
34. LARSSON, L. I. and O. SAMUELSON. — Acta Chem. Scand., 19(6):1357—1364. 1965.
35. ARWIDI, B. and O. SAMUELSON. — Svensk Kem. Tidskr., 77(2):84—90. 1965.
36. JOHNSON, S. and O. SAMUELSON. — Sv. Papperstidn., 69(19):664—670. 1966.
37. JONES, J. K. N., R. A. WALL, and A. O. PITTET. — Chem. and Ind., No. 38:1196. 1959.
38. JONES, J. K. N., R. A. WALL, and A. O. PITTET. — Canad. J. Chem., 38(12):2285—2289. 1960.
39. JONES, J. K. N. and R. A. WALL. — Canad. J. Chem., 38(12):2290—2294. 1960.
40. SYAMANANDA, R., R. C. STAPLES, and R. BLOCK. — J. Contribs Boyce Thompson Inst., 21(6):363—369. 1952.
41. HOUGH, L., J. E. PRIDDLE, and R. S. THEOBALD. — Chem. and Ind., No. 28:900. 1960.
42. MACHELL, G. — J. Chem. Soc., pp. 3389—3393. Aug. 1957.
43. HALLEN, A. — Acta Chem. Scand., 14(10):2249—2250. 1960.
44. LEWIS, L. N., C. W. COGGINS, and J. C. F. KNAPP. — J. Chromatogr., 20(2):421—423. 1965.
45. ASHBY, T., T. BROOKS, and W. W. REID. — Chem. and Ind., No. 13:360. 1955.
46. KHYM, J. X. and D. G. DOHERTY. — J. Am. Chem. Soc., Vol. 74:3199. 1952.
47. LARSEN, B. and A. HUNG. — Acta Chem. Scand., Vol. 15:1397. 1961.
48. ROUDIER, A. and L. EBERHARD. — Compt. Rend., Vol. 240:2012. 1955.
49. ISHIDATE, M., S. TAKITANI, and T. NAKAJIMA. — J. Pharmac. Soc. Japan, 79(6):843—845. 1959.
50. HAUG, A. and B. LARSEN. — Acta Chem. Scand., 16(8):1908—1918. 1962.
51. GAPONENKOV, T. K. and Z. I. PROTSENKO. — ZhPKh, 34(3):709—711. 1961.
52. SAMUELSON, O. and L. WICTORIN. — Svensk Papperstidn., 67(14):555—557. 1964.
53. SAMUELSON, O. and R. SIMONSON. — Svensk Papperstidn., Vol. 65:685. 1962.

54. GLAUDEMANS, C. P. J. and T. E. TIMELL. – J. Am. Chem. Soc., Vol. 80 : 941. 1953; Vol. 80 : 1209. 1953.
55. SAMUELSON, O. and L. O. WALLENIUS. – J. Chromatogr., 12(2) : 236 – 241. 1963.
56. DZEWIATKOWSKI, D. – Biochim. Biophys. Acta, Vol. 56 : 167. 1962.
57. URBAS, B., C. T. BISHOP, and G. A. ADAMS. – Can. J. Chem., 41(6) : 1522 – 1524. 1963.
58. ROUDIER, A. and L. EBERHARD. – Compt. Rend., Vol. 247 : 1505. 1958.
59. ALFREDSSON, B., S. BERGDAHL, and O. SAMUELSON. – Anal. Chim. Acta, Vol. 28 : 371. 1963.
60. SAMUELSON, O. and R. SIMONSON. – Analyt. Chim. Acta, 26(2) : 110 – 119. 1962.
61. WETTERHOLM, A. Harald Nordenson Anniv., pp. 460 – 467. 1946.
62. LOIACONO, M. – Rassegna Chim., 16(3) : 126 – 128. 1964.
63. JONES, J. K. N. – J. Chem. Soc., p. 2. London. 1944.
64. LINDBERG, B. and B. WICKBERG. – Acta Chem. Scand., 8(4) : 569 – 573. 1954.
65. WHELEAN, W. J. and K. MORGAN. – Chem. and Ind., Jan., No. 3 : 78. 1954.
66. GEERDES, J. D. et al. – Analyt. Chem., 26(2) : 264 – 266. 1954.
67. HURD, C. D. and H. T. MILES. – Analyt. Chem., 36(7) : 1375 – 1378. 1964.
68. BLOM, J. – Acta Chem. Scand., 16(7) : 1779 – 1784. 1962.
69. OTAKE, T. – Proc. Res. Soc. Japan Sugar Refin. Technol., 12(12) : 25 – 34. 1963.
70. AUGESTAD, I., E. BERNER, and E. WEIGNER. – Chem. and Ind., No. 16 : 376 – 377. 1953.
71. TURVEY, J. R. and M. J. CLANCY. – Nature, 183(4660) : 537 – 538. 1959.
72. COLEMAN, G. and A. HOLT. – Chem. and Ind., No. 8 : 364. 1962.
73. AUSTIN, P. W. et al. – J. Chem. Soc., Nov., pp. 5350 – 5353. 1963.
74. LOCK, M. W. and G. N. RICHARDS. – J. Chem. Soc., Sept., pp. 3024 – 3027. 1955.
75. LEFEBVRE, M. J., N. S. GONZALES, and H. G. PONTIS. – J. Chromatogr., 15(4) : 495 – 500. 1964.
76. HOROWITZ, S. T., S. ROSEMAN, and H. J. BLUMENTHAL. – J. Am. Chem. Soc., 79(18) : 5046 – 5049. 1957.
77. KARABINOS, J. V. – Enclides, 14(160 – 161) : 263 – 264. 1954.
78. ALFREDSSON, B. and O. SAMUELSON. – Acta Chem. Scand., 16(4) : 1059 – 1061. 1962.
79. TÄUFEL, K., K. J. STEINBACH, and K. S. GRUNERT. – Nahrung, 5(1) : 66 – 83. 1961.
80. REBENFELD, L. and E. PACSU. – J. Am. Chem. Soc., 75(17) : 4370 – 4371. 1953.
81. TURTON, C. N. and E. PACSU. – J. Am. Chem. Soc., 77(4) : 1959 – 1961. 1955.
82. PHILLIPS, J. D. and A. POLLARD. – Nature, 171(4340) : 41 – 42. 1953.
83. BUHLER, D. R. et al. – J. Am. Chem. Soc., 77(2) : 481 – 482.
84. O'COLLA, P. S., E. E. LEE, and D. McGRATH. – J. Chem. Soc., July, pp. 2730 – 2733. 1962.

## 2. Paper chromatography

The development of paper chromatography resulted in considerable advances in carbohydrate chemistry, mainly in the studies of polysaccharide structure and of reactions given by carbohydrates.

During the ten years which followed the publication of the first report /1/ of sugar separation by paper chromatography, more than 1000 papers were published on the subject; during the last decade the number of publications was several times larger than this figure.

For a review of paper chromatography of carbohydrates and their derivatives, the reader is referred to the book by Hais and Macek /2/. This section will only deal with a number of papers which are of interest to wood chemistry.

**Preparation of samples for analysis.** Prior to the chromatographic analysis of carbohydrate-containing industrial products or the products of hydrolysis of polysaccharides, the solution must be prepared for analytical operations.

Fateeva /3/, who studied the products of metabolism of yeast grown on glucose-containing nutrient media, used ion exchange resins of Soviet manufacture to purify the organic acids and sugars before chromatographic separation on paper. The resins used were the medium-basic anion exchanger N – O and the strongly acidic cation exchanger SDV- 3.

The purification was conducted on the column represented in Figure 16.

The sample solution is introduced into the upper widened part of the column; the solution passes through the resin layer and then through the capillary tube into the collector vessel or into a second column. The advantage of this shape of the outlet tube is that the resin always remains under a layer of liquid. Before being filled into the column, the resin is swollen in distilled water. The anion exchanger N — O is regenerated with a 3% solution of NaOH, the cation exchanger SDV- 3 with a 6% solution of HCl; 25 grams of the resin require 200 — 250 ml alkali and 500 — 600 ml acid, passed at the rate of 50 ml/hour. After regeneration the resin is carefully washed with distilled water.

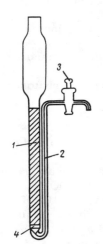

FIGURE 16. Diagram of column with ion exchange resin:

1 — resin; 2 — thin capillary tube; 3 — stopcock; 4 — thin layer of glass wool.

Under these conditions the organic acids are readily absorbed and are then eluted from the anion exchanger column with 3% NaOH; the eluate is then passed through the column with the cation exchanger, the resulting aqueous solution of acids is evaporated and analyzed by paper chromatography using the solvent system n- amyl alcohol: 5 M formic acid = 1:1; the spots are revealed by a solution of bromocresol green and an alkaline solution of silver nitrate /4/. Sugars are not sorbed on these resins, so that the method can be used to separate sugars from acids and also to purify the sugar solutions from cations and anions prior to analysis. Further chromatographic analysis of sugars may be conducted in the system ethyl acetate: ethanol: water (12:2:1) /5/, and the spots revealed according to Boyarkin /6/. Ion exchangers manufactured in the Soviet Union do not decompose sugars, whereas resins IRA- 400 and Dowex- 2, which are widely utilized abroad, absorb sugars in hydroxyl form, up to 50% of which are decomposed as a result, with the formation of organic acids /7 — 9/.

**Selection of solvent system.** In selecting a solvent system for the separation of sugars, it should be borne in mind that sugars are readily soluble in water and in lower alcohols, and are practically insoluble in hydrophobic and medium- hydrophilic solvents.

The solvent used in sugar chromatography should ensure the maximum possible differences in the $R_f$-values and should not be too viscous or the time of separation will be too long.

In view of these requirements, sugars are frequently separated with the aid of systems which contain the highly mobile ethyl acetate, to which a third component, readily soluble in both water and the ester, has been added in order to enhance the solubility of water and thus also of sugars in it. Such components are lower fatty acids (acetic and formic), pyridine, methanol and ethanol.

The following systems /2/ are extensively employed in the separation of sugars:

n- butanol: acetic acid: water = 4:1:5
n- butanol: formic acid: water (12:1:1)
ethyl acetate: acetic acid: water = 3:1:3
n- butanol: butyric acid: water = 1:1:1

n-butanol: pyridine: water = 6:4:3;
ethyl acetate: pyridine: water = 2:1:2;
n-butanol: acetone: water = 2:7:1.

The following systems are used in the separation of mixtures of some sugars with similar $R_f$-values:

n-butanol: pyridine: water = 6:4:3 to separate glucose from galactose;
n-butanol: acetic acid: water = 4:1:5;
ethyl acetate: pyridine: water = 2:1:2 to separate glucose, saccharose and fructose;

phenol saturated with water to separate xylose, arabinose and fructose, and also mannose and fructose;

n-butanol: pyridine: water = 6:4:3 to separate oligosaccharides containing up to 14 monosaccharide residues.

Repeated chromatographic separation is often employed to improve the separation of sugars.

The separation of D-glucose and D-galactose by repeated chromatography on paper with a solvent system n-$C_4H_9OH$ — $CH_3COOC_4H_9$ — $CH_3COOH$ — $CH_3OH$ — $H_2O$ (2:2:3:1:1) served as the basis for the calculation /10/ of the conditions of separation of the components. It was found, in particular, that the optimum number of passes $n$ for known values $a$ and $b$ of $R_f$ for glucose and galactose respectively may be described by the equation:

$$n = \log \; [ \; \log \; (1 - a)/ \log \; (1 - b)]/ \log \; [(1 - b)/(1 - a)].$$

**Detection of sugars on chromatograms.** Sugar spots on chromatograms are revealed by numerous reagents, in accordance with the specific reactions given by each reagent.

Table 11 gives a list of the main color reagents for the different sugars /2/. Thiobarbituric acid has been proposed /11/ for the detection of sugar spots on chromatograms; the reagent forms colored compounds with malonic dialdehyde, which is formed as a result of the reaction between $HIO_4$ and 2-deoxy-sugars, with β-formylpyruvic acid formed in the same manner from 2-keto-3-deoxyaldonic and N-acetylneuraminic acids, with hydroxymethylfurfural which is readily formed, mainly from ketoses and oligosaccharides with ketose residues, and with polyaldehydes which are the products of oxidation of glycosides and oligosaccharides by periodic acid.

Sugars can also be revealed by iodine /12/, $Ag^{110}$ isotope compounds /13/, p-anisidine /14/, dimethyl-α-naphthylamine /15/, p-anisidine hydrochloride /16/, p-toluidine hydrochloride /17/, cerium sulfate /18/, ammonium molybdate /19/, alkaline solution of the complex $K_7[Cu(IO_6)_2]$ /20/, potassium permanganate with bromothymol blue /21/, triphenyl-tetrazolium chloride /22/, ammoniacal solutions of silver nitrate /23/, potassium 3,6-dinitrophthalate /24/, dimedone /25/, anthrone /26/ and other compounds /27/. It has been recommended /28/ that carbohydrates be detected by spraying the chromatogram with a 1% solution of $NaIO_4$ and then with a 1% solution of potassium permanganate. Modified reactions with phloroglucinol /29/ and benzidine /30/ have been employed. Multiple spraying is employed /31/ to reveal the spots of sugars and polyhydric alcohols on the same chromatogram.

In certain methods of sugar determination, spraying of chromatograms can be dispensed with. In one such method /32/ the color reagents are introduced into the solvent system. Thus, when sugars are developed by

TABLE 11. Reactions for the detection of sugar

| Reagent | Aldopentoses | Aldohexoses | Ketopentoses | Ketohexoses | Methylpentoses | Nonreducing disaccharides | Reducing disaccharides | Alcohols | Nonreducing acids | Ketoacids and uronic acids | Acid lactones | Deoxy sugars | Methylated aldoses | Methylated ketoses | Sugar phosphates | Amino sugars | Sensitivity, µg |
|---|---|---|---|---|---|---|---|---|---|---|---|---|---|---|---|---|---|
| Silver nitrate | + | + | + | + | + |  | + | (+) | − | + | − |  | + | + | + | + | 1–5 |
| Triphenyltetrazolium chloride | + | + | + | + | + | − | + | − | − | + | − |  |  |  |  | + | 1–5 |
| Benzidine periodate | + | + | + | + | + | + | + | + | + | + | + | + | + | + | + | + | 5–10 |
| Periodate-KMnO$_4$-benzidine | + | + | + | + | + | + | + | + | + | + | + | + | + | + | + | + | 3–10 |
| Resorcinol | + | − | + | + | + | + | − | − |  | + |  |  |  | + | + |  | 5–10 |
| Anthrone | − | − |  | + | − | + | + | − |  |  |  |  |  |  | + |  | 10 |
| Acid aniline phthalate | + | + | − | − | + | − | + | − | − | + | − |  | + | (+) | + | (+) | 2–5 |
| Anilinodiphenylamine | + | + | + | + | + | + | + | − | − | + | − |  |  |  | + | + | 5 |
| Ammonium molybdate | − | − | − | − | − | − | − | − | − | + | − | − | − | − | + | − |  |
| Ninhydrin | − | − | − | − | − | − | − | − | − | − | − | − | − | − | − | + |  |

55

the system n-butanol: acetic acid: water = 40:10:50 (upper layer), benzidine or p-anisidine is introduced. The spots appear on the paper after the chromatogram has been dried at 100° for 10 minutes; glucose, arabinose, galactose and rhamnose can be separated in this manner.

Quantitative sugar determination is conducted by direct photometric measurements carried out on the chromatogram, or else the sugars are extracted from the paper and then determined in a suitable manner.

Irrespective of the large number of solvent systems and color reagents which may be used in the paper chromatography of sugars, the technique proposed by Emel'yanova and Batrakova /34/ (see also /33/) has found extensive application in the studies on the chemistry of wood performed in the Soviet Union. We shall now discuss this analytical technique.

Sugars are separated by the descending method and the solvent which drains from the lower end of the paper strip is collected in special receiving vessels. The dimensions of the paper strips are $3 \times 45$ cm. The glass chamber contains 12 — 14 such strips. The solvent is the upper layer of the mixture ethyl acetate: pyridine: water = 5:1:5. Control solutions are also applied to some of the strips with the aid of a micropipet.

Xylose is separated from rhamnose in 24 hours; the separation of other sugars takes 50 hours. The spots are revealed by spraying the strips with a solution of aniline phthalate (1.66 g phthalic acid and 0.92 ml freshly distilled aniline in 100 ml ethanol). The chromatograms are dried in the air and then placed in a drying oven at 105° for 5 minutes.

The $R_f$-values of different sugars obtained by this method are listed in Table 12.

TABLE 12. $R_f$-values of different sugars

| Sugar | $R_f$ | Sugar | $R_f$ |
|---|---|---|---|
| Galactose . . . . . . . . | 0.15 | Arabinose . . . . . . . . | 0.25 |
| Glucose . . . . . . . . . | 0.18 | Xylose . . . . . . . . . | 0.33 |
| Mannose . . . . . . . . . | 0.22 | Rhamnose . . . . . . . . | 0.47 |
| Fructose . . . . . . . . . | 0.23 | | |

Quantitative determinations of sugars may be performed by different methods. An accurate, though laborious method /34/ is to extract the sugars with water from the unrevealed parts of the paper, corresponding to the zones of individual sugars and then to determine the sugars in the extract by the potentiometric ebulliostatic method.

In a more convenient method /33/ the colored products of the reaction between the sugars and aniline phthalate are extracted. The extraction is usually effected with glacial acetic acid, methanol or ethanolic solution of hydrochloric acid. The determination is carried out by the photometric method, using a FEK-n-57 photoelectrocolorimeter, and the contents of the individual sugars are read off the calibration graphs. This method is more convenient than the ebulliostatic termination.

The colored compounds need not be extracted from the paper strips if the photometer employed measures the intensity of the light reflected by the chromatogram (e.g., Zeiss ERJ-10 automatic recorder).

Paper chromatography is very extensively employed in the studies of wood chemistry /35 — 37/. All studies which have appeared in the last few years involve the use of chromatography as the main technique of the research.

BIBLIOGRAPHY

1. PARTRIDGE, S. M. — Nature, Vol. 158: 270. 1946.
2. HAIS, I. M. and K. MACEK, editors. Paper Chromatography. [Russian translation from the Czech. 1962.]
3. FATEEVA, M. V. — ZhPKh, No. 11: 2576 — 2581. 1965.
4. BUCH, M. L., R. MONTGOMERY, and W. L. PORTER. — Analyt. Chem., 24(3): 489. 1952.
5. BORECKÝ, J. and J. GASPARIC. — Collect. Czech. Chem. Communs, Vol. 25: 1287. 1960.
6. BOYARKIN, A. N. — Fiziologiya Rastenii, No. 2: 298. 1955.
7. PHILLIPS, J. D. and A. POLLARD. — Nature, Vol. 171: 41. 1953.
8. HULME, A. C. — Nature, Vol. 171: 610. 1953.
9. HULME, A. C. and A. RICHARDSON. — J. Sci. Food and Agric., 5(5): 221. 1954.
10. RÜDIGER, R. and H. RÜDIGER. — J. Chrom., 17(1): 186 — 187. 1965.
11. PERCHERON, F. — Bull. Soc. Chim. France, No. 1: 255 — 259. 1965.
12. GREENWAY, R. M., P. W. KENT, and M. W. WHITEHOUSE. — Research Corr., Suppl. to Research, 6(1): 63. 1953.
13. JAARMA, M. — Acta Chem. Scand., 8(5): 860 — 862. 1954.
14. TORRACA, G. — Ricerca Scient., 24(1): 113 — 114. 1954.
15. AIRAN, J. W. and R. M. DESAI. — Sci. and Culture, 20(10): 505 — 506. 1955.
16. PRIDHAM, J. B. — Analyt. Chem., 28(12): 1967 — 1968. 1956.
17. STAGGEMEIER, O. M. — Dansk tidsskr. farmaci, Suppl. No. 2: 267 — 270. 1956.
18. THALER, H. — Nahrung, 2(2): 111 — 116. 1958.
19. EL KHADEM, H. and S. HANESSIAN. — Analyt. Chem., 30(12): 1965. 1958.
20. BONNER, T. G. — Chem. and Ind., No. 13: 345. 1960.
21. AKITA, E. and T. IKEKAWA. — J. Chrom., 12(2): 250 — 251. 1963.
22. FRIČ, F. and O. KUBANIOVÁ. — J. Chrom., 11(1): 127 — 130. 1963.
23. BEER, J. Z. — J. Chrom., 11(2): 247 — 252. 1963.
24. MOMOSE, T. and M. NAKAMURA. — Talanta, 10(1): 115 — 116. 1963.
25. ADACHI, S. — Analyt. Biochem., 9(2): 224 — 227. 1964.
26. SUNDERWIRTH, S. G. and G. G. OLSON. — J. Chrom., 16(1): 176 — 180. 1964.
27. GONZÁLES-ALONSO, M. — Fyton, 19(2): 95 — 100. 1962.
28. WOLFROM, M. L. and J. B. MILLER. — Analyt. Chem., 28(6): 1037. 1956.
29. BORENFREUND, E. and Z. DISCHE. — Arch. Biochem. and Biophys., 67(1): 239 — 240. 1957.
30. CHAN, B. G. and J. C. CAIN. — Nature, 192(4797): 69 — 70. 1961.
31. LAMBOU, M. G. — Analyt. Chem., 28(7): 1216. 1956.
32. EL KHADEM, H. S., Z. M. EL SHAFEI, and M. A. A. RAHMAN. — Analyt. Chem., 35(11): 1766. 1963.
33. OBOLENSKAYA, A. V. et al. Prakticheskie raboty po khimii drevesiny i tsellyulozy (Practical Work in the Chemistry of Cellulose and Wood). — Izdatel'stvo Lesnaya Promyshlennost'. 1965.
34. EMEL'YANOVA, I. Z. and T. A. BATRAKOVA. — ZhAKh, 13(1): 142. 1958.
35. SAEMAN, J. E., W. E. MOORE, and M. A. MILLETT. — Carb. Chem., Vol. 3: 54 — 69. London. 1963.
36. SHARKOV, V. I. et al. — Sbornik Trudov VNIIGS, No. 14: 7 — 12. 1965.
37. VARAKSINA, T. N., Yu. I. KHOL'KIN, and V. A. BAZHENOV. — Izvestiya VUZov, Lesnoi Zhurnal, No. 2: 137 — 139. 1967.

## 3. Thin layer chromatography

Even though thin layer chromatography began to be employed in carbo-hydrate chemistry only in 1960, while the first studies on the subject appeared only in 1961 /1, 2/, it is now very extensively applied. The method, which is almost as accurate as paper chromatography, is rapid and makes it possible to analyze multicomponent mixtures within $0.5 - 2$ hours instead of the $0.5 - 2$ days which are required for paper chromatography. A comparison /3/ between thin layer and paper chromatography shows that the former method is in certain respects preferable. In the chemistry of wood this method is employed to a rapidly increasing extent.

## Chromatography of simple sugars and oligosaccharides

For reviews of the first separations of sugars by thin layer chromatography the reader is referred to books /4, 5/ and papers /7/. Tabulated $R_f$-values of various sugars are given in /6/.

Thin layer sorbents used for the purpose are mainly those usually employed in column chromatography. The inorganic sorbents include different brands of silica gel, alumina, plaster of Paris and other materials. Sugars have been successfully separated on organic materials such as powdered cellulose and its derivatives, etc.

**Separation on kieselguhr.** The first studies on the separation of carbohydrates by thin layer chromatography were carried out on kieselguhr with an admixture of plaster of Paris (kieselguhr G).

Stahl and Kaltenbach /1/ used $250 \mu$ thick layers of kieselguhr G, which was mixed with a 0.02 M solution of sodium acetate before application on a $20 \times 20$ cm plate. The best solvent system for this layer proved to be 65 ml ethyl acetate — 35 ml of a 2:1 mixture of isopropanol with water. In order to improve the separation of di- and trisaccharides the content of the latter mixture was increased. The application of this method resulted in a qualitative group separation of mixtures of mono-, di- and trisaccharides containing up to 15 components (see also /8/).

A somewhat improved technique /9/ resulted in the separation on a thin kieselguhr G layer of a mixture of lactose, saccharose, D(+)-galactose, fructose, D (+)-glucose, D (—)-arabinose, D (+)-xylose and L (+)-rhamnose.

The experimental conditions were as follows. The concentration of each sugar in the model mixture was $2 \mu g/\mu l$. A mixture of 3 g kieselguhr G powder (Merck Co.) in 7.5 ml of a 0.02 M sodium acetate or boric acid solution was brought onto a $10 \times 15$ cm plate. The plate was dried at 105° for 40 minutes. The separation was effected by the ascending method at 20° during $30 - 120$ minutes. A $2 \mu g$ amount of each sugar was applied to the plate.

The solvents were (volume ratios): A) chloroform:methanol = 6:4; B) 2-propanol:water = 4:1; C) acetone:water = 9:1; D) acetone:water: chloroform:methanol = 8:0.5:1:1; E) methanol:chloroform:acetone: ammonia 28°Be' = 5:2:3:2; F) methanol:chloroform:ammonia 28°Be' = 6:4:0.7. The spots were revealed by spraying the chromatogram with ammonia and diphenylamine dissolved in acetone, with subsequent heating of the plates at 85° during 10 minutes. The $R_f$-values of different sugars are shown in Table 13.

All components of the mixture were satisfactorily separated by the use of solvent systems A and E.

TABLE 13. $R_f$-values of different sugars

| Compound | Solvent | | | | | |
|---|---|---|---|---|---|---|
| | A | B | C | D | E | F |
| Lactose . . . . . . . . | 0.12 | 0.35 | 0.29 | 0.13 | 0.06 | 0.05 |
| Saccharose . . . . . . | 0.19 | 0.56 | 0.48 | 0.24 | + | 0.11 |
| D(+)-Galactose . . . . | 0.27 | 0.48 | 0.45 | 0.35 | 0.25 | 0.14 |
| Fructose . . . . . . . . | 0.30 | 0.50 | 0.47 | 0.34 | 0.14 | 0.17 |
| D(+)-Glucose . . . . . | 0.37 | 0.56 | 0.55 | 0.42 | 0.20 | 0.19 |
| D(–)-Arabinose . . . . | 0.41 | 0.52 | 0.53 | 0.46 | 0.37 | 0.26 |
| D(+)-Xylose . . . . . | 0.46 | 0.65 | 0.65 | 0.55 | 0.40 | 0.33 |
| L(+)-Rhamnose . . . . | 0.54 | 0.70 | 0.71 | 0.61 | 0.47 | 0.40 |
| Sodium acetate . . . . | + | + | + | + | | + |
| Boric acid . . . . . . | | | | | + | |
| Time, minutes . . . . | 30 | 120 | 30 | 40 | 30 | 30 |

Waldi /10/ studied the chromatographic behavior of 20 sugars and
alcohols on a thin layer of kieselguhr G 250 $\mu$ thick. The kieselguhr (20 g)
was stirred with 40 ml of phosphate buffer made of equal volumes of 0.1 M
$H_3PO_4$ and 0.1 M $Na_2HPO_4$ (pH 4.8). The mixture was brought onto a
20 × 20 cm plate and dried in the air overnight. The sugar solution
(concentration 0.5%) was applied in amounts between 5 and 25 $\mu$g from a
micropipet. The solvent was n-butanol: acetone: phosphate buffer =
40: 50:10, and the duration of the separation was 30 — 35 minutes. The
sugars were revealed by spraying the chromatogram with a 0.1% solution of
sodium metaperiodate, and, after drying, with a solution of benzidine.
The benzidine solution was prepared by dissolving 2.8 g benzidine in 80 ml
of 96% alcohol, and adding 70 ml water, 30 ml acetone and 1.5 ml HCl to
the solution. The plate was placed during 5 minutes in a vessel containing
ammonia vapors, and was then sprayed with a solution of silver nitrate.

Sugars have also been separated /4/ on a thin layer of alusil (mixture
of alumina G with silica gel G (1:1)).

Glucose, maltose and maltooligosaccharides with up to 10 glucose units
have been separated /11/ on a thin layer of kieselguhr. Best results were
obtained with the following solvent systems: butanol: 2, 6-lutidine: water =
6:3:1; butanol: ethanol: water = 5:3:2 and butanol: pyridine: water =
75:15:10. Thin layer chromatography was also applied /12/ in separating
mixtures of oligosaccharides with up to 6 glucose residues.

Sugars have been separated /13/ on a 6:4 mixtures of kieselguhr with
silica gel; such mixtures are successfully separated with the solvent
system isopropanol: ethyl acetate: water = 27:3.1:1, while the zones are
revealed with a solution of $Pb(CH_3COO)_2$.

Sugar separation in a thin layer of kieselguhr takes place mainly by the
partition mechanism, so that the amount of the sample to be applied is
small (not more than 5 $\mu$g sugar). On the other hand, silica gel or alumina
do not fully lose their adsorptive properties during sugar separation, and
10 times more sugar may be applied to these layers than to the kieselguhr
layer. For this reason most sugar separations by thin layer chromatography have been performed on the more active sorbent — silica gel.

**Separation on silica gel.** In quantitative determination of sugars /14/
these are separated on a layer of silica gel G which is prepared using
0.1 N solution of boric acid instead of water. This treatment is designed

to prevent splitting the spots given by certain sugars into two /1/. Simple model mixtures of monosaccharides, disaccharides and uronic acids may be separated, for example, by the system benzene: glacial acetic acid: methanol = 20:20:60.

The spots are revealed with the aid of 1, 3-dihydroxynaphthalene (naphthoresorcinol) in sulfuric acid. The quantitative determination is performed as follows: the sugar spot together with the sorbent is cut into strips, mixed with excess 0.01 N or 0.05 N solution of potassium dichromate in 70% sulfuric acid, heated for 60 minutes at 90°, cooled, and 20 ml water and 5 ml of 5% KI are added. The liberated iodine is titrated after 20 minutes against 0.01 N sodium thiosulfate. The accuracy of the determination is ± 5%.

One of the first studies on the application of thin layer chromatography to carbohydrate chemistry /2/ deals with the selection of the experimental conditions suitable for the separation of polyhydroxy compounds. Model mixtures of these substances included not only carbohydrates and related compounds (glucose, lactose, glucosaccharinic acid), but also polyhydric alcohols (ethylene and propylene glycols, glycerol, 3-methylhexyne-1-diol-3, 4) and polyhydroxy acids (tartaric and 2, 3-dihydroxy-2-methylpentanoic acid).

The mixtures were separated on a thin layer of KSK (150 — 200 mesh) silica gel, on 13 × 18 cm plates. The layer was bound with plaster of Paris (6 g silica gel, 0.35 g plaster of Paris, 15 ml water); the drying lasted for 6 — 12 hours in the air and for 40 minutes at 104 — 106°. The best systems for the separation of carbohydrates proved to be ethanol: water = 96:5 and ethanol: ammonia: water = 16:1:3; the system chloroform: methanol = 9:1 proved to be best for the separation of polyhydric alcohols. The most sensitive reagent for spot detection proved to be a mixture of 5% aqueous silver nitrate with 25% ammonia /15/, which is used in paper chromatography. It has been noted that the sensitivity of the reagents studied (alkaline sodium periodate and potassium permanganate, lead tetraacetate with subsequent spraying with rosaniline and potassium periodate with benzidine) is 2 — 5 times lower than when they are used in paper chromatography.

Mono-, di- and trisaccharides of interest to the starch and molasses industry have been separated /16/ on a thin layer of silica gel. Silica gel is an active sorbent, and may alter the sugars in the process of chromatographic analysis; it is accordingly frequently modified /4/ by impregnation with various solutions.

Thin layer chromatography on silica gel G, impregnated with a 0.2 M solution of $NaH_2PO_4$ has been applied /17/ in the separation and identification of mono-, di- and trisaccharides. The best solvent system is $C_4H_9OH — CH_3COCH_3 — H_2O$ (4:5:1).

Very different solvent systems may be utilized in carbohydrate chromatography on thin layers. In particular, glucose, galactose, mannose, fructose, sorbose, arabinose, xylose and ribose on silica gel are developed by $CH_3COOC_2H_5 — HCON(CH_3)_2 — H_2O$ = 30:6:2 /18/; if separated on kieselguhr treated with 0.1 M sodium acetate, the system ethyl acetate: isopropanol: water = 32:12:6 should be utilized. Glucose may be separated from galactose on silica gel by developing with $CH_3COOC_2H_5 — n-C_3H_7OH — H_2O$ = 2:7:1. The sugar zones are revealed with the aid of the mixture aniline: diphenylamine: phosphoric acid.

Quantitative determination of aldoses was performed by revealing the spots and drying the plate which had been treated with a 0.2% solution of benzidine in acetic acid (in the case of disaccharides the solution also contained a small amount of concentrated sulfuric acid), and heating the plate at 100° for 10 minutes. The parts of the sorbent corresponding to the zones of aldoses were removed from the plate, 0.2 ml of a 3:2 mixture of alcohol with water was added and then 0.2 ml of 0.2% benzidine in acetic acid, and the mixture heated at 100° for 15 minutes for pentoses, 30 minutes for hexoses, 1 hour for disaccharides, and a photometric determination of the resulting solutions performed at 350 m$\mu$. Between 1 and 50 $\gamma$ of aldoses may be determined by this method.

Thin layer chromatography on silica gel G was applied /19/ to a study of a number of mixtures of mannoses and oligosaccharides. The following solvent systems ensure a satisfactory separation of the compounds within 3 — 5 hours by the ascending technique: n-butanol:isopropanol:water = 5:3:1 or 1:7:2 and n-butanol:methanol:water = 5:3:1. Under these conditions stachyose, raffinose, lactose, saccharose, galactose, glucose, mannose, fructose, arabinose and rhamnose can be separated. Spots of galactose are not separated from saccharose, while spots of lactose are not separated from raffinose; in order to improve the separation of these sugars the chromatographic development must be repeated.

Studies of carbohydrates and their derivatives /7/ resulted in the development of the procedure for the separation and identification on a thin layer of silica gel of numerous sugars, polyhydric alcohols, glucosides and their methyl ethers, acetals and mercaptals of sugars and polyhydric alcohols, sugar acids and their derivatives. The solvent systems used included benzene:ethanol:water:conc.ammonia = 200:47:15:1, n-butanol: acetic acid:ether:water = 9:6:3:1 and n-butanol:acetic acid:water = 2:1:1. The zones were revealed with the aid of concentrated sulfuric acid or a 0.5% solution of $KMnO_4$ in 1 N NaOH. For quantitative determination of 3-o-methyl-D-glucopyranose, 2, 3, 6-tri-o-methyl-D-glucopyranose and 2, 3, 4, 6-tetra-o-methyl-D-glucose in the presence of each other, solvent system $A$ * was employed, the silica gel zones with the substances were withdrawn, the compounds eluted with water and determined spectrophoto-metrically.

Spots of radioactive compounds do not require spraying. Sugars and polyhydric alcohols tagged with $C^{14}$ are chromatogrammed /20/ on a thin layer of silica gel G or kieselguhr G. After analysis, the plate is treated with a solution of 11.2 g polystyrene and 1.4 — 2.3 ml dibutyl phthalate in 100 ml benzene, held at room temperature, then for 30 minutes at 70°, soaked in water at 55° for 5 minutes and the sorbent is peeled off as film. The zones of the components are located by their activity or by radioautography.

Carbohydrates can also be separated /21/ on mixtures of silica gel and kieselguhr in proportions varying between 1:2 and 1:4, which were used without any preliminary treatment or else were treated with 0.02 M sodium acetate and 2% aqueous poly(vinyl alcohol).

A comparison has been made /22/ between the separation efficiency of sugars and sugar derivatives on a thin layer of silica gel and on paper.

* [Unclear in Russian.]

Aldohexoses, ketohexoses and oligosaccharides have been separated /23/ on a thin layer of silica gel impregnated with 0.02 N sodium acetate or a 0.5% solution of poly(vinyl alcohol); by development with ethyl acetate: dimethylformamide: water = 60: 30:5 or silica gel G, using the system ethyl acetate: n-propanol: water = 2: 7:1.

After the chromatographic development, the solvent is evaporated by heating the strip at 50 — 60° in the case of mixtures containing dimethyl-formamide and the chromatogram is sprayed with a 0.5% solution of $KMnO_4$ in sodium carbonate. The carbohydrates are quantitatively determined by a color reaction with diphenylamine. To do this, parts of the sorbent which contain the spots are mixed with a known volume of the reagent containing 10 parts concentrated HCl, 8 parts glacial acetic acid and 2 parts of a 10% alcoholic solution of diphenylamine. The mixture is heated on a water bath, cooled, diluted with glacial acetic acid, separated from the silica gel by centrifugation and photometric determination performed on the solution at 640 m$\mu$.

Sugar separation in a thin silica gel layer on mat glass has certain advantages /24/.

Sugars may be separated /25/ on a thin layer of silica gel in the presence of bisulfite and also on a thin silica gel layer, impregnated with borate /26/. Raffinose and saccharose have been separated /27/ on a thin layer of silica gel containing 5% starch. The determination of sugars during an investigation of glucosides has been described /28/.

It should be noted that silica gel is best suited to thin layer chromato-graphic detection and determination of carbohydrates, in preference to all other inorganic sorbents. Accordingly, the analytical procedures described in the present section may also be applied in the analysis of carbohydrate-containing products of chemical processing of wood.

**Chromatography on other inorganic sorbents.** $R_f$-values for a number of mono- and disaccharides and polyhydric alcohols on a thin layer of plaster of Paris have been determined. It has been shown /29/ that certain two-component mixtures of carbohydrates can be separated with chloroform: methanol = 19: 2.

Mixtures of n-propanol: water = 5:5 and n-propanol: water: n-propyl-amine = 5:3:2 have been employed in the separation of mixtures of carbohydrates and polyhydric alcohols on a thin layer of magnesium silicate /30/. n-Propylamine could also be replaced by isopropylamine, n-butylamine, diethylamine, triethylamine and pyridine. The components are revealed as light-colored spots on a violet-colored background when the chromatogram is sprayed with 1% $KMnO_4$. The dried chromatograms may also be sprayed with a solution of 1.7 g of diphenylamine in 75 ml n-butanol saturated with water, dried again and held for 20 minutes at 130°. Aldoses and ketones give bright blue spots, while polyhydric alcohols remain colorless.

It has been proposed /31/ that sugars and sugar phenylhydrazones be separated and identified on a thin layer (0.5 mm) of a 4:1 mixture of acid $Al_2O_3$ with plaster of Paris, by developing with mixtures of n-butanol: acetone: water = 4:5:1 and 7:2:1. The substances are applied as 1% solutions in pyridine (15 — 20 $\gamma$ each). The spots are revealed by spraying with the mixture anisaldehyde: conc. $H_2SO_4$: 95% ethanol = 1:1:18 and heating at 110°. After 2 — 3 minutes the hydrazones form yellow-green spots; after 10 minutes the sugars form green, blue or violet spots. It has been reported, however /29/, that monosaccharides cannot be effectively separated on a thin layer of alumina.

Sugars have also been separated /32/ on a thin (0.2 mm) layer of hydrated calcium silicate.

Even though sugars can be separated on a large number of sorbents, for routine work it is recommended to use standard chromatographic grade sorbents (e. g., silica gel) which are sold specially for purposes of chromatographic analysis and which answer definite quality specifications.

**Chromatography on organic sorbents.** The organic sorbents which are chiefly used in sugar separations are powdered cellulose and cellulose derivatives, which are usually bound to the glass plate with the aid of plaster of Paris.

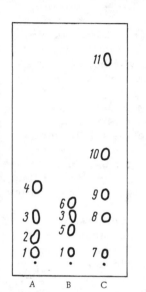

FIGURE 17. Separation of mixtures of polyhydroxy compounds:

A and B — system tert-butanol: ethyl acetate: water = 6 : 13 : 3. 1 — lactose; 2 — galactose; 3 — mannose; 4 — ribose; 5 — glucose; 6 — lyxose; C — system n-butanol: 25% NH₄OH: water = 16 : 1 : 2; 7 — inositol; 8 — mannitol; 9 — 2, 3-dihydroxy-2-methylpentanoic acid; 10 — glycerol; 11 — 2-methyl-pentanetriol-1, 2, 3.

Dyatlovitskaya et al. /33/ described a method for the separation of mixtures of simple sugars and polyhydric alcohols on a thin layer of cellulose powder. The cellulose powder was prepared by boiling 800 g cotton cellulose in 5 liters of a 10% solution of HCl in absolute ethanol for 20 — 25 minutes with subsequent washing with water and methanol and drying in the air. The layer was bound (5 g cellulose, 0.3 g plaster of Paris and 15 ml water) on 13×18 cm plates. In separating carbohydrates by the ascending technique, best results were obtained using the following solvent systems: tert-butanol: n-propanol: water = 8:2:3 (I), tert-butanol: ethyl acetate: water = 6:13:3 (II), sec-butanol: ethyl acetate: water = 8:12:3 (III), isopropanol: ethyl acetate: water = 25:65:11 (IV), n-butanol: pyridine: water = 10:3:3 (V), acetone: butanol: water = 7:2:1 (VI) and n-propanol: ethyl acetate: water = 15:2:3 (VII). The $R_f$-values of the sugars obtained with these solvent systems are shown in Table 14; Figure 17 gives an example of the chromatographic separation of three different mixtures.

The sugars were revealed by the Partridge reaction /34/, viz., with aniline—phthalic acid or aniline — diphenylamine — phosphoric acid /35/. When carbohydrates are separated on a thin cellulose layer, the sensitivity of the reagents is much higher than on silica gel.

Descending chromatography on a thin layer of cellulose was successfully employed /36/ to separate mixtures of sugars with similar $R_f$-values, which cannot be separated by the ascending technique on thin layers. Optimum separation of sugar mixtures was attained in the following solvent systems: n-butanol: pyridine: water = 10:3:3 for mixtures of galactose, glucose, mannose, xylose, ribose and rhamnose; n-butanol: 25% NH₄OH: water = 16:1:2 for a mixture of arabinose, xylose, ribose and rhamnose; phenol: n-butanol: acetic acid: water = 5:5:2:10 for mixtures of mannose, arabinose, lyxose and ribose. This method will detect 0.5 — 1 γ of the compound if the mixture is applied as spots and 5 — 10 γ if it is applied as thin strip.

TABLE 14. $R_f$-values of sugars

| Sugar | Solvent system | | | | | | |
|---|---|---|---|---|---|---|---|
| | I | II | III | IV | V | VI | VII |
| Lactose . . . . . . . . | 0.19 | 0.03 | 0.01 | 0.01 | 0.12 | 0.03 | 0.07 |
| Galactose . . . . . . . | 0.37 | 0.11 | 0.06 | 0.07 | 0.27 | 0.12 | 0.21 |
| Glucose . . . . . . . . | 0.40 | 0.13 | 0.08 | 0.09 | 0.32 | 0.14 | 0.23 |
| Mannose. . . . . . . . | 0.44 | 0.19 | 0.12 | 0.14 | 0.37 | 0.22 | 0.32 |
| Lyxose. . . . . . . . . | 0.48 | 0.24 | 0.17 | 0.19 | 0.44 | 0.38 | 0.42 |
| Ribose . . . . . . . . . | 0.52 | 0.32 | 0.21 | 0.23 | 0.46 | 0.44 | 0.40 |

Microcrystalline cellulose in the form of a preparation known as Avirin has been recommended /37/ as sorbent for thin layer chromatography of unsubstituted sugars, amino sugars, glucosides, methyl ethers of sugars, hydroxy acids and lactones. For the preparation of the sorbent, see /38/. The properties of powdered cellulose are greatly superior to those of silica gel G usually employed in chromatography. The plates are prepared by mixing 100 g of the cellulose with 430 ml water and applied to a $20 \times 20 \times 0.4$ cm glass plate; the sorbent film has a thickness of 1.0 mm. The plate is dried at 80°. The glass plate must be very pure, when the cellulose layer firmly adheres to the glass after drying; thus, the plates may be stored for a long time. Mixture separation takes $1 - 3$ hours; the experimental procedure is that used in paper chromatography, but a better separation is obtained.

In another method of plate preparation /39/ 15 grams of powdered cellulose in 90 ml of a 5:1 mixture of water with methanol are applied to the plate and dried for 2 hours at room temperature. The most effective sugar separation is attained using the solvent system formic acid: methyl ethyl ketone: tert-butanol: water = 15:30:40:15. The zones are revealed with the aid of a solution of 2-aminodiphenyl and oxalic acid in 85% ethanol.

For sugar separation on a thin cellulose layer see also /40/.

Powdered cellulose for chromatographic analysis is commercially available in a large number of countries, so that the methods just discussed may be extensively applied to the analysis of sugars contained in the products of chemical processing of wood.

Thin layer chromatography is now employed for the determination of carbohydrates in various technical products, mainly in the sugar and starch molasses industry.


Chromatography of polyhydric alcohols

Polyhydric alcohols are prepared on an industrial scale by hydrogenation of the corresponding monosaccharides. Modern procedures for the preparation of polyhydric alcohols by hydrogenolysis of monosaccharides and polysaccharides yield glycerol, ethylene glycol, propylene glycol and other alcohols. Accordingly, methods for the analysis of mixtures of sugars and polyhydric alcohols are of high interest to hydrolysis industries.

This section represents a review of the general methods of analysis of polyhydric alcohols and their derivatives by thin layer chromatography;

Chapter VI gives examples of analyses of various industrial products containing polyhydric alcohols.

A number of studies on the chromatography of simple sugars quoted above /2, 7, 13, 20, 29, 30, 33, 36, 41/ provide information on the chromatographic behavior of polyhydric alcohols. For separation of a mixture of glycerol, glycol, mannitol and sorbitol see /42/.

Thin layer chromatography is used in the detection and determination of ethylene glycol in propylene glycol /43/, in studying the $C_2$ through $C_5$-glycols, $C_4$ through $C_8$ aliphatic alcohols and diketones /44/, in the separation of industrially valuable polyhydric alcohols /45/ and in the separation of alcohols and glycols with an acetylenic triple bond /46/.

A number of aliphatic glycols, including ethylene glycol, propylene glycol, butanediols and others, have been separated /47/ on a thin alumina layer by development with benzene:ethanol = 9:1.

Higher fatty alcohols with various contents of hydroxyl groups have been separated /48/ on a layer of silica gel G by development with petroleum ether:ether = 70:30.

Methods are available for quantitative thin layer chromatography of isomeric monoglycerides /49/, and for the separation of mono-, di- and triglycerides of higher aliphatic acids /50/. Molecular distillation of mono-, di- and triglycerides has been carried out in conjunction with thin layer chromatography /51/; a method has been developed for the separation and identification of polyol and glucide acetates /52/.


Chromatography of substituted sugars and carbohydrate derivatives

Methylation is an important operation in the study of the structure of carbohydrates. A quantitative analysis of the methylation products will determine the number and the location of hydroxyl groups in carbohydrates of complex structure. A number of carbohydrate ethers and other derivatives are of practical interest.

Chromatographic procedures for the separation of various mixtures of simple sugars and sugar derivatives have been discussed above, in the section on thin layer chromatography of simple sugars. In particular, we have reviewed studies on the separation of glucosides, their o-methyl ethers, sugar acetals and mercaptals and polyhydric alcohols, sugar acids and their derivatives /7/, saccharose ethers /27/, amino sugars, glucosides, methyl ethers of sugars, hydroxy acids and lactones /37/, sugar phenylhydrazones /31/ and also glucosides, mercaptals, methylated sugars, acetylated sugars, benzoylated sugars, tosylated, benzylated and tritylated sugars, acetone derivatives of sugars and various mixtures of sugar ethers and esters /22/.

Kinosita /53/ published a review on thin layer chromatography of sugar ethers. Qualitative /54/ and quantitative /55/ analysis of saccharose ethers and fatty acids is conducted on a thin layer of silica gel containing 15% plaster of Paris. The solvent systems include methanol:chloroform: acetic acid:water = 10:80:8:2, methanol:chloroform:acetic acid = 15:80:5 and tetrahydrofuran:n-hexane:acetic acid = 29:70:1. The zones are revealed by treating the plates with 50% sulfuric acid and heating. In quantitative analysis the first-named solvent system is used, the sugars are extracted from the silica gel, reacted with anthrone and determined photometrically.

Thin layer chromatography on silica gel served to isolate the isomeric fatty acid monoesters of saccharose /56/ and to determine mono-, di-, tri- and polyesters formed between saccharose and long chain fatty acids /57/. Monosaccharide phosphates and nucleotides have been separated on a thin layer of cellulose /58/.

When determining the structure of carbohydrates by methylation, the determination of the methylated sugars is a particularly important step. The system toluene : methyl ethyl ketone = 1:1 has been used /59/ in the separation of methylated glucoses from methylated mannoses. A 0.3 mm thick layer of silica gel was applied to a $20 \times 10 \times 0.3$ cm plate, the plate dried for 4 hours at 105°, held over $P_2O_5$ in vacuo for about 18 hours and then for 72 hours at 75% relative atmospheric humidity. Chromatographic separation was effected by the descending technique, the plates were sprayed with aniline acid phthalate reagent /34/ and the plates heated for 10 — 12 minutes at 105°. Under these conditions a good separation of tetramethylated and trimethylated glucoses and mannoses could be achieved. A comparison (p. 16) of $R_f$ and $R_p$ values of methylated glucoses, mannoses and xyloses when determined on a thin layer and on paper showed that the two methods are mutually complementary.

Separation and identification of methylated sugars and sugar acetates has been conducted /60/ on a thin layer of magnesol (hydrated magnesium silicate). The plaster of Paris-bound sorbent should have a neutral reaction. The acetates are separated in the solvent system ethyl acetate : benzene = 1:1, while the system methanol : benzene = 7:93 is used for methyl ethers.

Silica gel G was employed to separate some methylated sugars and for a partial separation of the products of decomposition of sugars: dihydroxyacetone, glyceraldehyde and its ethyleneacetal, hydroxymethylfurfural, glycerol, glycol, mannitol and sorbitol /42/.

The same sorbent was also used for a micropreparative separation of sugar acetates by development with benzene : methanol = 96:4, in two 17-cm passes.

Analysis of sugar $\beta$-naphthylhydrazones /62/ has been performed on a silica gel layer. Development was effected by ethyl acetate : n-butanol = 90 : 10 and the spots located by UV irradiation of the chromatogram.

Analytical results obtained for the anomers and isomers of methylated glycosides by thin layer chromatography on silica gel have been compared /28/ with those obtained by gas-liquid chromatography.

A mixture of glycosides with steroid and triterpenic aglycones has been separated /63/ on a nonbound alumina layer of II and III activity grades /63/. A thin silica gel-starch layer has been employed /64/ in the separation of acylated sugar derivatives.

Kochetkov et al. /65/ used thin layer chromatography on alumina to determine the $R_f$-values of 12 mercaptal derivatives of monosaccharides and 9 hexitol derivatives and cyclic monosaccharides, 8 aldehydo-monosaccharides, 15 sugar derivatives with a free OH-group and 7 derivatives with two or more free hydroxyl groups.

Sugar phenylosazones have been separated and identified /66/ by thin layer chromatography on a layer of polyamide. The system dimethylformamide : benzene = 7:93 was used to separate the phenylosazones of trioses, tetroses, pentoses, methylpentoses and hexoses; oligosaccharide phenylosazones remain on the starting line.

Fourteen glycosides, with rhamnose, arabinose, glucose and galactose as their carbohydrate constituents have been separated /67/ on a thin layer of polyamide (Perlon) powder.

Mono- and di-o-isopropylidene derivatives of monosaccharides were separated and identified /68/ on a thin layer of silica gel bound with plaster of Paris. The solvent system used was acetone: n-hexane = 4:1, and the zones were revealed by a mixture of a 0.2% solution of naphthoresorcinol or phloroglucinol in methanol and 20% sulfuric acid (1:1), the plates being subsequently heated at 110° for 10 — 15 minutes. Sugar o-isopropylidene derivatives have also been separated /69/ on a film of acetylcellulose.

Lower hydroxy compounds derived from carbohydrates, sugar acids and their lactones and sugar osazones have been separated /70/ on a thin layer of silica gel or cellulose. In preparative separation, the mixture was applied to the plate as a continuous line; the elution was conducted in a perpendicular direction to the line.

Mono- and di-2, 4-dinitrophenylhydrazones of hydroxycarbonyl compounds have been separated /71/ on aluminum G and silica gel G layers.

These examples show the vast potentialities of thin layer chromatography in the studies of the composition of the products of conversion of carbohydrates, including the products of chemical processing of wood.

BIBLIOGRAPHY

1. STAHL, E. and U.KALTENBACH. — J.Chromatogr., 5(4) : 351 — 355. 1961.
2. BERGEL'SON, L.D., E.V.DYATLOVITSKAYA, and V.V.VORONKOVA. — DAN SSSR, 141(1) : 84 — 86. 1961.
3. PERPAP, M., J.PERKAVAC, and P.BANIC. — Farmac.Vestn., 14(10 — 12) : 191 — 202. 1963.
4. STAHL, E., editor. Dünnschicht-Chromatographie, ein Laboratoriumshandbuch. Berlin 1962. [Russian translation from the German. 1965.]
5. AKHREM, A.A. and A.I.KUZNETSOVA. Tonkosloinaya khromatografiya (Thin Layer Chromatography), p.85. — Izdatel'stvo Nauka. 1964.*
6. Chromatographic Data. — J.Chromatogr., 15(4), Suppl.D13 — D26. 1964.
7. HAY, G.W., B.A.LEWIS, and F.SMITH. — J.Chromatogr., 11(4) : 479 — 486. 1963.
8. STAHL, E. — Z.Anal.Chem., Vol.181 : 303. 1961.
9. PIFFERI, P.G. — Analyt.Chem., 37(7) : 925. 1965.
10. WALDI, D. — J.Chromatogr., 18(2) : 417 — 418. 1965.
11. WEILL, C.E. and P.HANKE. — Analyt.Chem., 34(13) : 1736 — 1737. 1962.
12. CHIBA, S. and T.SHIMOMURA. — Agric.and Biol.Chem., 29(5) : 486 — 487. 1965.
13. WASSERMANN, L. and H.HANUS. — Naturwissenschaften, 50(9) : 361. 1963.
14. PASTUSKA, G. — Z.Analyt.Chem., 179(6) : 427 — 429. 1961.
15. HAIS, I.M. and K.MACEK, editors. Paper Chromatography. [Russian translation from the Czech. 1962.]
16. PREY, V., H.BERBALK, and M.KAUSZ. — Mikrochim.Acta, No.6 : 968 — 978. 1961.
17. KRINGSTAD, K. — Acta Chem.Scand., 18(10) : 2399. 1964.
18. BANCHER, E., H.SCHERZ, and K.KAINDL. — Mikrochim.Acta, No.5 : 652 — 659. 1964.
19. GUILLOUX, E. and S.BEAUGIRAUD. — Bull.Soc.Chim., No.1 : 259 — 262. France. 1965.
20. SCHWANE, R.A. and R.S.NAKON. — Analyt.Chem., 37(2) : 315 — 316. 1965.
21. PREY, V., H.SCHERZ, and E.BANCHER. — Mikrochim.Acta, No.3 : 567 — 577. 1963.
22. MICHEEL, F. and O.BERENDES. — Mikrochim.Acta, No.3 : 519 — 524. 1963.
23. SCHERZ, H., W.RUCKER, and E.BANCHER. — Mikrochim.Acta, No.5 — 6 : 876 — 879. 1965.
----------------
* [Available in English translation as IPST No.2174.]

24. WOHNLICH, J.J. — Bull.Soc.Chim.Biol., 46 (5—6) : 729—737. 1964.
25. ADACHI, S. — J.Chromatogr., 17(2) : 295—299. 1965.
26. IACIN, H. and A.R.MISHKIN. — J.Chromatogr., 18(1) : 170—173. 1965.
27. GEE, M. — J.Chromatogr., 9(3) : 278—282. 1962.
28. GEE, M. — Analyt.Chem., 35(3) : 350—353. 1963.
29. ZHDANOV, Yu.A., G.N.DOROFEENKO, and S.V.ZELENSKAYA. — DAN SSSR, 149(6) : 1322—1333. 1963.
30. GRASSHOF, H. — J.Chromatogr., 14(3) : 513—515. 1964.
31. STROH, H.H. and W.SCHÜLER. — Z.Chem., 4(5) : 188—189. 1964.
32. PER TORE JÖSSANG. — J.Chromatogr., 12 (3) : 413—415. 1963.
33. DYATLOVITSKAYA, E.V., V.V.VORONKOVA, and L.D.BERGEL'SON. — DAN SSSR, 145(2) : 325—327. 1962.
34. PARTRIDGE, S.M. — Nature, Vol.164 : 443. 1949.
35. BUCHAN, J.L. and R.I.SAVAGE. — Analyst, Vol.77 : 401. 1952.
36. BERGEL'SON, L.D., E.V.DYATLOVITSKAYA, and V.V.VORONKOVA. — DAN SSSR, 149(6) : 1319—1321. 1963.
37. WOLFROM, M.L., D.L.PATIN, and R.M.LEDERKREMER. — Chem.and Ind., No.25 : 1065. 1964.
38. WOLFROM, M.L., D.L.PATIN, and R.M.LEDERKREMER. — J.Chromatogr., 17(3) : 488—494. 1965.
39. VOMHOF, D.W. and T.C.TUCKER. — J.Chromatogr., 17(2) : 300—306. 1965.
40. SCHWEIGER, A. — J.Chromatogr., 9(3) : 374—376. 1962.
41. BERGEL'SON, L.D. et al. — Izv.AN SSSR, OKhN, p.1612. 1962.
42. PREY, V., H.BERBALK, and M.KAUSZ. — Mikrochim.Acta, No.3 : 449—454. 1962.
43. CONACHER, H.B.S. and D.I.REES. — Analyst, 91(1078) : 55—56. 1966.
44. KUČERA, J. — Collect.Czechos.Chem.Communs, 28(5) : 1341—1344. 1963.
45. KNAPPE, E., D.PETERI, and I.ROHDEWALD. — Z.Analyt.Chem., 199(4) : 270—276. 1964.
46. AKHREM, A.A. et al. — Izv.AN SSSR, OKhN, No.4 : 657—661. 1962.
47. HEŘMANEK, S., V. SCHWARZ, and Z.ČEKAN. — Pharmazie, Vol.16 : 566. 1961.
48. SUBBARAO, R., M.W.ROOMI, M.R.SUBBARAM, and K.T.ACHAYA. — J.Chromatogr., Vol.9 : 295. 1962
49. THOMAS, A.E., J.E.SCHAROUN, and H.RALSTON. — J.Amer.Oil.Chemists Soc., 42(9) : 789—792. 1965.
50. POKORNÝ, J. and O.HERODEK. — Sb.Vysoké Školy chem.technol. v Praze, Potravin.technol., 8(1) : 87—92. 1964.
51. PRIVETT, O.S., M.L.BLANK, and W.O.LUNDBERG. — J.Amer.Oil Chemists Soc., 38(6) : 312—316. 1961.
52. DUMAZERT, C., C.GHIGLIONE, and T.PUGNET. — Bull.Soc.Chim., No.3 : 475—476. France. 1963.
53. KINOSITA, C. — J.Japan Chem., No.65 : 2, 79—101. 1964.
54. KINOSITA, C. — J.Chem.Soc.Japan, Industr.Chem.Sec., 66(4) : 450—455. 1963.
55. KINOSITA, C. and M.OYAMA. — J.Chem.Soc.Japan, Industr.Chem.Sec., 66(4) : 455—458. 1963.
56. OTAKE, T. and E.TAMATE. — J.Chem.Soc.Japan, Industr.Chem.Sec., 68(10) : 1896—1900. 1965.
57. MIMA, H. and N.KITAMORI. — J.Amer.Oil Chemists Soc., 41(3) : 198—200. 1964.
58. DIETRICH, C.P., S.M.C.DIETRICH, and H.G.PONTIS. — J.Chromatogr., 15(2) : 277—278. 1964.
59. ROUDIER, A. — Bull.Soc.Chim.France, No.1 : 271—273. 1965.
60. WOLFROM, M.L., R.M.LEDERKREMER, and L.E.ANDERSON. — Analyt.Chem., 35(10) : 1357—1359. 1963.
61. TATE, M.E. and C.T.BISHOP. — Can.J.Chem., Vol.40 : 1043. 1962.
62. KOWALEWSKI, Z., O.SCHINDLER, H.JÄGER, and T.REICHSTEIN. — Helv.Chim.Acta, Vol.43 : 1280. 1960.
63. KHORLIN, A.Ya. and A.F.BOCHKOV. — Izv.AN SSSR, OKhN, No.6 : 1120—1121. 1962.
64. DEFERRARI, J.O., R.M.LEDERKREMER, B.MATSUHIRO, and J.F.SPROVIERO. — J.Chromatogr., 9(3) : 283—290. 1962.
65. KOCHETKOV, N.K., B.A.DMITRIEV, and A.I.USOV. — Doklady AN SSSR, 143(4) : 863—866. 1962.
66. HAAS, H.J. and A.SEELIGER. — J.Chromat., 13 (2) : 573—574. 1964.
67. EGGER, K. — Z.Anal.Chem., Vol.182 : 161. 1961.
68. MODI, B.D., J.R.PATIL, and J.L.BOSE. — Indian J.Chem., 2(1) : 32—34. 1964.
69. BARNETT, J.E.G. and P.W.KENST. — Nature (Engl.), 192(4802) : 556. 1961.
70. BANCHER, E., H.SCHERZ, and H.KAINDL. — Mikrochim.Acta, No.6 : 1043—1051. 1964.
71. ANET, E.F.L.J. — J.Chromatogr., Vol.9 : 291. 1962.
72. PITRA, J. and J.ŠTĚRBA. — Chem.Listy, Vol.56 : 544. 1962; Vol.57 : 389. 1963.

## 4. Gas chromatography of sugar derivatives

In the past few years sugars have been frequently analyzed by the
technique of gas-liquid chromatography. Since sugars are not volatile,
chromatographic analysis is preceded by the synthesis of their volatile
derivatives, mainly ethers.

Since a recent detailed review of the literature on gas-liquid chromatography of sugar derivatives is available /1/, this section will deal only
with the most interesting procedures of the past few years.

In gas-liquid chromatography methyl ethers, acetates, acetals and
trimethylsilyl ethers of sugars are mostly employed.

Table 15 shows the liquid stationary phases used by different workers
in separating the sugar derivatives. We shall discuss a few techniques of
separation of carbohydrate derivatives by gas-liquid chromatography.

**Analysis of methyl ethers.** It has been recommended /16/ to separate
methylglycosides at 202° on two columns — $40 \times 0.5$ and $77 \times 0.5$ cm —
connected in series, carrying 20% Apiezone M and 20% buranediol succinate
on Chromosorb W (60 — 80 mesh) and 1% silicone SE-30 in glass beads
(60 mesh), and also at 210° on a $117 \times 0.5$ cm column with a 1:1 mixture of
20% Apiezone M and 20% butanediol succinate on Chromosorb W and 0.1%
Apiezone M on glass beads. The flow rate of carrier gas (argon) is
200 ml/min; RaD ionization detector; the sample should contain 5— 20 γ
of the compounds to be analyzed in methanol or chloroform.

Complex mixtures of methylated and partly methylated methylglycosides
may also be separated /23/ at 175 — 200° on a $120 \times 0.5$ cm column with
15% butanediol-1, 4 succinate or 10% m-bis-(m-phenoxyphenoxy)-benzene
on celite (80 — 100 mesh); flow rate of carrier gas 80 — 100 ml/min.

**Analysis of sugar acetates.** Acetylated disaccharides have been
separated /16/ on a $117 \times 0.5$ cm column with a 1:2 mixture of 1% polyphenyl
ether and 1% DS-710 silicone on glass beads or 1% of SE-30 silicone on
glass beads; the flow rate of carrier gas (argon) was 100— 150 ml/minute, and
the temperature of the column was 236 — 238°. Acetates of reducing
disaccharides give wide peaks, anomers are not separated. Compounds
(0.05 — 0.15 gram) have also been preparatively separated on a $250 \times 1.3$ cm
column; detection by thermal conductance.

During gas-liquid chromatography, sugar derivatives, in the first
instance sugar acetates, can undergo different alterations /35/. Such
alterations mainly comprise deamination, change in ring size, migration
of acetal or ketal groups and rearrangement of fully acetylated amino
sugars, accompanied by marked degradation of sugar derivatives. The
pentaacetates of D-glucosamine and D-galactosamine are quite unsuitable
for analysis by gas-liquid chromatography, since they are decomposed
during the analysis.

**Analysis of trimethylsilyl (TMS) ethers.** Trimethylsilyl sugar ethers
are the most stable to gas-liquid chromatography, owing to which this
method is now most frequently used in analyzing sugars in the form of
ethers.

To prepare TMS sugar ethers /11/ the sample (0.01 — 0.05 g) is weighed
into a tube, a 100% excess of trimethylchlorosilane is added and then a
125% excess of pyridine, the mixture is cooled by dipping into dry ice, the
tube is sealed, heated for 10 — 15 hours at 100 — 150°, cooled, opened and
the contents are extracted with 0.5 ml benzene. The benzene extract is

TABLE 15. Stationary phases used in the separation of carbohydrate derivatives

| Liquid stationary phase | Maximum heating temperature, °C | Sugar derivative | References |
|---|---|---|---|
| **Hydrocarbon polymers** | | | |
| Apiezone M | 275 | Methyl ethers | 2−9 |
| | | Acetates | 3 |
| | | TMS ethers | 10, 11 |
| Apiezone L | 300 | Acetates | 12, 13 |
| | | TMS-ethers | 13 |
| **Polysilicones** | | | |
| Silicone oil DS-710 | 225 | Anhydroglucosides | 14 |
| | | Acetals | 15 |
| Methylsilicone SE-30 | 400 | Disaccharide acetates | 16 |
| | | TMS-ethers | 11 |
| Methylphenylsilicone SE-52 | 400 | TMS-ethers | 17 |
| Fluorinated alkylsilicone OF-1 | 225 | Acetates | 18−20 |
| | | Acetals | 21 |
| **Methylated polysaccharides** | | | |
| Methylated o-(2-hydroxyethyl)-cellulose | − | Methyl ethers | 9−22 |
| **Polyarylic compounds** | | | |
| Polyphenyl ethers | 250 | Methyl ethers | 5−9, 23−26 |
| **Polyesters** | | | |
| 1,4-Butanediol succinate | 225 | Methyl ethers | 3, 5−9, 23, 24, 26−31 |
| | | Acetates | 32 |
| 2,2-Dimethyl-1,3-propanediol succinate | 225 | Methyl ethers | 33, 34 |
| | | Methylated aldonolactones | 35 |
| | | Anhydroglucosides | 35 |
| Diethylene glycol succinate | 225 | Methyl ethers | 29, 33 |
| | | Anhydroglucosides | 36 |
| Diethylene glycol adipate | 225 | Methyl ethers | 37, 38 |
| 2,2-Dimethyl-1,3-propanediol (neopentyl glycol) sebacate | 225 | TMS-ethers | 39 |
| Ethylene glycol isophthalate | 225 | Acetates | 18 |
| 1,2-Propanediol adipate | − | Acetals | 40 |
| Ethylene glycol succinate | 225 | TMS-ethers | 17 |
| Diethylene glycol-pentaerythritol adipate and phosphoric acid | − | Methyl ethers | 41 |
| **Polyglycols** | | | |
| Carbowax 6000 | 175 | Methyl ethers | 18, 42, 43 |
| Carbowax 20M | 250 | Methyl ethers | 43 |
| | | Acetals | 35 |
| | | Acetates | 44 |
| **Mixed phases** | | | |
| − | − | Acetates | 16, 45 |
| − | − | Glucoside acetates | 16 |
| − | − | Aminodeoxyglucose acetates | 46 |
| − | − | Acetals | 46 |

chromatogrammed at 184 — 215° on a 100×0.4 cm column with 20% SE-30 silicone or Apiezone M on celite (60 — 100 mesh); flow rate of carrier gas (helium) 70 — 75 ml/min; katharometric detection.

Bilik et al. /49, 50/ prepared TMS-ethers of sugars in this manner. The reaction product was analyzed at 155 — 185° on 170×0.6 cm columns with 5, 10 and 15% of 1, 4-butanediol succinate on kieselguhr (0.1 — 0.2 mm). The flow rate of carrier gas (nitrogen) was 30 ml/min, flame ionization detector, "Chrom-1" chromatograph.

Figure 18 shows a comparison of the results of chromatographic separation of methylated sugars and their TMS derivatives.

A more convenient procedure was developed by Sweeley et al. /47/, in which the synthesis of TMS ethers of sugars is rapid and proceeds in a quantitative yield. The sample, which should contain 0.01 g of carbohydrates, is treated in a test tube with a mixture of 1 ml anhydrous pyridine, 0.2 ml of hexamethyldisilazane and 0.1 ml of trimethylchlorosilane. The tube is closed with a plastic stopper and is vigorously shaken for 30 seconds, held at room temperature for not less than 5 minutes and the mixture is chromatogrammed. In order to increase the solubility of some of the carbohydrates, the mixture may be heated at 75 — 85° for 2 — 3 minutes.

The chromatographic analysis is conducted at 125 — 250° under isothermal conditions or else at a programmed temperature increase within this range at the rate of 2.3° minutes. The 183×0.6 cm column used contains 3% SE-52 silicone or 15% Apiezone M or 4% of nitrilesilicone; a 244.0×0.6 cm column with 10% Carbowax 1540 or 15% polyethylene glycol succinate on Chromosorb W (80 — 100 mesh) or Gasochrome P may also be used. The flow rate of the carrier gas is 75 — 100 ml/min, gage pressure at inlet 1.1 — 1.4 atm, volume of sample 0.0001 — 0.0005 ml, flame ionization or argon ionization detector. More than one hundred TMS derivatives of carbohydrates and related compounds were studied under these conditions and anomers and spatial

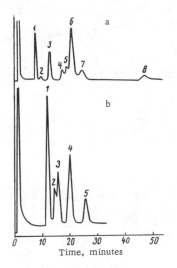

FIGURE 18. Separation chromatograms:

a — methylated sugars; 1, 2 — methyl-2, 3, 5-tri-o-methyl-α, β-L-arabinoside; 3 — methyl-2, 3, 4-tri-o-methyl-β-L-arabinoside; 4 — methyl-2, 3, 4, 6-tetra-o-methyl-α -D-glucoside; 5 — methyl-2, 3-di-o-methyl-α, β-L-arabofuranoside; 6 — methyl-2, 3, 4, 6-tetra-o-methyl-β-D-galactoside; 7 — methyl-3, 4-di-o-methyl-β-D-arabinoside; 8 — methyl-2, 4, 6-tri-o-methyl-β-D-galactoside; b — TMS sugar ethers: 1 — trimethylsilyl-2, 3, 4, 6-tetra-o-trimethylsilyl-α -D-glucoside; 2 — methyl-2, 3, 4, 6-tetra-o-trimethylsilyl-β-D-glucoside; 3 — methyl-2, 3, 4, 6-tetra-o-trimetylsilyl-β-D-glucoside; 4 — trimethylsilyl-2, 3, 4, 6-tetra-o-trimethylsilyl-β-D-glucoside; 5 — methyl-2, 3, 4, 6-tetra-o-methyl-α -D-glucoside.

isomers could be satisfactorily separated.

This method /47/ found extensive application in carbohydrate chemistry.

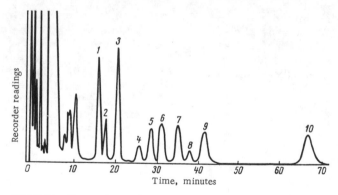

FIGURE 19. Chromatogram of a mixture of sugar TMS ethers:

1 and 2 – ribose; 3 – $\alpha$-mannose; 4 – $\gamma$-galactose; 5 – $\alpha$-galactose; 6 – internal standard; 7 – $\alpha$-glucose; 8 – $\beta$-mannose; 9 – $\beta$-galactose; 10 – $\beta$-glucose.

Qualitative and quantitative analysis of TMS ethers thus prepared was conducted /48/ at 170° on a 366×0.6 cm column with 15% Carbowax 20M on silicone-coated Chromosorb W (80 – 100 mesh); flow rate of carrier gas (helium) 100 ml/min. Methyl $\alpha$-D-mannopyranoside was used as an internal standard in quantitative work; sample volume was 4 $\mu$l of a 0.2% solution of sugar TMS ethers in anhydrous pyridine. Figure 19 shows a chromatogram which illustrates a successful separation of a mixture of sugar derivatives under these conditions.

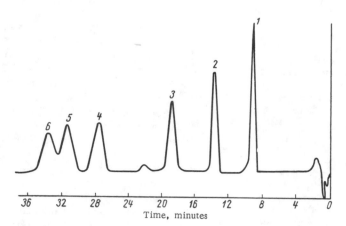

FIGURE 20. Chromatographic separation of trimethylsilyl derivatives of a number of sugars:

1 – arabinose; 2 – xylose; 3 – $\alpha$-methylmannoside; 4 – galactose; 5 – glucose; 6 – mannose.

Stepovaya and Khol'kin made a comparative study of the effectiveness of various stationary phases in the chromatographic separation of TMS ethers of simple sugars. The separations were effected on a 120×0.4 cm

72

column with the following phases: 10% polyethylene glycol adipate on celite 545 (100 — 120 mesh); 10% Apiezone M and 10% Apiezone L on celite 545 (100 — 120 mesh); 14% polyethylene glycol succinate on Chromosorb W (80 — 100 mesh); 3% silicone oil on Chromosorb W (80 — 100 mesh). Isomeric sugars could be successfully separated on the two last-named phases.

In the analytical practice in the chemistry and chemical technology of wood, determinations of the overall amount of all isomeric forms of each sugar are usually required. For this purpose the authors recommend the following experimental conditions: a $120 \times 0.4$ cm column with 10% silicone oil on celite 545 (100 — 120 mesh), column temperature 175°, flow rate of carrier gas (argon) 60 ml/min, sample size $0.1 \mu$l, chromatograph manufactured by Pye Co., $Co^{60}$-$\gamma$-ray ionization detector. Figure 20 shows an example of a successful separation of a model mixture of sugars formed by hydrolysis of wood under these conditions.

Gas-liquid chromatography as a means of separation of sugars as the TMS derivatives may be applied on studying the composition of wood hydrolyzates (cf. Chapter VI). The method is of major importance in the study of wood and products of its chemical processing.

BIBLIOGRAPHY

1.  BISHOP, C. T. — Advanc. Carb. Chem., Vol. 19: 95 —147. 1964.
2.  McINNES, A. G., D. H. BALL, F. P. COOPER, and C. T. BISHOP. — J. Chromatogr., Vol. 1: 556. 1958.
3.  BISHOP, C. T. and F. P. COOPER. — Can. J. Chem., Vol. 38: 388, 793. 1960.
4.  BISHOP, C. T., F. BLANK, and P. E. GARDNER. — Can. J. Chem., Vol. 38: 869. 1960.
5.  ASPINALL, G. O. and T. M. WOOD. — J. Chem. Soc., p. 1683. 1963.
6.  ASPINALL, G. O., A. J. CHARLSON, E. L. HIRST, and R. YOUNG. — J. Chem. Soc., p. 1696. 1963.
7.  ASPINALL, G. O. and J. BAILLIE. — J. Chem. Soc., p. 1714. 1963.
8.  ASPINALL, G. O., I. M. CAIRNCROSS, and K. M. ROSS. — J. Chem. Soc., p. 1721. 1963.
9.  PERILA, O. and C. T. BISHOP. — Can. J. Chem., Vol. 39: 815. 1961.
10. HEDGLEY, E. J. and W. G. OVEREND. — Chem. Ind., p. 378. London. 1960.
11. SMITH, B. and O. CARLSSON. — Acta Chem. Scand., 17(2): 455 —460. 1963.
12. FERRIEN, R. J. — Chem. Ind., p. 831. London. 1961.
13. FERRIEN, R. J. — Tetrahedron, Vol. 18: 1149 —1154. 1962.
14. ANDERSON, C. D., L. GOODMAN, and B. R. BAKER. — J. Am. Chem. Soc., Vol. 81: 898. 1959.
15. BUKHARI, M. A., A. B. FOSTER, J. LEHMANN, J. M. WEBBER, and J. H. WESTWOOD. — J. Chem. Soc., p. 2291. 1963.
16. JONES, H. G. and M. B. PERRY. — Can. J. Chem., Vol. 40(7): 1339 —1343. 1962.
17. BENTLEY, R. S., C. C. SWEELEY, M. MAKITA, and W. W. WELLS. — Biochem. Biophys. Res. Commun., Vol. 11: 14. 1963.
18. BISHOP, C. T. and F. P. COOPER. — Can. J. Chem., Vol. 41: 2743. 1963.
19. HEUVEL, Van der W. J. A. and E. C. HORNING. — Biochem. Biophys. Res. Commun., Vol. 4: 399. 1961.
20. HAUSE, J. A., J. A. HUBICKI, and G. G. HAZEN. — Analyt. Chem., Vol. 34: 1567. 1962.
21. MILES, H. T. and H. M. FALES. — Analyt. Chem., Vol. 34: 860. 1962.
22. KIRCHER, H. W. — Analyt. Chem., Vol. 32: 1103. 1960.
23. ASPINALL, G. O. — J. Chem. Soc., pp. 1676 —1680. 1963.
24. ASPINALL, G. O. and J. BAILLIE. — J. Chem. Soc., p. 1702. 1963.
25. SIDDIQUI, I. R. and C. T. BISHOP. — Can. J. Chem., Vol. 40: 233. 1962.
26. SIDDIQUI, I. R., C. T. BISHOP, and G. A. ADAMS. — Can. J. Chem., Vol. 39: 1595. 1961.
27. ADAMS, G. A. and C. T. BISHOP. — Can. J. Chem., Vol. 38: 2380. 1960.
28. KIRCHER, H. W. — In: "Methods in Carbohydr. Chem.," Vol. 1: 13. 1962.
29. KLEIN, E. and C. J. BARTE. — Textile Res. J., Vol. 31: 486. 1961.
30. ASPINALL, G. O. and K. M. ROSS. — J. Chem. Soc., p. 1681. 1963.
31. LEMIEUX, R. U. and A. G. McINNES. — Can. J. Chem., Vol. 40: 2376. 1962.

32. KIRCHER, H. W. − Tappi., Vol. 45: 143. 1962.
33. GEE, M. and H. G. WALKER. − Analyt. Chem., Vol. 34: 650. 1962.
34. ALFES, H., C. T. BISHOP, and F. BLANK. − Can. J. Chem., Vol. 41: 2621. 1963.
35. BISHOP, C. T., F. P. COOPER, and R. K. MURRAY. − Can. J. Chem., 41(9): 2245−2250. 1963.
36. NEWMAN, H. − Chem. Ind., p. 372. London. 1963.
37. JAMAKAWA, T., N. KISO, S. HANDA, A. MAKITA, and S. YOKOYAMA. − J. Biochem., Vol. 52: 226.
    Tokyo. 1962.
38. YAMAKAWA, T., S. YOKOYAMA, and N. KISO. − J. Biochem., Vol. 52: 228. Tokyo. 1962.
39. PERRY, M. B. − Can. J. Biochem., Vol. 42: 451. 1964.
40. HEDGLEY, E. J., O. MERESZ, W. G. OVEREND, and R. RENNIE. − Chem. Ind., p. 938. London. 1960.
41. NEELY, W. B., J. NOTT, and C. B. ROBERTS. − Analyt. Chem., Vol. 34: 1423. 1962.
42. BISHOP, C. T. and F. P. COOPER. − Can. J. Chem., Vol. 40: 224. 1962.
43. BISHOP, C. T., F. BLANK, and M. HRANISAVLJEVIC-JAKOVLJEVIC. − Can. J. Chem., Vol. 40: 1816. 1962.
44. ESPOSITO, G. G. and M. H. SWANN. − Analyt. Chem., Vol. 33: 1854. 1961.
45. GUNNER, S. W., J. K. N. JONES, and M. B. PERRY. − Chem. Ind., p. 255. London. 1961; Can. J. Chem.,
    Vol. 39: 1892. 1961.
46. JONES, H. G., J. K. N. JONES, and M. B. PERRY. − Can. J. Chem., Vol. 40: 1559. 1962.
47. SWEELEY, C. C., R. BENTLEY, M. MAKITA, and W. W. WELLS. − J. Amer. Chem. Soc., 85(16): 2497−
    2505. 1963.
48. SAWARDEKER, J. S. and J. H. SLONEKER. − Analyt. Chem., 37(7): 945−947. 1965.
49. BILIK, V., and I. JEŽO. − Chem. Zvesti, 17(12): 861−864. 1963.
50. BILIK, V., S. BAUER, I. JEŽO, and M. FURDIK. − Chem. Zvesti, 19(1): 28−33. 1965.

## B. CHROMATOGRAPHY OF POLYSACCHARIDES AND THEIR DERIVATIVES

### 1. Special features of chromatographic separation of high polymers

Chromatographic separations of high polymers on a large scale are only a few years old. Such separations involve special difficulties on account of the lower solubility of high polymers as compared with low-molecular compounds and of their different sorptional and partition properties. The distribution coefficients of high-molecular compounds are either very low or very high as compared with the small-sized molecules in the same homologous series. Accordingly, it becomes very difficult to select the stationary and the mobile phases suitable for use in partition chromatography. It is easier to achieve polymer separation by adsorption chromatography, but even here difficulties arise owing to the limited accessibility of the fine sorbent pores to the large-sized molecules; the adsorptional equilibrium is established slowly and an irreversible adsorption is noted in several cases. The potential applications of gas chromatography in the chemistry of high polymers are even more restricted, owing to the nonvolatile character of these compounds. Accordingly, recourse is now had to reaction gas chromatography, which is based on the analysis of the volatile products formed by thermal or chemical degradation of the polymer.

For the characteristic features of different chromatographic methods in the study of high polymers, the reader is referred to /1/.

Column chromatography on active sorbents and inert carriers has been widely employed during the past few years in the fractionation of polymers of different structures. For reviews of chromatographic fractionations of some synthetic high-molecular compounds, see /2, 3/.

## 2. Column chromatography of polysaccharides and their derivatives

Chromatographic methods serve mainly to separate low-molecular polysaccharides and their derivatives. Both organic and inorganic sorbents, and also ion exchangers, can be employed.

A recent method in the chemistry of polysaccharides is gel filtration, which is based on the different penetration of macromolecules into the dextran gel. This method is very important in molecular weight fractionations of polysaccharides.

**Separations on activated charcoal.** Countercurrent fractionation of cellulose derivatives was effected on porous wood charcoal /4/, in particular, of cellulose acetate /5, 6/. The method is based on the selective diffusion of different materials in the porous charcoal.

Jayme and Tröften /7/ studied the adsorption of cellulose from a 0.1% solution in the system $Fe(OH)_3$ — tartaric acid — NaOH on activated charcoal at different solution ratios of cellulose and adsorbent. When the amount of the adsorbent was increased, the average molecular weight of the nonadsorbed cellulose increased, which meant that low-molecular cellulose fractions were the first to be adsorbed on activated charcoal. Data on the degree of polymerization of the cellulose sample may be obtained by this method.

**Separations on inorganic sorbents.** Chromatographic fractionation on $Al_2O_3$ columns has been widely employed in the structural studies on starch. The method has been used in the study of amylose /8/ and amylopectin /9/ of potato starch, and of the products of acid hydrolysis of potato starch /10/.

Other authors /11, 12/ also employed chromatographic methods in their studies of starch.

Balandina and Novikova /13/ developed a method of column chromatography on silica gel to determine the bound butyric and acetic acids in cellulose acetate butyrate with a low content of butyrate groups.

Polysaccharides are successfully separated on columns of cellulose and cellulose derivatives. Amylopectin has been purified /14/ on a cellulose column. Diethylaminoethylcellulose, which has ion exchanger properties, has been used in the fractionation of polysaccharides /15/ and pectic substances /16/ and in the study of water-soluble sulfated polysaccharides of the green algae Codium fragile /17/.

Hydrolysis of polysaccharides may be performed on a number of cation exchangers /18/.

Chromatography on diethylaminoethylcellulose in the $OH^-$-form was employed /19/ to separate the mixture of polysaccharides isolated from the tree Picea mariana and which contains mainly arabomethoxy-glucuronoxylan and galactoglucomannan; the elution was effected with solutions of urea. Elution with a 7 M solution of urea yielded fractions not containing xylose which on being hydrolyzed gave galactose, glucose, mannose and 3-o-methylrhamnose in the ratio 1.0:2.2:2.5:3.8. Further elution with 2 N ammonium acetate in 7 M urea yielded fractions consisting mainly of xylose polymers. 3-o-Methylrhamnose was identified by its chromatographic behavior in solvent systems $CH_3COOC_2H_5$ — $CH_3COOH$ — $HCOOH$ — $H_2O$ = 18:3:1:4 and $CH_3COOC_2H_5$ — $C_5H_5N$ — $H_2O$ = 9:2:2.

Molecular weight fractionation of nitrocellulose has been performed /20/ by passing solutions of nitrocellulose in acetone (mobile systems cyclohexane : acetone = 3 : 7, acetone : methanol = 7 : 3) through columns filled with cellulose powder.

**Gel filtration of carbohydrates.** The method of gel filtration (gel penetration) proved to be a very successful technique of fractionation of polysaccharides by molecular weights and for purifying polysaccharides from low-molecular admixtures /21/. Elements of this method are present in the fractionation of polysaccharides, in particular starch, by electro-kinetic ultrafiltration through collodion membranes, which involves a combination of electrophoresis and molecular sieve effect /22/.

Partial distribution of dextran (MW 5000 — 300,000) was attained by the diffusion method /23/ on a column with 6 — 9% agar-agar gel or 4% agarose gel. Water or a 0.05 M solution of trimethylolaminomethane, containing HCl, were used as eluents. Polysaccharides may also be separated on synthetic polymers /24/, but cross-linked dextran gel is more frequently employed — Sephadex. Recently biogel-P has been employed, which has a somewhat better separating power than Sephadex /25/.

Interesting results were obtained in fractionating wood hemicelluloses on Sephadex of different brands /26/. Hemicelluloses were extracted from pine holocellulose with a 10% solution of NaOH in an atmosphere of nitrogen; the yield of water-soluble hemicelluloses was 20% on the original wood material. The hemicelluloses contain 18% lignin. Fractionation was effected by placing a solution of 1.5 gram of hemicelluloses in 50 ml water in a 110×4.8 cm column with Sephadex G-100 and eluting with 0.05 M aqueous sodium sulfate at an efflux rate of $0.04$ ml $\cdot$ min$^{-1}$ $\cdot$ cm$^{-2}$. The second column (38×2.6 cm) was filled with Sephadex G-25 and eluted with water at $0.30$ ml $\cdot$ min$^{-1}$ $\cdot$ cm$^{-2}$. The third column (3.2×90 cm) was also filled with Sephadex G-100.

The analytical data obtained for the filtrate served to plot the elution curves which contained one maximum. Successive fractionations of hemicelluloses on these columns made it possible to study the distribution of lignin in hemicelluloses, to confirm the presence of a chemical bond between lignin and hemicelluloses and to study the behavior of hemicelluloses and lignin during acid and alkaline treatments.

Cereal polysaccharides have been fractionated /27/ on Sephadex G-25. The water-alcohol extract was passed through a 70×4 cm column at 4°; elution was carried out with water; rate of filtration 20 ml/hr; total duration of analysis 22 hours. The first fractions of the filtrate contained the polysaccharides, the middle fractions contained oligosaccharides, while the last contained saccharose and fructose. The analysis of carbohydrates in the resulting fractions was effected by paper chromatography. Prior to the fractionation of carbohydrates the proteins were precipitated by basic lead acetate and $H_2S$.

Gel filtration on Sephadex was utilized in the synthesis of polysaccharides /28/. Kochetkov et al. /29/ used Sephadex G-50 and showed that the polysaccharide synthesized by their method had an average molecular weight of several thousands.

Gel filtration served in the separation of acid oligosaccharides from hyaluronic acid /30/. A Sephadex G-25 column was used to effect a molecular weight separation of coloring substances from maple syrup and other syrups /31/.

Sephadex chromatography — on sulfosephadex C-50, diethylaminoethyl-sephadex A-50, diethylaminoethylcellulose and sulfomethylcellulose — was employed /32/ in the separation of carbohydrates and nitrogenous compounds from the humic substances in the soil.

It should be stressed again that gel filtration is an important method in studying the structure of polysaccharides and their alteration as a result of various physical and chemical effects. So far, the method has been only rarely employed in wood chemistry.

The method may be employed in studying the products of chemical degradation of wood polysaccharides, for example products of partial hydrolysis.

## 3. Paper chromatography

Paper chromatography is utilized in the study of starch polysaccharides /33/. The method served in the study /34/ of individual starch fractions and the products of its thermolysis, hydrolysis, radiolysis by $\gamma$-rays and products of decomposition by ultra-sound. The mobile phase consists of a 0.2 N solution of NaOH; amylose and amylopectin spots were revealed by a solution of iodine.

The mobility of different starch fractions chromatogrammed on paper is very different /35/. A stationary zone, and a zone which moves with the solvent front were noted. Gradient analysis with 0.8 — 6.4 M perchloric acid (concentration gradient 0.8 M) showed /36/ that the mobility of amylose fractions is a function of its degree of polymerization.

Fractionation of starch by paper chromatography is the principle of a method /37/ for the determination of the amylose content of starches.

A method for the simultaneous determination of amylose and amylopectin in starch and starch fractions has been proposed /38/. The starch is extracted with water at 130 — 140°, the extracts are diluted with water and chromatogrammed on paper. In the elution of amylose 20% dioxane is the mobile phase, while amylopectin is eluted with 40 — 50% dioxane. The spots are detected by spraying with a saturated aqueous solution of iodine; amylopectin gives red spots, while the spots of amylose are blue. These colors fade on standing, and it is accordingly recommended /39/ to reveal the spots in iodine vapor and to photograph the chromatograms.

A relationship exists between the chemical structure, $R_f$-values and colorations given by glucobiose and other oligosaccharides /40/. Paper chromatography is employed in a rapid identification of cellulose ethers and esters /41/.

A more accurate method of determination of the content of soluble polysaccharides in wood hydrolyzates /42/ involves the use of chromato-graphic technique.

Paper chromatography is successfully employed mainly in the study of low-molecular polysaccharides. It is practically impossible to separate, say, cellulose by this method, since cellulose solvents will also dissolve the chromatographic paper.

## 4. Reaction gas chromatography in the chemistry of carbohydrates

One of the preceding sections dealt with the analysis of carbohydrates by gas-liquid chromatography, which involved their preliminary conversion to volatile compounds by preparing the respective ethers. However, not all compounds have volatile derivatives; this applies, most particularly, to polysaccharides.

A recent development in polymer chemistry is analytical reaction gas chromatography. This technique is based on the simultaneous utilization of chemical reactions and chromatographic separation of the reaction products /43, 44/. A special reactor unit is included in the chromatographic apparatus in front of the chromatographic columns, behind them or between two columns connected in series. Occasionally the chromatographic column itself may serve as the reactor.

Polysaccharides are most often determined by pyrolytic chromatography which is a particular case of reaction gas chromatography. An additional unit — a reactor in which the sample is rapidly heated to the desired temperature — is inserted into the chromatographic apparatus.

The rapid thermal decomposition of polysaccharides and their derivatives results in the formation of a multi-component mixture of the reaction products, the separation of which yields a "chromatographic spectrum." The identity of the products in the spectrum may furnish a qualitative indication of the nature of the different polymeric materials. Qualitative and quantitative analysis of the products of pyrolysis yields information on the mechanism of thermal decomposition and on the structural features of the initial polymers.

### Pyrolysis and gas chromatography of polysaccharides

Early studies of the thermal decomposition of cellulose include the work of Martin and Ramstad /45/ who determined the gases which are invariably evolved — mainly $CO$ and $CO_2$ — and other products of pyrolysis by gas-adsorption chromatography.

Most studies of pyrolytic gas chromatography of polysaccharides involved qualitative identification of materials of different origins.

Kirret and Kyullik /47/ (see also /48/) studied about 20 natural and chemical polymeric fibers by this method. They used a KhL-3 chromatograph with a pyrolytic block; the pyrolysis was conducted at 900° in a stream of helium (carrier gas) and the resulting chromatograms contained up to 8 peaks. Much more complex chromatograms were obtained /48, 49/ using the UKh-1 chromatograph with a pyrolytic block heated by a platinum spiral. The fiber samples 1.8 — 2.0 mg in weight were introduced into a thin-walled tube in the center of the spiral and heated to 300 — 900°. The most typical chromatograms were obtained for the pyrolysis temperature of 500°, irrespective of the packing of the chromatographic column; time of pyrolysis 10 — 12 seconds.

The separation of the hydrolysis products took place on a column with 25% poly(ethylene glycol) 1000 on Chromosorb P (0.16 — 0.31 mm); column temperature 100°, flow rate of carrier gas (helium) 3.8 liters/hour, katharometric detection, duration of determination 20 — 30 minutes.

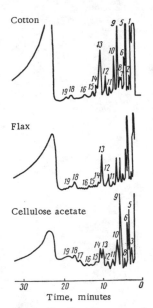

FIGURE 21. Chromatograms of pyrolysis products of cellulose and cellulose esters (numbers of peaks correspond to those in Table 16).

The chromatograms obtained during the analysis of natural and artificial cellulosic fibers are shown in Figure 21; Table 16 shows the relative peak retention times.

It is seen that the cellulose fibers give what are essentially identical peaks. A wide water peak terminates the chromatogram. In order to differentiate the cellulosic fibers by their pyrolysis products, the surface areas under the largest peaks may be determined. The pyrolysis products were found to include acetaldehyde, propionaldehyde, acrolein, acetone, methanol, ethanol, benzene and toluene.

Pyrolysis of saccharose, maltose, cellulose and starch conducted in nitrogen at 300° yielded /46, 50/ peaks of $CO_2$, acetaldehyde, furane, propionaldehyde, acetone, acrolein, 2-methyl-furane and water; pyrolysis of jute hemicelluloses also yielded peaks of methyl formate, methanol and ethanol. These compounds were merely qualitatively identified. The disadvantage of the method is that the product of pyrolysis is trapped in a U-shaped vessel, which is then connected to the chromatograph. The components of the mixture were separated on a 150 cm long column with 10% of a 2:1 mixture of dibutyl phthalate and poly(ethylene glycol) 400 on celite (60 — 80 mesh); column temperature 50°; carrier gas: nitrogen; detector: katharometer.

Schwenker and Beck /51/ studied the products of hydrolysis of preliminarily purified cotton cellulose. Unlike in pyrolytic chromatography, these authors conducted a macropyrolysis of 10-gram samples of cellulose in air or on purified nitrogen. The cellulose samples were dried at 110° to remove the sorbed water and were then heated to 370° at 15 degrees per minute. The pyrolyzate was trapped at 75 and −78°. Samples (10 $\mu$l) of the resulting condensate were withdrawn and introduced into the chromatograph.

In addition, test pyrolyses were conducted on 10 mg cellulose samples during 10 — 12 sec, after which the resulting mixture was immediately introduced into the chromatograph. Best separations of pyrolysis products were obtained with Carbowax 20M as the liquid stationary phase.

The analytical conditions were as follows: the column (366×0.6 cm) was filled with 10% poly(ethylene glycol) Carbowax 20M on Haloport F (30 — 60 mesh). A linear programmed temperature increase at the rate of 7.9 degrees/minute was produced up to 225°, and the analysis was thereafter conducted isothermally; temperature at the sample inlet 225°, temperature of detector 275°, flow rate of carrier gas (helium) 60 ml/min, chromatograph F and M. Mark 500.

TABLE 16. Relative retention times of pyrolysis products of cellulosic fibers ($t^\circ$ benzene = 100)

| Number of peak | Cotton | Flax | Viscose rayon | Cellulose acetate |
|---|---|---|---|---|
| 1 | 10.2 | 10.1 | 10.4 | 10.9 |
| 2 | 16.5 | 16.7 | 16.0 | 16.4 |
| 3 | 19.4 | (18.4) | 18.9 | 19.1 |
| 4 | + | 20.6 | 20.7 | (20.0) |
| 5 | 24.8 | 24.8 | 24.5 | 24.6 |
| 6 | 30.2 | 30.3 | 30.2 | 30.0 |
| 7 | 40.3 | 38.6 | 38.6 | 39.1 |
| 8 | 41.3 | 40.4 | 40.5 | + |
| 9 | 50.5 | 49.6 | 50.0 | 51.0 |
| 10 | 57.8 | 56.9 | 57.5 | 57.3 |
| 11 | 69.5 | 68.9 | 69.8 | 69.2 |
| 12 | 82.5 | 80.7 | 82.0 | 81.8 |
| 13 | 100.0 | 100.0 | 100.0 | 100.0 |
| 14 | 107.2 | 107.3 | 106.6 | 107.2 |
| 15 | 118.3 | 118.3 | 117.0 | 118.2 |
| 16 | 137.9 | 137.6 | 137.6 | 137.2 |
| 17 | – | + | 157.6 | 158.0 |
| 18 | 175.2 | 175.0 | 176.5 | 176.4 |
| 19 | 191.0 | 190.0 | 189.0 | 190.0 |

Figure 22 shows a comparison of the composition of pyrolysis products in an uncondensed mixture and in condensates obtained at 75 and $-78^\circ$. The following compounds were identified (number corresponds to peak number in Figure 22): 1 — uncondensed gases; 2 — formaldehyde; 3 — acetaldehyde; 4 — propionaldehyde; 5 — acetone; 6 — acrolein; 7 — butyraldehyde and methanol; 8 — methyl ethyl ketone; 10 — water; 14 — glyoxal; 15 — acetic acid; 16 — formic acid and furfural; 18 — carboxylated compound; 30 — lactic acid; 34 — 5-hydroxymethylfurfural.

When the temperature of the column with 3% Carbowax 20M was raised to 245° another peak was obtained which may have originated from levoglucosan, the volatility of which is very low (mp 180°). Levoglucosan is the main reaction product, so that its determination is of major interest. The authors found up to 37 products in each of the reaction mixtures, most of which remained unidentified. Linear temperature programming ensured a better separation of the products. The results confirm that the mechanism of pyrolysis of cellulose is not oxidative, since the compositions of the pyrolysis products obtained in nitrogen and in the air are practically identical.

Gas-liquid chromatography with a programmed raise in temperature was also employed /52/ in a study of the pyrolysis of paper and levoglucosan. The products of pyrolysis of $\alpha$-cellulose were analyzed for comparison. Samples of 300, 100 and 25 mg of paper, cellulose and levoglucosan, respectively, were taken for pyrolysis. Prior to the determination the weighed samples were dried at 110° for 40 minutes. Different conditions of pyrolysis were tried out. It was found that the decomposition of cellulose begins at 170° and the composition of the mixture becomes more complex as the temperature is increased. Figure 23 shows the chromatogram of pyrolysis products of paper at 365° during 6 minutes.

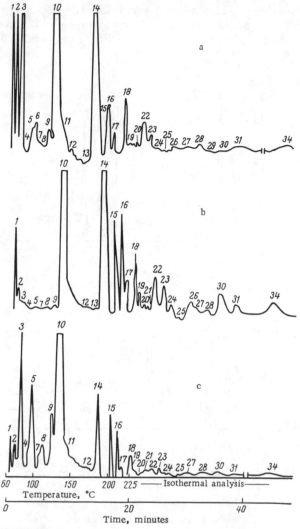

FIGURE 22. Chromatogram of pyrolysis products of cellulose:

a – vapor products from microreactor, pyrolysis in helium; b –
substances condensed at 75°C, macropyrolysis in nitrogen; c –
substances condensed at –78°C, macropyrolysis in nitrogen.

The analysis was conducted on a 366×0.6 cm column with 5%
Carbowax 20M on Haloport F (30 — 60 mesh). The retention times of the
components were checked on a second column (183×0.6 cm) with 5%
diethylene glycol succinate on the same carrier. The temperature of the
analysis was raised from 50 to 245° at the rate of 5° per minute. The flow
rate of the carrier gas (helium) was 30 ml/min. Katharometric detection,
detector temperature 380°, current intensity of detector 150 mA.

It is seen from Figure 23 that the reaction mixture contains more than
30 compounds. They were identified by their retention times on two columns;
some of them were additionally identified by their odor and by chemical
tests. The following products of decomposition of cellulose were identified

(peak number shown in parentheses): formaldehyde (2), acetaldehyde (3), propionaldehyde (4), acetone (5), acrolein (6), n-butyraldehyde and methanol (7), methyl ethyl ketone (8), water (11), glyoxal (15), acetic acid (18) and furfural (20).

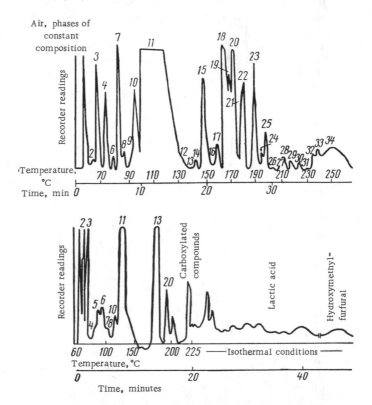

FIGURE 23. Comparison of volatile products formed during pyrolysis of cellulose in chamber and a more complete pyrolysis in the flame.

Pyrolyses of cellulose and levoglucosan carried out under the same conditions result in almost identical mixtures, in agreement with the prevailing view to the effect that levoglucosan is an intermediate product of pyrolysis of cellulose.

For applications of pyrolytic chromatography to the analysis of cellulose and other polymers see also /53/.

Gas-liquid chromatography and paper chromatography have also been used /54/ in a study of the mechanism of thermal decomposition of cellulose.

Analysis of the products of thermal decomposition of starch at 300° was conducted /55/ on a column containing 10% of a 9:1 mixture of poly(ethylene glycol) 400 with dibutyl phthalate on celite. Aldehydes, ketones and furanes formed in the pyrolysis of starch and other carbohydrates could be identified in this way.

Gridyushko et al. /56/ applied the technique of pyrolytic gas-liquid chromatography to the study of bleached sulfite pulp to develop a method for the determination of rubber content in latex-sized papers (cf. Chap. VI.).

The applications of pyrolytic chromatography to the chemistry of wood polysaccharides are very promising. The technique may result not only in the information regarding the identity of the polymer, but may also lead to important conclusions on its chemical transformations which take place during its isolation from the raw material and during subsequent chemical treatment.

Reaction gas chromatography of
polysaccharide derivatives

   Gas-liquid chromatography is suitable /57/ for the determination of hydroxyethyl groups in hydroxyethylstarch. To do this, starch samples are pyrolyzed in sealed ampules and the product mixture is chromatogrammed. For quantitative determination, the pyrolysis products are separated and acetaldehyde determined.

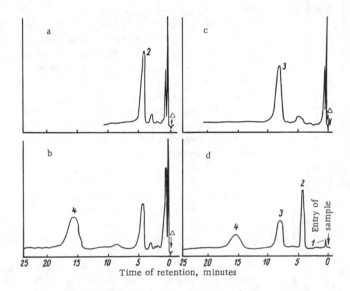

FIGURE 24. Chromatograms of pyrolysis products of cellulose esters:

a — cellulose acetate; b — cellulose butyrate; c — cellulose propionate; d — mixture of acids; 1 — air; 2 — acetic acid; 3 — propionic acid; 4 — butyric acid.

   A 0.001 gram sample is placed in a capillary tube (9.0×0.1 cm) sealed at one end, the tube is evacuated, sealed, heated for 10 minutes at 400° in a furnace, taken out, placed in the sample inlet chamber of the chromatograph, broken and the pyrolysis products are chromatogrammed at 90° on a 244×0.6 cm column with poly(ethylene glycol) on Burrell 341 — 133 carrier. The flow rate of carrier gas (helium) is 75 ml/min; flame ionization detector; flow rate of air 600 ml/min, that of hydrogen 50 ml/minute. Ordinary starch not containing ethoxy groups also forms acetaldehyde which is then deducted from the analytical results. The dependence between the peak height and the ethoxy group content in the

83

hydroxyethylstarch is linear. The method is reproducible and fairly accurate and may be of interest in the analyses of other starch derivatives and polysaccharide derivatives in general.

A combination of several methods, including gas-liquid chromatography, has been recommended /58/ for the determination of the functional groups and degree of substitution of starch derivatives.

A number of interesting papers deal with the study of cellulose esters by pyrolytic chromatography. The quantitative determination is based on the measurement of the peak heights of organic acids formed as a result of the pyrolysis of the corresponding cellulose esters /59/.

Figure 24 shows the chromatograms of the products of pyrolysis of cellulose acetate, butyrate and propionate, and the chromatogram of a model mixture of acetic, propionic and butyric acids.

The analytical parameters were as follows: pyrolysis temperature 700°; mixture components separated on 244×0.6 cm column with 5% water-insoluble Ucon on Haloport F; column temperature 100°— flow rate of carrier gas (helium) 45 ml/min; Perkin-Elmer 154 isothermal chromatograph.

In addition, qualitative studies were performed /59/ on about 150 other materials, including plastics, elastomers, resins, natural products, etc.

Cellulose esters are also analyzed /60/ by reaction gas chromatography, which is based on the formation of methyl esters of organic acids by the reaction of cellulose esters in methanol in the presence of $BF_3$ as catalyst. A 30 — 300 mg sample of the cellulose ester is mixed in a tube with 0.5 — 2.0 ml anhydrous methanol containing 10% $BF_3$. The tube is sealed, and the contents are heated for 3 hours at 140°. A sample of the cooled reaction mixture is introduced into Perkin-Elmer 116E gas chromatograph provided with a flame ionization detector. A 2-meter long glass column, filled with 30% poly(ethylene glycol) P200 on kieselguhr (0.2 — 0.3 mm) is used; temperature 50°, flow rate of carrier gas (helium) 60 ml/min, sample volume 5 — 30 $\mu$l; alternatively, a 3 meter long glass column with 10% of $\beta, \beta'$-oxydipropionitrile on kieselguhr (0.2 — 0.3 mm) at 60° can be used; flow rate of helium 40 ml/min; sample volume 5 — 30 $\mu$l.

Figure 25 shows chromatograms of reaction products obtained during the analysis of cellulose acetate, propionate and acetobutyrate according to this method. The components were separated on a column of 30% poly(ethylene glycol) P200 on kieselguhr. The recommended internal standard for quantitative analysis is n-heptane which appears on the chromatogram prior to methyl acetate.

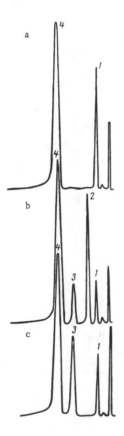

FIGURE 25. Chromatograms of trans-esterification products:

a — cellulose acetate;
b — cellulose propionate;
c — cellulose acetate butyrate; 1 — methyl acetate; 2 — methyl propionate; 3 — methyl butyrate; 4 — methanol.

Reaction gas chromatography may be used in the determination of cellulose ethers as well as esters.

Quantitative determination of the alkoxy groups in methyl-, ethyl- and propylcellulose /61/ is based on the formation of the corresponding alkyl iodides according to Zeisel and their determination by gas-liquid chromatography. Alkyl iodide samples in 1, 2, 5-trimethylhexane are analyzed at 75° on a 213.5×0.6 cm column with di-2-ethylhexyl sebacate on refractory brick; the flow rate of carrier gas (helium) is 68 ml/min.

Gas-liquid chromatography with preliminary pyrolysis has also been used /62/ in the analysis of methyl- and ethyl-cellulose.

Instantaneous pyrolysis of nitrocellulose yields nitrous oxides, carbon oxides and water in the product mixture /63/. The method is used to determine plasticizers in nitrocellulose varnishes.

Pyrolytic gas-liquid chromatography is used not only in qualitative and quantitative analysis of cellulose and cellulose esters and ethers, but also in the studies of kinetics and mechanism of formation and pyrolysis of homopolymers and copolymers. The reaction /64/ of alkali cellulose and sodium cellulosate with acrylonitrile and other vinyl monomers (vinyl acetate, vinyl butyrate, methyl acrylate and styrene) yields products which have been studied by differential thermal analysis and gas chromatography of the products of thermal decomposition of high polymers. It was shown that the reaction between cellulose and vinyl monomers yields graft copolymers in all cases.

Double-exposure pyrolytic gas-liquid chromatography was used by Khol'kin and Gridyushko in the analysis of wood modified by furane resins. The low-temperature stage of the analysis comprises the determination of the unreacted monomer; the high-temperature stage of pyrolysis determines the content of the polymer in modified wood. Clearly, the method can be used in the study of numerous copolymerizations and graft polymerizations.

BIBLIOGRAPHY

1. CASSEL, J. M. and G. M. KLEIN. Analytical Chemistry of Polymers. — Interscience Publishers. 1959 –1962.
2. RAFIKOV, S. R., S. A. PAVLOVA, and I. I. TVERDOKHLEBOVA. Metody opredeleniya molekulyarnykh vesov i polidispersnosti vysokomolekulyarnykh soedinenii (Determination of Molecular Weights and Polydispersity of High Polymers), pp. 56 –57. — Izdatel'stvo AN SSSR. 1963.*
3. BALANDINA, V. A. et al. Analiza polimerizatsionnykh plastmass (prakticheskoe rukovodstvo) (Analysis of Polymerized Plastics. A Practical Textbook), pp. 53 –67. — Izdatel'stvo Khimiya. 1965.
4. SWENSON, H. A. and A. ROSENBERG. — Acta chem. scand., 10(9): 1393 –1403. 1956.
5. SWENSON, H. A. — Acta Chem. Scand., 9(4): 572 –582. 1955.
6. SWENSON, H. A. — Svensk Papperstidn., 58(15): 550 –553. 1955.
7. JAYME, G. and J. TRÖFTEN. — Naturwissenschaften, 52(17): 496. 1965.
8. ULMANN, M. — Makromolek. Chem., 9(1): 76 –95. 1953.
9. ULMANN, M. and B. WENDT. — Makromolek. Chem., 12(3): 155 –167. 1954.
10. ULMANN, M. — Makromolek. Chem., 10(2): 147 –157. 1953.
11. FISCHER, E. H. and W. SETTELE. — Helv. Chim. Acta, 36(4): 811 –819. 1953.
12. TAKI, M. — J. Agric. Chem. Soc. Japan, 33(9): 781 –785. 1959.
13. BALANDINA, V. A. and E. M. NOVIKOVA. — Plasticheskie Massy, No. 12: 53 –54. 1960.
14. ROSENTHAL, F. R. T., S. T. TOLAMSQUIM, and E. TOLMASQUIM. — Anals Acad. Brasil. Scienc., 33(3 –4): 305 –307. 1961.
15. NEUKOM, H., H. DEUEL, W. J. HERI, and W. KÜNDIG. — Helv. Chim. Acta, 43(1): 64 –71. 1960.
16. HERI, W. — Diss. Dokt. Techn. Wiss., Eidgenöss. Techn. Hochschule. Zürich, Basel. 1962.
17. LOVE, J. and E. PERCIVAL. — J. Chem. Soc., Sept., pp. 3338 –3345. 1964.
---------------

* [Available in English translation as IPST No. 2097.]

18. GLEGG, R.E. and D.EIDINGER. — Analyt. Chem., 26(8):1365−1367. 1954.
19. APPLEGARTH, D.A. and G.G.S.DUTTON. — J. Chromatogr., 15(2):246. 1964.
20. REISER, V. — Papier et celul., 20(2):41−43. 1965.
21. HOGLUND, A. — Focus (Sver.), No.1:5−7. 1964.
22. MOULD, D.L. and R.L.M.SYNGE. — Biochem.J., 58(4):571−585. 1954.
23. HUMMEL, B.C.W. and D.C.SMITH. — J.Chromatogr., 8(4):491−500. 1962.
24. LEA, D.J. and A.H.SEHON. — Canad.J.Chem., 40(1):159−160. 1962.
25. ANDERSON, D.M.W., I.C.M.DEA, S.RAHMAN, and J.F.STODDART. — Chem. Communs, No.8:145−
    146. 1965.
26. KRINGSTAD, K. and G.ELLEFSEN. — Papier, 18(10, A):583−591. 1964.
27. SCHLUBACH, H.H. and M.GREHN. — Liebigs Ann. Chem., Vol.668:180−183. 1963.
28. BOUVENG, H.O., H.KIESSLING, B.LINDBERG, and J.McKAY. — Acta Chem. Scand., 17(5):1351−1356.
    1963.
29. KOCHETKOV, N.K. et al. — Izv.AN SSSR, Seriya Khimicheskaya, No.2:385. 1966.
30. FLODIN, P., J.D.GREGORY, and L.RODÉN. — Analyt. Biochem., 8(4):424−433. 1964.
31. STINSON, E.E. and C.O.WILLITS. — J.Assoc.Offic. Agric.Chemists, 48(3):493−497. 1965.
32. ROULET, N., N.C.MEHTA, P.DUBACH, and H.Z.DEUEL. — Z.Pflanzenernähr., Düng., Bodenkunde,
    103(1):1−9. 1963.
33. ULMANN, M. and M.RICHTER. — Kolloid-Z., 169(1−2):136−148. 1960; Monatsber.Dtsch.Akad.Wiss.,
    2(10):603−607, Berlin. 1960; Ernährungsforschung, 5(4):462−477. 1960.
34. ULMANN, M. — Stärke, 14(5):175−179. 1962; 16(5):151−157. 1964.
35. RICHTER, M. — Stärke, 14(10):337−342. 1962.
36. RICHTER, M. and H.H.STROH. — Stärke, 14(11):415−424. 1962.
37. TAKI, M. — J.Agric.Chem.Soc.Japan, 33(3):216−218; 218−220; No.4:245−249; No.6:445−448;
    448−452. 1959; Agric. and Biol.Chem., 26(1):1−9. 1962.
38. WINKLER, S. — Stärke, 14(5):168−175. 1962.
39. SEIDEMANN, J. — Photogr.Korresp., 101(12):189−191. 1965.
40. ASO, K., F.YAMAUCHI, and J.TOHOKU. — J.Agric.Res., 5(4):305−316. 1955.
41. MANO, E.B. and L.C.O.LIMA. — Analyt.Chem., 32(13):1772−1773. 1960.
42. LIKHONOS, E.F. and I.I.KOROL'KOV. — ZhPKh, 36(5):1152−1154. 1963.
43. BEREZKIN, V.G. and O.L.GORSHUNOV. — Uspekhi Khimii, 34(6):1108−1126. 1965.
44. BEREZKIN, V.G., O.A.GORSHUNOV, and M.A.GEIDERIKH. — Plasticheskie Massy, No.11:53−57.1965.
45. MARTIN, S.B. and R.W.RAMSTAD. — Anal. Chem., Vol.33:982. 1961.
46. GREENWOOD, C.T., J.H.KNOX, and E.MILNE. — Chem. Ind., No.46:1878. London. 1961.
47. KIRRET, O. and E.KYULLIK. — Izv.AN EstSSR, Seriya Fiziko-Matematicheskikh i Tekhnicheskikh Nauk,
    13(1):15−24. 1964.
48. KYULLIK, E.A. — Author's Summary of Candidate's Thesis. Tallin. 1966.
49. KIRRET, O. and E.KYULLIK. — Izv.AN EstSSR, Seriya Fiziko-Matematicheskikh i Tekhnicheskikh Nauk,
    15(2):252. 1966.
50. GREENWOOD, C.T., J.H.KNOX, and E.MILNE. — Chem. and Ind., No.46:1878−1879. 1961.
51. SCHWENKER, R.F. and L.R.Beck. — J.Polymer Sci., C., No.2:331−340. 1963.
52. GLASSNER, S. and A.R.PIERCE. — Analyt.Chem., 37(4):525−527. 1965.
53. FEUERBERG, H. and H.WEIGEL. — Z.Analyt.Chem., 199(2):121−132. 1964.
54. KULZER, F.J. and A.BROIDO. — Pyrodynamics, 2(2−3):151−163. 1965.
55. BRYCE, D.J. and C.T.GREENWOOD. — Stärke, 15(8):285−290. 1963.
56. GRIDYUSHKO, G.S., Yu.M.KHOL'KIN, and V.L.KOLESNIKOV. — Obshchaya i Prikladnaya Khimiya,
    Vol.1, No.2. 1968.
57. TAI, H., R.M.POWERS, and T.F.PROTZMAN. — Analyt.Chem., 36(1):108−110. 1964.
58. HUCHETTE, M. — Stärke, 15(8):275−280. 1963.
59. GROTEN, B. — Analyt. Chem., 36(7):1206−1212. 1964.
60. WANDEL, M. and H.TENGLER. — Gummi-Asbest-Kunststoffe, 19(2):141−143. 1966.
61. COBLER, J.G., E.P.SAMSEL, and G.H.BEAVER. — Talanta, 9(6):473−481. 1962.
62. FUDZIHARA, F. and T.CUGIMOTO. — Sci. and Ind., 39(5):284−293. 1965.
63. Chem. Process., 9(10):34−36; 10(4):4−7. 1964.
64. SCHWENKER, R.F. and E.PASCU. — Tappi, 46(11):665−672. 1963.

*Chapter IV*

## CHROMATOGRAPHY IN THE CHEMISTRY OF LIGNIN

Lignin, just like polysaccharides, is a high-molecular component of wood, so that the chromatographic analysis must be preceded by the cleavage of the molecule into simpler structural units. As distinct from polysaccharides, lignin is not hydrolyzed to elementary units by the action of acid catalysts, owing to which it is the products of its advanced degretion (oxidative, hydrogenolytic, thermal, etc.) which are studied by the chromatographic technique. The study of the sulfur products of lignin and the products of its alkaline treatment are particularly important, since these treatments form the base for the preparation of pulp from wood.

At present chromatographic methods are only utilized in the study of certain reactions of lignin. The size and the content of the individual sections of the present chapter will thus necessarily be determined by the number of publications available on each particular subject.

Chromatographic methods yielded a number of valuable data on the chemical mechanism of formation of lignin. This chapter is a review of the chromatographic methods employed in the study of various preparations of lignin, except for lignosulfonates and sulfate lignin, which are discussed in Chapter VI.

Chromatographic methods are extensively employed in the structural studies on lignin, but special monographs on the subject are not available. For a few examples of the application of chromatography to the chemistry of lignin, see monograph by Brauns and other publications /2 — 5/.

The chemistry of lignin has been studied by different chromatographic techniques, the general tendency being a gradual transition from column chromatography /6, 7/ via paper chromatography /8 — 15/ to thin sorbent layer chromatography /16/. Gel filtration /17/ and gas-liquid chromatography /18/ are now used with increasing frequency.

## 1. CHROMATOGRAPHY IN THE STUDY OF BIOSYNTHESIS OF LIGNIN

Chromatographic methods have been extensively employed in the study of biosynthesis and enzymatic synthesis of lignin, mainly in the separation of the intermediate products of the biosynthesis, in order to identify its precursors.

Manskaya and Bardinskaya /19/ studied ligninlike preparations isolated by alkaline extraction from peat moss. The products of alkaline nitrobenzene oxidation of the resulting preparations were studied by paper chromatography. It was found that vanillin, syringaldehyde and p-hydroxy-benzaldehyde present in the reaction mixture can be separated on No. 2 chromatographic grade paper with n-butanol saturated with $2-3\%$ ammonia as developer and a solution of 2, 4-dinitrophenylhydrazine in 2 N HCl as spot detector. Other authors /8, 20/ developed with a 6:1 mixture of petroleum ether with n-butyl ether saturated with water.

The results indicate that the cell wall of peat moss contains mobile aromatic precursors of lignin; there is no high-molecular lignin in the moss. This is in contradiction to the conclusion arrived at by Lindberg and Theander /22/ who carried out a chromatographic analysis of the products of alkaline nitrobenzene oxidation of peat moss and established the presence of lignin which mainly consisted of p-hydroxyphenolic compounds.

A similar paper chromatographic technique (development with butanol + $3\%$ ammonia, spot detection with $5\%$ alcoholic solution of phloroglucinol and concentrated HCl) was subsequently employed /23/ in a study of ether-soluble phenolic components isolated by extraction accompanied by mechanical grinding of the buds of a number of shrubs. It was found that the constituents of the ether extracts appear on the chromatogram in the zone of the oxidation products of coniferyl alcohol. The individual components in the mixture were not identified.

Paper chromatography was also employed in the study of the biosynthesis of lignin involving the use of isotopic carbon /24/.

Chromatographic methods have been widely employed in the studies of enzymatic synthesis of lignin carried out by the school of Freudenberg. Model compounds used in the synthesis of lignin have been successfully separated by paper chromatography /25/; synthetic d,l-pinoresinol ($R_f = 0.87$) has been characterized by this method /26/; intermediate products of enzymatic synthesis of lignin have been separated /27/ on cellulose columns and on columns with a mixture of $SiO_2$ and cellite; dehydrodiconiferyl alcohol has been detected /28/.

Enzymatic synthesis of lignin was also achieved by Okabe and Kratzl /29/. They conducted enzymatic polymerization of coniferyl alcohol or its mixture with sinapyl alcohol in the presence of radioactive p-hydroxybenzoic acid, using peroxydase or hydrogen peroxide as a catalyst according to Freudenberg /30/. The yield of the dehydropolymerizate in the synthesis was 85% on the coniferyl alcohol; when a 1:1 mixture of the two alcohols was employed, the yield was 47.9% on the combined amount of the alcohols and 85% on the coniferyl alcohol. The dehydropolymerizate was fractionated by stepwise fractionation, the UV- and IR-spectra of the fractions were studied, their elementary compositions determined and conductometric titrations performed in order to compare the acidic properties of the preparations. When the ligninlike preparations were hydrolyzed in boiling 1 N NaOH under reflux for 6 hours, $40-80\%$ of p-hydroxybenzoic acid became solubilized. These results were also obtained by paper chromatographic analysis of the products of the alkaline hydrolysis /31/ and their radioactivities. The mobile phase in the chromatographic analysis was benzene saturated with formic acid; the spots were revealed by spraying with diazotized sulfanilic acid, the colored compounds extracted and determined by photometry at 276 m$\mu$.

Paper chromatography was also employed /32/ in the study of many simple compounds serving as mockup for lignin. In particular, the

$R_f$-values of 25 ligninlike phenylpropane derivatives have been determined /33/. Shikimic and quinic acids are determined in this manner.

Thin layer chromatography on silica gel G has been employed /35/ in the separation of aromatic amino acids which are precursors of lignin.

The dimer D, L-syringoresinol /36/, formed in the intermediate stages of biosynthesis of lignin, has been isolated from beechwood extracts on a silica gel column.

As distinct from the chemical methods, chromatography is a very convenient technique in the study of intermediate products of biosynthesis of lignin, as in this way the separated compounds do not undergo any secondary chemical alterations. It may accordingly be expected that chromatography will in future be used to a much greater extent in the study of these complex enzymatic reactions.

## 2. CHROMATOGRAPHY OF DIFFERENT PREPARATIONS OF LIGNIN

The isolation of lignin from wood is always accompanied by a partial change in its structure. The closest to native lignin are preparations extracted with ethanol according to Brauns, those isolated by a combination of mechanical grinding with Bjorkman extraction and certain other preparations. These preparations are usually characterized by the electrophoretic method. .

The structure of native lignin preparations is variable. It has been shown, by way of fractional precipitation, that native lignin of aspen wood includes four fractions /37, 38/. It has been established by paper electrophoresis /39/ that these fractions are also heterogeneous; the total number of fractions obtained from the native aspen lignin was fourteen. Some of them have a natural yellow coloration, others fluoresce in UV light. When the chromatograms were treated with phloroglucinol in hydrochloric acid, an intensely colored red-violet zone appeared, the color of the zone varying with time.

The electrophoretic method was also extensively employed /40, 41/ in studying the native lignin and lignin preparations isolated from wood by the enzymatic method. The oxidation products of these lignin preparations were studied /42/ by paper chromatography. The electrophoretic method was applied by Bjorkman /44 — 46/ in his study of lignin-containing materials.

Lignin preparations from samples of reeds, isolated by ethanol extraction according to Brauns and by dioxane according to Nikitin, have been studied /47/. The properties of the native lignin and dioxane lignin thus obtained had similar properties. The solubility, the UV and IR spectra and the electrophoretic properties of the lignin preparations were studied, and their elementary composition and functional group contents determined. In its structure and properties, reed lignin resembles lignin from wood of deciduous trees.

Sukhaya, Morozov and Khol'kin compared different preparations of lignin with the aid of pyrolytic gas-liquid chromatography. The pyrolysis was conducted in a modified pyrolytic block of a KhL-7 chromatograph at 500°; the duration of the pyrolysis was 10 seconds. The separation of the

hydrolysis products was effected on a 200×0.6 cm column with 15%
Provacel W-OF-100 on celite 545 (45 — 100 mesh), column temperature
100°, flow rate of carrier gas (nitrogen) 31 ml/min, current intensity of
detector 100 mA, temperature of detector 100°, sample weight of lignin
16 mg, potentiometer sensitivity 1 mV over the entire scale range.

The following lignin preparations were studied by this method: Bjorkman
lignin isolated from fir and oak trees, Pepper lignin, dioxane lignin,
sulfuric acid Claesson lignin, hydrolysis and sulfate lignins, phenol lignin
and also a number of lignin preparations which had undergone different
thermal treatments.

The pyrolysis products of most of these lignin preparations contained
formaldehyde, acetone, acetaldehyde, propionaldehyde, methanol, methyl
ethyl ketone, etc. The composition of the hydrolysis products is a function
of the mode of preparation of the lignin.


## 3. STUDIES OF THE LIGNIN-CARBOHYDRATE COMPLEX

Chromatographic methods are widely employed in the isolation,
purification and study of the lignin-carbohydrate complex. The complex
has been purified /48/ by chromatography on $Al_2O_3$. The chromatographic
isolation of lignin confirmed /49/ the presence of a chemical bond between
xylan and lignin in a preparation of lignin acetate from beechwood. In a
study of the lignin-carbohydrate complex of straw /50/, the lignin-xylan
complex was isolated by chromatography from wheat straw /51/ and it was
shown that there is a phenyl-$\beta$-glucoside link between the carbohydrate and
the lignin components of the complex /52/.

Freudenberg /53/ studied the mechanism of formation of lignin and
lignin-carbohydrate links by the chromatographic method; the results
served to establish tentative /54/ model links between lignin and
carbohydrates.

The lignin-carbohydrate complex isolated from $\gamma$-irradiated wood has
been studied /55/ by paper chromatography.

Wood, finely ground in a ball mill and treated at 100° with ethylene
oxide and dimethylformamide was fractionated into components by fractional
precipitation, column and paper chromatography and separation of individual
fractions by electrophoresis /56/.

In a study of the lignin-carbohydrate complex of jute /57/ the partly
hydrolyzed preparations were analyzed by paper chromatography.


## 4. OXIDATION OF LIGNIN

Chromatographic methods are most frequently employed in the study of
the chemical reactions of lignin, in particular its oxidation reactions. The
products of oxidation of lignosulfates on CuO were studied /58/ by
adsorption chromatography on columns. This catalyst also served for the
oxidation of model compounds, and the composition of the reaction mixture
was studied by paper chromatography /59, 60/ and by chromatography on

magnesol /61/. The oxidation of lignosulfonates in alkaline medium on silver oxide was also studied /62/.

A recent study /63/ deals with the oxidation of model compounds of lignin by hydrogen peroxide. Sixteen different ligninlike substances were studied; these were phenylpropane derivatives, including $\alpha, \beta$-unsaturated aldehydes ($Ar - CH = CH - CHO$), $\alpha$-ketones ($Ar - CO - CH_2 - CH_3$), $\beta$-ketones ($Ar - CH_2 - CO - CH_3$) and unsaturated acids ($Ar - CH = CH - COOH$). All model compounds were oxidized under the same conditions. Hydrogen peroxide (1 M solution) was added to the model compounds dissolved in 1 N NaOH (molar ratio $H_2O_2$/model = 1.5 : 1.2). The reaction was allowed to proceed for one hour at 25°, the excess $H_2O_2$ was reduced by sodium bisulfite and the reaction mixture was made acidic to litmus. The reaction products were extracted from the mixture with ether, the extract washed with a saturated solution of sodium bicarbonate, the acid substances removed, and the residual ether extract studied by gas-liquid chromatography (Aerograph A-90-S chromatograph).

The mixture was separated on columns with 20% diethylene glycol succinate on Chromosorb W at 175°, flow rate of carrier gas 100 ml/min. In quantitative analysis of the reaction mixture 2-phenylethanol was employed as the internal standard. The compounds were identified by preparative gas-liquid chromatography followed by a study of the IR spectra of the separated components. It was found that the identity of the side chain greatly affects the oxidation of the model compounds by hydrogen peroxide. In unsaturated aromatic aldehydes the double bond is broken with the formation of the corresponding aldehydes. $\alpha$-Ketones react only in the presence of a free hydroxyl group in the para-position to the side chain. $\beta$-Ketones probably react with the formation of enol tautomers as intermediate products, with subsequent scission of the double bonds. Phenolic and primary alcohol groups and alkylaryl ether bonds are not oxidized. Some of the reactions studied may be of importance in connection with alkaline hydrogen peroxide bleaching of wood pulp.

Chromatography was employed /64/ in studying the products of oxidation of methylated and nonmethylated hydrochloric acid lignin and in the study /65/ of the composition of the oxidation products of lignin from the bark of Japanese red pine.

Quantitative determination of the products of oxidation of lignin was effected by chromatography on paper impregnated with sodium tetraborate /66/. The oxidation products could be identified by the variation of $R_f$-values with the change in pH /67/. It was found by this method that the oxidation products of hydrotropic beechwood lignin contained vanillin and syringaldehyde /68/; oxidation in alkaline medium yielded syringyl-ethane /69/.

Oxalic, maleic, fumaric and other acids have been isolated by the chromatographic technique /70/ from the oxidation products of model lignin compounds. These acids are also formed under similar conditions during the oxidation of lignin hydrochloride.

Brunow /71/ determined the yields of benzenepolycarboxylic acids during the oxidation of D-pinoresinol after preliminary Willstatter condensation with concentrated HCl, after Claesson condensation with 72% sulfuric acid and after concentrated alkali treatment. The oxidation was performed in 2.5% KOH by potassium permanganate at 80 — 90° during 24 hours. The acids in the form of esters were separated on chromatographic columns and identified by thin layer chromatography from their IR-spectra and their melting points. The maximum yield of the acids (up to 3.45%) was obtained by the oxidation of the product of 72% $H_2SO_4$ condensation of D-pinoresinol; benzenepolycarboxylic acids were not detected in the oxidation products of pinoresinol condensed in alkaline medium.

Up to 37.3% of ether-soluble substances (in the presence of a 5% catalyst) were isolated /72/ from the oxidation products of the lignin hydrolyzate in alkaline medium under a pressure of $18 - 20$ atm at $180 - 200°$ during 4 hours in the presence of different amounts of $V_2O_5$ as catalyst. Paper chromatography showed the presence of vanillin, vanillic and protocatechuic acids, guaiacol and pyrocatechol in these substances.

Let us now discuss in detail the technique of oxidation of lignin, which is most often employed in structural studies.

**Alkaline nitrobenzene oxidation of lignin.** The oxidation method most often employed in the study of lignin is nitrobenzene oxidation in alkaline medium. A high yield of vanillin is thus obtained from conifers and a high yield of vanillin and syringaldehyde from deciduous trees; a number of other compounds are also formed, the chromatographic study of which gives additional information on the nature of oxidative transformations of lignin.

A technique recently used in research work is the micromethod of Stone and Blundell /8/ who utilized paper chromatography in semiquantitative analysis of the reaction mixture. This method includes the separation of vanillin, syringaldehyde and p-hydroxybenzaldehyde on chromatographic paper, after which the paper strips were cut up to separate individual components, the sections extracted and the components determined spectrophotometrically. If reproducible results are to be obtained, the procedure must be rigorously followed; this particularly applies to the sampling of the oxidation products.

A modified procedure has been described /73/ in which a number of experimental difficulties are eliminated. The products of oxidation of lignin may also be separated on a cellulose column /74/.

The micromethod /8/ has been greatly simplified by Pen /75/, who determined vanillin only in the reaction mixture.

Nitrobenzene oxidation is conducted in stainless steel micro-bombs of 5 ml volume, with continuous shaking. A sample corresponding to $20 - 25$ mg lignin is taken for the oxidation, mixed with 2 ml of 2 N NaOH and 0.12 ml nitrobenzene and heated at $170°$ during $2^1/_2$ hours.

To separate the oxidation products the reaction mixture is centrifuged, 0.02 ml of the clarified liquid is applied as a spot $6 - 8$ mm in diameter to a $35 \times 3$ cm strip of chromatographic paper. The chromatogram is developed with n-butanol saturated with a 3% solution of ammonia by the descending method. The vanillin spot ($R_f = 0.46$) is eluted in a test tube with 5 ml alcohol during 3 hours, 1 ml of 0.1% solution of 2, 4-dinitrophenylhydrazine in 14% $H_2SO_4$ is added to the eluate and the color intensity of the solution is determined 30 minutes later at 413 m$\mu$ (FEK-N-57 photoelectric colorimeter was employed). The coloration is stable, and the optical density remains perfectly constant for the first three hours. The average relative error of the determination was 0.85% in experiments performed on solutions of pure vanillin of concentrations between 3 and 40 $\mu$g/ml; vanillin could be determined to within 1.6% in the oxidation products of periodate lignin.

The micromethod /8/ is extensively employed in the study of preparations of lignin from different vegetal materials.

The method was utilized by Vil'kova and Murygina /76/ in their study of lignin from guza-paya (stems and bolls of cotton plant). Since guza-paya has a high content of extractable substances, the isolation of lignin was preceded by a Soxhlet extraction of the comminuted preparation with an alcohol-benzene mixture to remove waxes and tars; the sample was then treated with water at $70-75°$ during 24 hours to eliminate the water-extractable substances and for 24 hours at $70-75°$ with a 5% solution of sodium bicarbonate to extract the humic acids. The extraction of lignin from this preparation was effected with a 5% solution of alkali at $70-75°$ during 9 hours. The lignin was precipitated from solution by adding concentrated hydrochloric acid. The precipitate was purified by sixfold reprecipitation from alkaline solution.

The preparations were oxidized during $2-2^1/_2$ hours at $160°$ by shaking in stainless steel autoclaves 2 ml in volume, which contained about 40 mg lignin, 0.06 ml nitrobenzene and 1 ml of 2 N solution of NaOH. The reaction mixture was cooled, filtered and developed by the ascending method for $18-20$ hours with the mixture petroleum ether:butanol:water = 3:1:4.

The study of the chromatogram in UV light shows the presence of four spots, the first two of which were identified as vanillin and syringaldehyde.

The homogeneity of alkaline solutions of guza-paya lignin has also been chromatographically studied. It has been shown /76/, by using the technique described above, that lignin can be separated on paper (without nitrobenzene cleavage) into three zones, two with $R_f = 0.8$ and one with $R_f = 0.95$. UV spectra, luminescence spectra and polarographic investigations showed that the lignin fractions are very similar.

The method of nitrobenzene oxidation with chromatographic analysis of the reaction mixture was utilized /77/ in the study of the effect of $\gamma$-irradiation on the guza-paya lignin. It was shown that vanillin is evolved from the dry guza-paya lignin acted upon by $Co^{60}$ $\gamma$-radiation. The effect of $\gamma$-radiation of the alkali-dissolved lignin produces deeper changes than nitrobenzene oxidation.

Shorygina and Niyazov /78/ studied the structure of the lignin isolated from individual parts of the cotton plant-seed husks, bolls and stems.

Alkaline nitrobenzene oxidation of the ground preparations yielded a mixture of aldehydes, the total yield of which was 3.55% on the stem weight, 1.9% on the boll weight and 1.66% on the weight of the seeds and husks of the cotton plant. The composition of the aldehyde mixture was studied by paper chromatography. As distinct from the method /8/, the solvent systems used contained hydrocarbons: hexane, heptane, octane, nonane. A sharp separation of a mixture of vanillin, syringaldehyde and p-hydroxy-benzaldehyde was attained by development with octane:heptane:hexane = 1:1:1, butyl ether:water = 1:0.2:0.2. Formerly the system ligroin: n-butanol:water = 6:1:1 had been employed for the purpose. The elution was conducted in two passes of 3 hours each, the chromatogram being dried after each separation stage. The detection of the aldehydes on paper was effected with the aid of a 0.2% solution of 2,4-dinitrophenylhydrazine in 2 N HCl. The $R_f$-values are 0.056 and 0.254 for syringaldehyde and vanillin, respectively.

It has been shown in this way that the aldehyde mixtures contained vanillin and syringaldehyde and that p-hydroxybenzaldehyde was absent. The presence of syringaldehyde shows that the cotton lignin resembles the lignin of deciduous trees.

Chromatographic methods were utilized in the study /80/ of the products of alkaline nitrobenzene oxidation of lignin sulfate isolated from black liquor with sulfuric acid. For the sake of comparison lignin preparations isolated from wood by methanol /81/, dioxane /82/ and by a modified cuprammonium method /83/ were also studied. The oxidation was performed according to a macromethod /84/ in a rocking autoclave at 160° during three hours. The volatiles were removed from the reaction mixture by steam distillation, the aqueous condensate layer was acidified to pH 6 — 6.5 and extracted with benzene; the residual aqueous layer was acidified to pH 2 and extracted with benzene and ether in succession.

The first benzene and ether extracts were separated into the aldehyde, acid and phenol fractions, while the second benzene extract was chromatogrammed without preliminary fractionation. The study of the extracts was performed by two methods — paper chromatography and chromatography on columns. Paper chromatography was conducted by both ascending and descending methods; the time required for mixture separation was 6 — 18 hours, depending on the method of separation and the brand of the chromatographic paper. Three developer systems were utilized. The aldehyde fraction was successfully developed with n-butanol: 3% aqueous ammonia = 3:1 and with n-butanol: pyridine: water = 10:3:3; the spots were revealed with a 0.1% solution of 2, 4-dinitrophenylhydrazine in 2N HCl. The acid fraction was separated in n-butanol: acetic acid: water = 4:1:5; aromatic acids were detected by a solution of diazotized sulfanilic acid. The phenolic fractions were chromatogrammed by the ascending technique only; they were developed with n-butanol: acetic acid: water = 4:1:5; the same reagent as above was used for spot detection.

It has been shown by this method /80/ that the qualitative composition of the products of oxidative degradation of all the lignin samples studied are very similar. However, the quantitative content of vanillin in the mixture obtained by the oxidation of sulfate lignin is much lower than in the products of oxidative degradation of the other lignin preparations, whereas their acid content is, on the contrary, higher. These data indicate that lignin undergoes profound chemical changes during the sulfate cook.

The technique of column chromatography was also employed in a study of the products of alkaline nitrobenzene oxidation of sulfate lignin, dioxane lignin, methanol lignin and cupramonium lignin /80/.

The aldehyde fractions separated from the reaction mixture were studied as follows: 10 grams of $Al_2O_3$ sorbent with 10 wt% of water (III activity grade according to Brockmann) were suspended in 40 ml toluene, introduced into a 200×12 mm column and washed with 15 — 20 ml pure toluene. The sample (10 — 20 mg) of the mixture was dissolved in 2 — 3 ml toluene, introduced into the column, and was then eluted with pure toluene. The quantitative determination of aniline in the eluate was conducted by potentiometric titration against hydroxylamine hydrochloride.

Aromatic acids were separated on 340 — 380×10 — 11 mm columns with silica gel; the stationary phase was 0.5N sulfuric acid and the mobile solvent was a 20:80 mixture of butanol with chloroform. It was shown that the main component of the acid fractions was vanillic acid.

Phenolic fractions were separated on columns filled with silica gel suspended in cyclohexane saturated with water. A partial separation of the phenols in the reaction mixture was attained.

The method of alkaline nitrobenzene oxidation /8/ was applied to the study of the biosynthesis of lignin /24/, in the establishment of a relationship between the structure of lignin and the species of higher plants /85/, to the oxidation of model compounds of lignin /86/, of the lignin from the bark of red pine /87/, etc.

The products of alkaline nitrobenzene oxidation of lignin may also be separated on silica gel columns /88/. The method can be used for a quantitative determination of vanillin, syringaldehyde and p-hydroxy-benzaldehyde.

Chromatography on kieselguhr columns and thin layer chromatography was utilized /89/ in a study of the composition of the products of alkaline nitrobenzene oxidation of lignin synthesized by plant tissue grown in an artefact medium.

Many more examples of the applications of the method could be adduced.

**Analysis of the products of alkaline nitrobenzene oxidation of lignin by gas-liquid chromatography.** In 1962 Pepper et al. /90/ described a method for studying the products of alkaline nitrobenzene oxidation of lignin and lignin-containing plant materials with the aid of gas-liquid chromatography.

Oxidation and analytical procedure: Ten ml of 2N NaOH and about 200 mg isolated lignin or 400 — 800 mg wood or powdered straw are placed in a stainless steel autoclave of 20 ml capacity, and 0.6 ml of double-distilled nitrobenzene is added. The autoclave is rotated and heated for 2 hours at $180 \pm 2°$. After cooling, the dark reaction mixture is carefully washed with water and ether by continuous liquid extraction. The extraction is continued for 24 — 30 hours, in order to remove the excess nitrobenzene and the products of its regeneration.

The aqueous layer is acidified to pH 3 by slow addition of concentrated HCl and is again extracted with ether for 24 — 30 hours in order to isolate the products of oxidation of lignin. The ether extract is washed with water, dried over anhydrous $MgSO_4$ and concentrated to 2 — 3 ml. The resulting extract is quantitatively transferred to a 5 ml volumetric flask, the ether washings from the extract vessel are added and the flask is made up to mark with dry ether. The contents of the flask are mixed, two 60 — 100 $\mu l$ samples are withdrawn with the aid of a pipet and immediately injected into the chromatograph column.

Complete separation of vanillin, syringaldehyde and p-hydroxybenzal-dehyde was achieved on a $183 \times 0.6$ cm copper column with 15% Apiezone N on Fluoropak 80; temperature of analysis 220°, the flow rate of carrier gas (helium) was 42 ml/min, pressure at entry 2.1 atm. Beckman GC-2 chromatograph; katharometric detection.

Under the above conditions the retention times were 5.8, 8.2 and 19.3 minutes for p-hydroxybenzaldehyde, vanillin and syringaldehyde, respectively.

Studies were carried out on the oxidation products of lignins of various tree species, and also on the lignin of wheat straw. The resulting quantitative analysis of the reaction products is important in the structural studies of lignins of plants in different botanical classes. The main component of the mixture of the oxidation products of fir lignin was vanillin; aspen lignin yielded vanillin and syringaldehyde, while wheat straw lignin yielded vanillin, syringaldehyde and p-hydroxybenzaldehyde.

Hrutfiord /91/ used a more efficient type of chromatographic column and detector and thus could study the products of alkaline nitrobenzene oxidation of lignin in more detail.

Oxidation procedure: 50 ml of sulfite lye are neutralized, 5 g NaOH and 5 ml nitrobenzene are added and the mixture is heated for 2 hours in a stainless steel autoclave. Preliminarily extracted groundwood is treated in a similar manner: 10 grams of wood meal are added to 50 ml water, 5 g NaOH and 5 ml nitrobenzene are added and the mixture heated at 160° for two hours. The reaction mixture is filtered, extracted for 24 hours with ether, acidified and again extracted with ether for 24 hours. The ether extract is introduced into the chromatograph.

Analysis: capillary chromatographic columns (45 m × 0.15 cm) with 5 — 10% stationary phase operate at 150 — 175°, the temperature at the sample inlet is 300 — 325°, the flow rate of carrier gas (helium) is 120 — 140 ml/min; Perkin-Elmer 154C chromatograph with flame-ionization detector. Satisfactory mixture separation was obtained when diethylene glycol succinate was used as the stationary polar phase; a more rapid, but less complete separation was obtained on weakly polar phases (polyphenyl ether) OS-138 and Apiezone L).

Products of nitrobenzene oxidation of red alder tree were found to include vanillin, acetovanillone, p-hydroxybenzaldehyde, syringaldehyde, acetosyringone and 5-formylaniline.

An even more effective mixture separation was attained /93/ (see also /94/) in the study of the methylated products of alkaline nitrobenzene oxidation with programmed temperature increase of the chromatographic column.

Filings of the wood of white fir (Abies concolor) were subjected to alkaline nitrobenzene oxidation under conditions recommended by Leopold /92/. The oxidation products were extracted from the reaction mixture with ether, and methylated with dimethyl sulfate in the presence of added ammonium hydroxide at pH 11. The methyl ethers of the phenolic oxidation products were extracted with ether, the residue was acidified to pH 1—2 and again extracted with ether in order to isolate the carboxylic acids. The isolated acids were esterified with diazomethane.

The resulting preparations were studied by gas-liquid chromatography. The components were identified by methylation and gas-liquid chromatographic analysis of model mixtures. The oxidation products were analyzed both by the isothermal technique and with programmed temperature increase. Isothermal analysis was conducted on stainless steel columns (153 × 0.35 cm) with 10 or 20% phenylsilicone 550 on Chromosorb W (60 — 80 mesh) at 125°, 190° or 225°; sample inlet temperatures 285, 300 and 310°, respectively. The flow rate of carrier gas (nitrogen) was 40 ml/min, that of hydrogen was 30 ml/min, sample volume 1 — 2 $\mu$l, Aerograph A600-B chromatograph with flame ionization detector. A better separation of the components was attained with programmed temperature increase of the column from 65 to 250°, at 8° per minute followed by isothermal analysis at 250° on 183 × 0.35 cm column with 10% of fluorosilicone QF-1 on Chromosorb W, AW (100 — 120 mesh), treated with dimethylchlorosilane. The flow rates of $N_2$ and $H_2$ were 40 ml/min, the injector temperature was 275°, the detector temperature was 300° and the sample volume was 0.5 — 1.0 $\mu$l. The chromatograph used was Aerograph 204 with double flame ionization detector. In this way the following compounds could be detected in the mixture: veratrole, veratryl aldehyde, acetoveratrone,

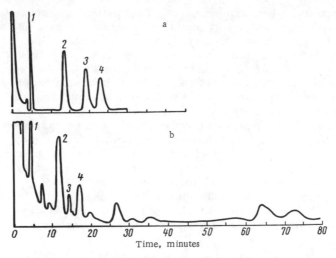

FIGURE 26. Chromatograms of:

a — model mixture; b — methylated products of alkaline nitrobenzene oxidation under isothermal conditions; 1 — anisaldehyde; 2 — veratryl aldehyde; 3 — acetoveratrone; 4 — 3,4,5-trimethoxybenzaldehyde.

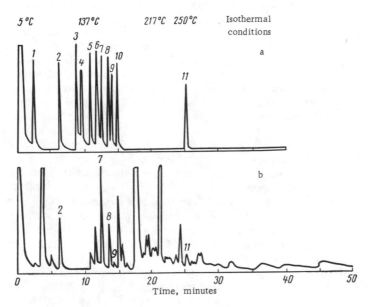

FIGURE 27. Chromatograms of:

a — model mixture; b — methylated products of alkaline nitrobenzene oxidation with programmed temperature increase; 1 — anisole; 2 — veratrole; 3 — 1,2,3-trimethoxybenzene; 4 — anisaldehyde; 5 — p-methoxyacetophenone; 6 — veratryl alcohol; 7 — veratryl aldehyde; 8 — acetoveratrone; 9 — 3,4,5-trimethoxybenzaldehyde; 10 — 3,4,5-trimethoxyacetophenone; 11 — dehydroveratryl aldehyde.

3, 4, 5-trimethoxybenzaldehyde, 3, 4, 5-trimethoxyacetophenone, dehydro-veratryl aldehyde and methyl esters of benzoic, anisic, phthalic, veratric, 3, 4, 5-trimethoxy benzoic, mellitic and other acids. The chromatograms contained numerous peaks which have remained unidentified.

Figures 26 and 27 show examples of chromatographic separation of mixtures of model compounds and oxidation products under isothermal conditions and with programmed temperature increase of the column.

If the results of analyses of the products of alkaline nitrobenzene oxidation of lignin by paper chromatography are compared with those obtained by gas-liquid chromatography, it will be seen that gas-liquid chromatography is more rapid and more accurate. In addition, gas-liquid chromatography permits to identify not only vanillin and syringaldehyde, but also numerous other reaction products, which is of great importance in the chemistry of lignin. The products of alkaline nitrobenzene oxidation of lignin should be examined with programmed temperature increase; it is desirable to utilize chromatographs with highly sensitive detectors.

## 5. CHROMATOGRAPHY OF THE PRODUCTS OF HYDROLYSIS AND ACIDOLYSIS OF LIGNIN

Catalytic degradation of lignin in aqueous medium (hydrolysis) or by acids in organic solvents and their mixtures with water (acidolysis) yields complex mixtures of reaction products, which can be qualitatively and quantitatively analyzed by applying chromatographic techniques.

Paper chromatography showed /95/ that the hydrolysis of lignin in aqueous medium forms a mixture of monomeric products which can be fractionated. Coniferyl aldehyde, vanillin, p-coumarilaldehyde, vaniloyl methyl ketone and guaiacylacetone have been identified in the mixture.

When lignin from the wood of fir trees is treated with dilute HCl, coniferyl aldehyde, vanillin and other compounds which can be studied by paper chromatography pass into the extract /96/. Chromatographic methods were also employed by Chudakov /97/ in his study of the alteration of lignin in the process of acid hydrolysis.

The acid degradation of lignin in the system dioxane-water has been intensively studied. A comparative study has been performed /98/ on the hydrolysis of fir and beechwood lignin in the system dioxane-water. Finely ground wood (2 grams, 60 — 100 mesh) was subjected to a preliminary extraction with alcohol-benzene mixture and with hot water and was then boiled with 15 ml of dioxane: water = 1:1 in 20 ml autoclaves; the treatment temperature was 140 — 180°.

The eluted fraction of the reaction mixture was separated by paper chromatography in the solvent systems xylene: dimethylformamide = 9:2, xylene: methyl ethyl ketone: formamide = 25:25:1 and with benzene-saturated water. The spots were revealed with diazotized sulfanilic acid in 2% aqueous sodium carbonate, phloroglucinol or 2, 4-dinitrophenyl-hydrazine in a solution of hydrochloric acid. They were also revealed in UV-light.

The following compounds were identified in the hydrolyzate of fir wood by the method: coniferyl alcohol, p-coumaril alcohol, coniferyl aldehyde, vanillin and p-hydroxybenzaldehyde; the hydrolyzate of beechwood contained in addition sinapic alcohol and sinapyl and syringyl aldehydes.

Cinnamic alcohols were not identified in the products of water hydrolysis or in the products of hydrolysis with water-acetone and water-dimethylformamide mixtures. Vanillic acid /99/ was also found in the dioxane-water hydrolyzates of conifers, while syringic acid was found in hydrolyzates of deciduous trees. The chromatograms given by hydrolyzates of Bjorkman and Brauns lignins were identical with those of wood hydrolyzates containing native lignin.

Ether-soluble products of the water-dioxane hydrolyzates of pinewood lignin were separated by chromatography on powdered cellulose columns on developing with xylene : dimethylformamide = 9:2 /100/. Coniferyl alcohol, coniferyl aldehyde and carbohydrate degradation products were isolated in this way.

Gardner and MacLean /101/ studied the composition of low-molecular products obtained during hydrolytic degradation of the lignin of hemlock (Tsuga heterophylla (Raf.) Sorg.) in the system dioxane-water in the presence of hydrochloric acid. The products were separated by paper chromatography, using the following solvent systems: tetrahydrofurane : petroleum ether (bp 65 — 110°); water = 3:7:5, butanol: ethanol: ammonia: water = 40:10:1:49 and benzene : petroleum ether (bp 80 — 100°): methanol: water = 50:50:1:50. The components were identified by their UV and IR spectra and by the chromatographic behavior of model compounds. The following products of acid hydrolysis of lignin were identified: 1-hydroxy-3-(4-hydroxy-3-methoxyphenyl)-propanone-2 ($\omega$-hydroxyguaiacylacetone), 1-hydroxy-1 (4-hydroxy-3-methoxyphenyl)-propanone-2 ($\alpha$-hydroxyguaiacylacetone) and 2-hydroxy-1-(4-hydroxy-3-methoxyphenyl-propanol-1 ($\alpha$-hydroxypropioguaiacone). 3-Hydroxy-1-(4-hydroxy-3-methoxyphenyl)-propanone-1 was not found in the reaction products.

Gel filtration through a Sephadex G-25 column has been employed /102/ in the study of the products of acidolysis of Bjorkman fir lignin. The acidolysis was effected with dilute hydrochloric acid in a dioxane-water mixture; the fractions were eluted with dioxane : benzene = 1:3, and further separation was performed on silica gel. In addition to those previously described, three new fractions were isolated in this manner. The first fraction contained vanillic acid, 1-(4-hydroxy-3-methoxyphenyl)-propanone-2 and 1-(4-hydroxy-3-methoxyphenyl)-propanedione-1, 2 and the previously unknown compound 3-hydroxy-1- (4-hydroxyphenyl)-propanone-2, mp 72 — 73°. 4, 4'-Dihydroxy-3, 3'-dimethoxystilbene and phenylcoumarone, mp 110°, were found in the second fraction. The third fraction contained unidentified polymeric products.

The acidolysis of lignin in the system dioxane-water was also studied by other workers /103, 73/.

Column chromatography on Sephadex C-25 was employed /104/ in the fractionation of conc. $H_2SO_4$-soluble lignin in the determination of lignin according to Claesson. During analysis of birchwood and eucalyptus wood, 12 — 13% of the total lignin passes into the hydrolyzate.

The products of mild hydrolysis of beechwood lignin have been studied /105/ by chromatography on a column of cellulose impregnated with dimethylformamide and also on a silica gel column. Dimethylpyrogallylglycerol and other compounds have been isolated.

The products of acidic hydrolysis of native lignin could be separated /106/ on a thin layer of silon (Perlon) and on silica gel. Silon was used in mixture with plaster of Paris. The best separation was attained for

99
UNIVERSITY OF VICTORIA
LIBRARY
Victoria B. C.

components of the phenolic fraction by developing with ammonia-saturated butanol. The spots were revealed by spraying with ferric chloride and $K_3Fe(CN)_6$; in addition, the spots could be located in UV-light. The components were extracted from the paper with ether.

Thin silica gel layer was not bound with plaster of Paris. The layer served to separate the components of different fractions: phenolic, acidic, neutral substances and carbonyl compounds. The following solvent systems were recommended. For carbonyl compounds: benzene : methanol : acetic acid = 45 : 8 : 4; carboxyl compounds: xylene : dimethylformamide = 5 : 2; phenols; ammonia-saturated butanol; neutral components: xylene : dimethyl-formamide = 5 : 2. The spots were revealed in UV light. The components were extracted with ether, and IR spectra of the solutions were then taken. It was noted that silica gel was a more universal sorbent in thin layer chromatography of the hydrolysis products of lignin.

Fukuzumi and Terasawa studied /107/ the composition of the products of acetolysis of wood. Wood meal was preliminarily extracted and then heated under reflux in the reactor for 24 hours with a mixture of glacial acetic acid and a solution of magnesium chloride in a stream of $CO_2$. The reaction mixture was concentrated at 100° in nitrogen under reduced pressure and acetylated with a mixture of pyridine and acetic anhydride at 37° for more than 12 hours. The acetylated lignin was precipitated by dispersing the reaction product in a large volume of ice water, the precipitate washed and dried over KOH. The filtrate was extracted with methylene chloride, and the acetyllignin extracted with ether in a Soxhlet apparatus during 35 hours. The resulting extracts were examined by paper chromatography. The spots were revealed by the color reaction with 2,4-dinitrophenylhydrazine. The extracts contained coniferyl aldehyde and other carbonyl derivatives of guaiacol, which resembled Hibbert's ketones.

Gas-liquid chromatography is now frequently used in the studies of hydrolytic degradation of lignin.

Dence et al. /108/ compared the behavior of isopropyl ethers of guaiacol and 2,6-dimethoxyphenol and their derivatives during hydrolysis in the presence of $Cl_2$ as catalyst. The former compounds were chosen as models of guaiacyl structural elements of conifer lignin, the latter as the models of the syringyl structure of lignin from deciduous trees. Owing to the low solubility of model compounds in water the reaction was conducted in aqueous acetic acid at room temperature during two hours in the presence of varying amounts of $Cl_2$. The alcohols formed by dealkylation of the model compounds were isolated from the reaction mixture by distillation and their amounts determined by gas-liquid chromatography on 720F and 720M chromatographs on columns with 20% glycerol (column I) or with 20% Carbowax (column II) on fire-resistant brick; rate of flow of carrier gas (helium) 110 — 135 ml/min (column I) or 50 — 65 ml/min (column II), column temperature 95°. It was found that isopropyl groups are cleaved off the guaiacyl type compounds to a much greater extent than off syringyl compounds, in the presence of the same amounts of $Cl_2$. These results are due to the presence of a steric effect, which is a function of the size of the alkyl groups and of the presence of halogen atoms ortho to the alkoxyl groups.

A study of the degradation of lignin by peracetic acid was conducted /109/ on veratryl and vanillyl alcohols as model compounds. The reaction products were identified and determined by gas-liquid chromatography and

UNIVERSITY OF VICTORIA
LIBRARY
Victoria, B. C.

paper chromatography. Peracetic acid treatment of vanillyl alcohol yielded vanillin, vanillic, acetylvanillic, $\beta$-carboxymuconic, maleic and oxalic acids and vanillyl alcohol diacetate. The treatment of veratryl alcohol yielded veratryl aldehyde, veratric acid and vanillyl alcohol.

Kinetics of alkaline catalytic hydrolysis of substances modeling lignin (guaiacol and veratrole derivatives) was studied /110/ by determining the amount of methanol formed during the hydrolysis; the methanol was determined by gas-liquid chromatography.

## 6. ETHANOLYSIS OF LIGNIN

Lignin is often studied with the aid of ethanolysis reaction — treatment with anhydrous ethanol in the presence of an acid catalyst. Hibbert's ketones, which are important products formed during ethanolysis were studied /111/ by paper chromatography. Vanillin, vanilloyl methyl ketone, 1-(4-hydroxy-3-methoxyphenyl)-2-propanone (guaiacylacetone) and ethoxypropiovanillone were determined in the products of ethanolysis of lignin by chromatography on paper /112/. This technique was also extensively used by other workers /113, 114/ in their studies of the ethanolysis of lignin.

In a later study /115/ gas-liquid chromatography was employed in the determination of the composition of the oily material obtained by distillation of the products of ethanolysis of fir lignin. The analysis was conducted at 210° on a 200×4.65 mm column with 25% silicone on celite. Flow rate of carrier gas (nitrogen) 50 ml/min. The main reaction product were $\alpha$-ethoxypropiovanillone and its isomers. Isoeugenol may have been present; traces of $\alpha$-hydroxypropiovanillone and other compounds were also found.

## 7. HYDROGENATION AND HYDROGENOLYSIS OF LIGNIN

Products of hydrogenolysis of lignin have been studied by column chromatography on activated carbon /116/ and alumina /117/ and also by paper chromatography /118/.

During the past few years gas-liquid chromatography has been widely used in studying the products of hydrogenation and hydrogenolysis of lignin /119, 120/.

Pepper and Steck /121/ (see also /122/) studied the chloroform-soluble products of hydrogenation of aspen wood. Hydrogenation of wood meal was conducted in a dioxane-water medium with Raney catalyst; initial hydrogen pressure 35 atm, temperature 150 — 220°, duration about 5 hours. The maximum yield of hydrogenation products (52% on the weight of lignin) was obtained at 195° after 5 hours. It was established by gas-liquid chromatography that these products include guaiacol (yield 1.8% on the lignin), 4-methylguaiacol and 4-ethylguaiacol (1.2%), 4-n-propylguaiacol (0.4%), dihydroconiferyl alcohol (11.0%), syringol (0.5%), 4-methylsyringol (2.1%), 4-ethylsyringol (4.0%), 4-n-propylsyringol (2.9%) and dihydrosinapyl alcohol (28.3%). The hydrogenation products of pinewood contained only guaiacol derivatives, their yield being 20.5 wt% on the lignin.

Gas-liquid chromatography was employed /123/ to study the products of delignification of wood by hydrogenation in the presence of cobalt octacarbonyl. Sawdust of spruce (P i c e a  e x c e l s a) were suspended in benzene and treated with a mixture of $H_2$ and CO (1:1) in the presence of cobalt octacarbonyl $Co_2(CO)_8$ as soluble catalyst. The reaction was conducted at 170° under a pressure of 100 atm during 24 hours; after cooling, the gaseous reaction products were vented and the mixture heated for 3 hours at 150° under 60 atm pressure of hydrogen. The insoluble residue consisted of cellulose, which contained 3% Claesson lignin. The soluble components were separated into a neutral, an acidic and a phenolic fraction. The mixture of phenolic materials was subjected to molecular distillation and separated by gas-liquid chromatography. Phenol, guaiacol, 4-methylguaiacol, 4-ethylguaiacol and 4-n-propylguaiacol were separated on a column (length 1.8 m, internal diameter 6.5 mm) filled with 10% Apiezone N on Fluoropak, at a flow rate of carrier gas (helium) of 36 ml/min and at 210°. One of the peaks could not be identified. The same components could be identified on a 0.9 m long column with 20% Carbowax 20M on fireproof brick (flow rate of He 60 ml/min) at 225°; at 235° 3-methoxy-5, 6, 7, 8-tetrahydro-2-naphthol, 3-guaiacyltetrahydrofurane, 3-guaiacylpropanol, 4-guaiacylbutanol, diguaiacylmethane, and 4, 4'-dipropyl-6, 6'-biguaiacol were also detected. Analyses were also performed on a 0.9 m long column with 20% silicone rubber on fireproof brick (flow rate of He 60 ml/min) at 215 and 260°. The retention times of the individual components on the various columns are shown in Table 17. The phenolic components were also separated by thin layer chromatography on neutral alumina; the development was affected with cyclohexane : chloroform : acetic acid = 8:1:1.

TABLE 17. Analysis of phenolic products of hydrogenation of wood by gas-liquid chromatography

| Compound | Yield, % on lignin | Retention time, minutes | | | |
|---|---|---|---|---|---|
| | | Apiezone N | Carbowax 20M | | Silicone rubber |
| | | 210°C | 225°C | 235°C | 215°C |
| Phenol . . . . . . . . . . . . . . | Traces | 3.3 | 1.1 | | |
| Guaiacol . . . . . . . . . . . . | 0.5 | 4.9 | 1.4 | | |
| 4-Methylguaiacol . . . . . . . . | Traces | 8.1 | 2.3 | | |
| 4-Ethylguaiacol . . . . . . . . . | Traces | 11.0 | 3.6 | | |
| 4-n-Propylguaiacol . . . . . . . | 7.6 | 15.2 | 4.2 | 3.1 | 2.3 |
| Not identified . . . . . . . . . . | 0.3 | 29.8 | | 13.1 | 4.2 |
| 3-Methoxy-5, 6, 7, 8-tetrahydro-2-naphthol . . . . . . . . . . | 0.5 | | | 9.1 | 4.9 |
| 3-Guaiacyltetrahydrofurane . . . | 2.7 | | | 17.1 | 5.7 |
| 3-Guaiacylpropanol . . . . . . . | 10.7 | | | 27.4 | 6.2 |
| 4-Guaiacylbutanol . . . . . . . | Traces | | | 34.3 | 8.9 |
| Diguaiacylmethane . . . . . . . | 0.3 | | | | 4.8 (at 260°C) |
| 4, 4'-Dipropyl-6, 6'-biguaiacol . | 1.9 | | | | 12.1 (at 260°C) |
| Total . . . . . . . . . . . . | 24.5 | | | | |

102

Several chromatographic methods were successfully combined in the analysis of the composition of phenolic fractions formed by hydrogenation of technical alkali lignin, acid lignin and lignite /124/. The reaction was conducted in a solution in phenol or pyrocatechol at $300 - 400°$ under a pressure of $200 - 400$ atm in the presence of $NiSWS_2$, mixtures of $Fe_2O_3$, CuO and S, and NiSWS and $MoO_2$ as catalysts. Alkali lignin thus treated for $2 - 2^1/_2$ hours yielded p-alkylphenols in $2 - 3\%$ yield. The reaction products included phenol, p-cresol, p-ethyl and p-propylphenol, guaiacol, 2, 4-, 2, 5- and 3, 5-xylenols and in certain experiments also m-cresol.

## 8. THERMAL DEGRADATION OF LIGNIN

The products of dry distillation of lignin were studied /125/ by the technique of paper chromatography. The application of gas-liquid chromatography in the identification of the pyrolysis products of lignin proved to be more successful /126, 127/.

Pyrolysis of lignin at $500°$ yielded /128/ 19 major and 17 minor components. The pyrolysis products were analyzed by gas-liquid chromatography, with a linear rise in the column temperature from 50 to $225°$; $4\%$ of nitrosilicone polymer on diatomaceous earth were used as stationary phase.

## 9. OTHER REACTIONS OF LIGNIN

This section deals with the applications of chromatographic methods to the study of the composition of mixtures formed as a result of different reactions of lignin, which have not so far been dsicussed.

**Degradation of lignin by metallic sodium.** Chromatography was utilized in the study of both model compounds /129/ and lignin /130/ degraded by metallic sodium. Semechkina and Shorygina /131/ used the technique of paper chromatography in the separation of phenols obtained from aspen lignin decomposed by metallic sodium in liquid ammonia. The total yield of phenols was 16% on the weight of the lignin. Dihydroeugenol, syringyl-propane, 1-(4-hydroxy-3-methoxyphenyl)-propanol-1 and 1-(4-hydroxy-3-methoxyphenyl)-propanol-3 were identified. It was noted that the chromatogram of phenols obtained from the lignin of aspen wood contained more spots than did the chromatogram of the degradation products of lignin from coniferous trees. The same products could also be identified by paper chromatography of the phenolic fraction obtained by reductive degradation of cotton plant lignin by metallic sodium /132/.

**Reaction between lignin and phenol.** Paper chromatography was used /133/ in the study of the composition of the condensation products in the formation of phenol-lignin-formaldehyde resins. It was shown that the condensation reaction of resol resins with lignin is similar to the condensation without lignin. The main intermediate reaction products are monocyclic phenol-alcohols with varying methylol group contents. It was noted that lignin had a retarding effect on the condensation rate. The structure of the intermediate reaction products depends on the nature of the catalyst: if an alkaline catalyst is employed, o- and p-hydroxybenzyl alcohols are formed, while in acid medium bicyclic phenols not containing methylol groups are produced.

Kratzl et al. /134/ studied the mechanism of the reaction between phenol and the components of wood, using $C^{14}$-labeled lignin and model compounds. The wood meal was treated with phenol, the phenol-lignin fraction was subjected to oxidative degradation and the products separated by thin layer chromatography, when $C^{14}$-containing vanillin, vanillic and salicylic acids, p-hydroxybenzaldehyde and p-hydroxybenzoic acid were obtained. It would appear that the condensation of phenol with lignin takes place in the $\alpha$-position in the side chains of the lignin and may take place ortho- or para- to the phenolic hydroxyl. Phenol does not react with polysaccharides.

**Other reactions.** The formation of dinitroguaiacol during the nitration of lignin and model compounds has been demonstrated /135/ by chromatographic techniques. The products of the nitration of model lignin compounds have been separated on an alumina column /136/. It has also been shown that nitrolignin is not homogeneous /137/.

The products of degradation of sprucewood formaldehydeperiodate lignin have been separated by chromatography on paper /138/. Dyes formed by the reaction between lignin and quinone monochloroamide have been isolated on alumina column /139/.

Paper chromatography has served to analyze different phenolic products of degradation of lignin /140, 141/, in particular, 4-substituted pyrocatechol and guaiacol derivatives /142/.

Gas-liquid chromatographic determinations of different alkoxy groups /143/ and of benzene rings in organic compounds /144/ are of interest to the chemistry of lignin.

We may finally stress once more the importance of chromatographic methods in the chemistry of lignin. The application of chromatographic methods yielded important new data on the formation, structure and chemical transformations of lignin. Future studies of lignin will involve in the first place gas-liquid (including the pyrolytic variant) chromatographic investigations on high-molecular preparations of lignin.

BIBLIOGRAPHY

1. BRAUNS, F. E. and D. A. BRAUNS. The Chemistry of Lignin. — Academic Press. 1960.
2. PEARL, I. A. — Forest Prod. J., 12(3):141—150. 1962; 8(9):373—385. 1963; 14(9):435—445. 1964; 15(9):379—393. 1964.
3. ROWE, J. W. and I. A. PEARL. — Forest Prod. J., 11(2):85—107. 1961.
4. CHUDAKOV, M. I. — Uspekhi Khimii, 30(2):184—219. 1961.
5. POLČIN, J., B. KOŠIKOVÁ, and V. KOVAČIK. — Drevársky Výskum., No. 4:193—210. 1965.
6. PEARL, I. A. and D. L. BEYER. — Tappi, 40(1):45—54. 1957.
7. ENKVIST, T. — Paperi ja puu, 43(11):657—662. 1961.
8. STONE, J. E. and M. J. BLUNDELL. — Analyt. Chem., 23(5):771. 1951.
9. FREUDENBERG, K. and G. A. SIDHU. — Holzforschung, 15(2):33—39. 1961.
10. ISHIHARA, T. and T. KONDO. — Bull. Agric. Chem. Soc. Japan, 23(3):178—185. 1954.
11. TURUNEN, J. — Paperi ja puu, 43(11):663. 1961.
12. BLAND, D. E. — Holzforschung, 12(2):36—43. 1958.
13. NAKANO, J., A. ISHIZU, and N. MIGITA. — Tappi, 44(1):30—32. 1961.
14. HATA, K. and B. SOGO. — J. Japan Wood Res. Soc., 4(3):85—90. 1958.

15.  KYOGOKY, Y. and Y. HACHIHAMA. – Technol. Repts Osaka Univ., 11(10) : 439–445. 1961.
16.  KRATZL, K. and G. PUSCHMANN. – Holzforschung, 14(1) : 1–4. 1960.
17.  LUNDQUIST, K. and G. E. MIKSCHE. – Tetrahedron Letters, No. 25 : 2131–2136. 1965.
18.  SPOREK, K. F. and M. D. DANYI. – Analyt. Chem., 34(12) : 1527–1529. 1962.
19.  MANSKAYA, S. M. and M. S. BARDINSKAYA. – Biokhimiya, 19(3) : 332–335. 1954.
20.  GAILEY, W. K. – Analyst, Vol. 39 : 3. 1950.
21.  STONE, J. and M. BLUNDELL. — J. Anal. Chem., 23(5) : 771. 1951.
22.  LINDBERG, B. and O. THEANDER. – Acta Chem. Scand., Vol. 6 : 311. 1952.
23.  BARDINSKAYA, M. S. and K. B. PYATIKRESTOVSKAYA. – Izv. AN SSSR, Seriya Biologicheskaya, No. 1 : 109–115. 1956.
24.  STONE, J. – Can. J. Chem., 31(3) : 207–213. 1953.
25.  FREUDENBERG, K. and H. G. MÜLLER. – Liebigs Ann. Chem., 584(1) : 40–53. 1953.
26.  FREUDENBERG, K. and H. DIETRICH. – Chem. Ber., 86(9) : 1157–1166. 1953.
27.  FREUDENBERG, K. and M. FRIEDMANN. – Chem. Ber., 93(9) : 2138–2148. 1960.
28.  FREUDENBERG, K. and K. C. RENNER. – Chem. Ber., Vol. 98 : 1879–1892. 1965.
29.  OKABE, J. and K. KRATZL. – Tappi, 48(6) : 347–354. 1965.
30.  FREUDENBERG, K. et al. – Chem Ber., Vol. 96 : 1844. 1963.
31.  PEARL, I. A., D. L. BEYER, B. JOHNSON, and S. WILKINSON. – Tappi, Vol. 40 : 374. 1957.
32.  BLAND, D. E. – Austral. J. Appl. Sci., 6(4) : 511–515. 1955.
33.  PEARL, I. A. – J. Organ. Chem., 24(6) : 736–740. 1959.
34.  MORIMOTO, I. and T. SAKO. – Japan Analyst, 12(6) : 566–567. 1963.
35.  SCHÜTTE, H. R. and R. FREYER. – Flora, 155(4) : 511–514. 1965.
36.  NIMZ, H. and H. GABER. – Chem. Ber., 98(2) : 538–539. 1965.
37.  DESMET, J. – Comptes Rendus, 250 : 3374. 1960.
38.  ROBERT, A. and J. DESMET. – Comptes Rendus, 251 : 430. 1960.
39.  DESMET, J. – Comptes Rendus, 251(5) : 780–782. 1960.
40.  SCHUBERT, W. J. et al. – J. Am. Chem. Soc., 75(8) : 1869–1873. 1953.
41.  SCHUBERT, W. J. and F. F. NORD. – Proc. Nat. Acad. Sci., Vol. 41 : 122–127. 1955.
42.  STEVENS, G. and F. F. NORD. – Proc. Nat. Acad. Sci., 39(2) : 80–84. 1953.
43.  LINDGREN, B. O. – Acta Chem. Scand., 12(3) : 447–452. 1958.
44.  BJÖRKMAN, A. – Svensk Papperstidn., 60(7) : 243–251. 1957; No. 9 : 329–335. 1957.
45.  BJÖRKMAN, A. and B. PERSSON. – Svensk Papperstidn., 60(8) : 285–292. 1957.
46.  BJÖRKMAN, A. – Ind. and Eng. Chem., 49(9) : 1395–1398. 1957.
47.  SIMIONESCU, C. and J. ANTON. – Papier (BRD), 19(4) : 150–158. 1965.
48.  TRAYNARD, P. and A. M. AUROUD. – Bull. Soc. Chim. France, No. 3 : 345–347. 1954.
49.  KAWAMURA, HIGUTI. – J. Soc. Text. Cell. Ind., Japan, 9(1) : 9–11. 1953.
50.  HAYASHI, A. and I. TACHI. – Tappi, 41(9) : A173–A178. 1958.
51.  HAYASHI, A. and I. TACHI. – J. Agric. Chem. Soc. Japan, 30(8) : 442–451. 1956; 33(9) : 806–809. 1959.
52.  HAYASHI, A. – J. Agric. Chem. Soc. Japan, 35(1) : 80–83; 83–86. 1961.
53.  FREUDENBERG, K. and G. GRION. – Chem. Ber., 92(6) : 1355–1363. 1959.
54.  FREUDENBERG, K. and J. M. HARKIN. – Chem. Ber., 93(12) : 2814–2819. 1960.
55.  TAKAMUKU, S. and Y. HATICHAMA. – J. Chem. Soc. Japan, Ind. Chem. Sec., 64(9) : 1662–1664. 1961.
56.  BROWNELL, H. H. and K. L. WEST. – Pulp and Paper Mag. Canada, 62(8) : T374–T384. 1961.
57.  GUPTA, A. B. S., A. S. DUTT, and W. G. MacMILLAN. – Indian J. Chem., 2(5) : 213–214. 1964.
58.  PEARL, I. A. and E. E. DICKEY. – J. Am. Chem. Soc., Vol. 74 : 614–617. 1952.
59.  PEARL, I. A. and D. L. BEYER. – J. Am. Chem. Soc., 76(8) : 2224–2226; No. 23 : 6106–6108. 1954.
60.  PEARL, I. A. and D. L. BEYER. – Tappi, 39(3) : 171–177. 1956.
61.  PEARL, I. A. – J. Am. Chem. Soc., 78(21) : 5672–5674. 1956.
62.  PEARL, I. A. and D. L. BEYER. – Tappi, 42(9) : 800–804. 1959.
63.  REEVES, R. H. and I. A. PEARL. – Tappi, 48(2) : 121–125. 1965.
64.  HLAVA, J. B. and F. E. BRAUNS. – Holzforschung, 7(2–3) : 62–66. 1953.
65.  HATA, K. and M. SOGO. – J. Japan Wood Res. Soc., 4(1) : 5–9. 1958.
66.  BLAND, D. E. and C. STAMP. – Austral. J. Appl. Sci., 6(3) : 353–358. 1955.
67.  GARDON, J. L. and B. LEOPOLD. – Publ. and Paper Mag. Canada, 59(8) : 148–154. 1958.
68.  SUZUKI, E. and T. YURUGI. – Bull. Text. Res. Inst., No. 44 : 29–34. 1958.
69.  TANAKA, J. – J. Japan Wood Res. Soc., 6(6) : 227–229. 1960.
70.  GIANOLA, G. and J. MEYBECK. – Bull. Assoc. Tech. Ind. Papet., No. 1 : 25. 1960.
71.  BRUNOW, G. – Suomen Kemistiseuran Tiedonantoja, 74(1) : 20–23. 1965.

72. PERSHINA, L. A., V. P. VASIL'EVA, and V. N. KUKSINA. − Khimicheskaya Pererabotka Drevesiny, Sbornik 14 : 11. 1964.
73. PEPPER, J. M. and M. SIDDIQUEULLAH. − Can. J. Chem., 39(2): 390−391. 1961.
74. PEPPER, J. M. and M. SIDDIQUEULLAH. − Can. J. Chem., 38(12): 2324−2331. 1960.
75. PEN, R. Z. − ZhAKh, 20(2): 277−278. 1965.
76. VIL'KOVA, S. N. and N. G. MURYGINA. − ZhPKh, 33(7): 1628−1632. 1960.
77. VIL'KOVA, S. N. and N. G. MURYGINA. − ZhPKh, 33(7): 1674−1676. 1960.
78. SHORYGINA, N. N. and Kh. R. NIYAZOV. − Izv. AN SSSR, OKhN, No. 9: 1689−1690. 1962.
79. SEMECHKINA, A. F. and N. N. SHORYGINA. − ZhOKh, 28(1): 119−121. 1958.
80. SOKOLOVA, A. A., E. V. NAZAR'EVA, and L. A. SEMAKOVA. − ZhPKh, 34(9): 2084−2095. 1961.
81. BRAUNS, F. and H. HIBBERT. − Can. J. Res., Vol. 1313: 28. 1935.
82. NIKITIN, N. I. and I. M. ORLOVA. − ZhPKh, No. 9: 2210. 1936.
83. FREUDENBERG, K. − Ber., Vol. 71: 1810. 1938.
84. FREUDENBERG, K. and W. LAUTSCH. − Ber., Vol. 73: 167. 1940.
85. TOWERS, G. H. and R. D. GIBBS. − Nature, 172(4366): 25−26. 1953.
86. KAVANAGH, K. R. and J. M. PEPPER. − Can. J. Chem., 33(1): 24−30. 1955.
87. SOGO, M., K. HATA, and A. HIRATA. − J. Japan Wood Res. Soc., 9(5): 194−198. 1963.
88. SIMPSON, W. G. and E. SONDHEIMER. − Tappi, 43(12): 1025−1026. 1960.
89. BARNOUD, F., T. HIGUCHI, J. -P. JOSELEAU, and A. C. MOLLARD. − R. Acad. Sci., 259(20): 3589−3591. 1964.
90. PEPPER, J. M., M. MANOLOPULO, and R. BURTON. − Can. J. Chem., 40(10): 1976−1980. 1962.
91. HRUTFIORD, B. F. − Tappi, 48(1): 48−54. 1965.
92. LEOPOLD, B. − Svensk Kem. Tidskr., Vol. 61: 1. 1952.
93. BICHO, J. G., E. ZAVARIN, and D. L. BRINK. − Tappi, 49(5): 218−226. 1966.
94. MERRIMAN, M. M., H. CHOULETT, and D. L. BRINK. − Tappi, Vol. 49: 34. 1966.
95. GOLDSCHMID, O. − Tappi, 38(12): 728−732. 1955.
96. FUKUZUMI, T. and T. SHIBAMOTO. − J. Japan Wood Res. Soc., 4(1): 15−22. 1958.
97. CHUDAKOV, M. I. − DAN SSSR, 137(6): 1389−1392. 1961.
98. SAKAKIBARA, A. and N. NAKAYAMA. − J. Japan Wood Res. Soc., 7(1): 13−18. 1961.
99. SAKAKIBARA, A. and N. NAKAYAMA. − J. Japan Wood Res. Soc., 8(4): 157−162. 1962.
100. SAKAKIBARA, A. and N. NAKAYAMA. − J. Japan Wood Res. Soc., 8(4): 153−156. 1962.
101. GARDNER, J. A. F. and H. MacLEAN. − Can. J. Chem., 43(8): 2421−2423. 1965.
102. LUNDQUIST, K. − Acta Chem. Scand., 18(5): 1316−1317. 1964.
103. PEPPER, J. M. and P. D. S. WOOD. − Can. J. Chem., 40(5): 1026−1028. 1962.
104. SWAN, B. − Svensk Papperstidn., 68(22): 791−795. 1965.
105. NIMZ, H. − Chem. Ber., 98(10): 3153−3159; 3160−3164. 1965.
106. KOŠIKOVÁ, B. and J. POLČIN. From "Stationary Phase in Paper and Thin-Layer Chromatography." − Publ. House CAS − Elsevier Publ. Co., Prague-New York, pp. 140−141. 1965.
107. FUKUZUMI, T. and M. TERASAWA. − J. Japan Wood Res. Soc., 8(2): 77−80. 1962.
108. DENCE, C. W., J. A. MEYER, K. UNGER, and J. SADOWSKI. − Tappi, 48(3): 148−157. 1965.
109. HATAKEYAMA, H., D. NAKANO, and H. J. MIGITA. − J. Chem. Soc. Japan, Ind. Chem. Sec., 68(5): 972−975. 1965.
110. SARKANEN, K. V., G. CHIRKIN, and B. F. HRUTFIORD. − Tappi, 46(6): 375−379. 1963.
111. TÖPPEL, O. − Holzforschung, 14(5): 139−146. 1960.
112. KODINA, L. A. − Doklady AN SSSR, 147(1): 227−230. 1962.
113. KRATZL, K. and W. SCHWEERS. − Monatsh. Chem., 85(5): 1046−1054. 1954.
114. KRATZL, K. and W. SCHWEERS. − Chem. Ber., 89(2): 186−192. 1956.
115. KRATZL, K. and H. CZEPEL. − Monath. Chem., 95(6): 1609−1612. 1964.
116. ARLT, H. G., S. K. GROSS, and C. SCHUERCH. − Tappi, 41(2): 64−70. 1958.
117. BHATTACHARYA, A. and C. SCHUERCH. − Tappi, 43(10): 840−844. 1960.
118. SAKAKIBARA, A. and T. ARAKI. − J. Japan Wood Res. Soc., 7(1): 19−23. 1961.
119. COSCIA, C. J., W. J. SCHUBERT, and F. F. NORD. − J. Organ. Chem., 26(12): 5085−5091. 1961.
120. OLCAY, A. − J. Organ. Chem., 27(5): 1783−1786. 1962.
121. PEPPER, J. M. and W. STECK. − Can. J. Chem., 41(11): 2867−2875. 1963.
122. PEPPER, J. M. − Pulp and Paper Mag. Canada, 65(2): T35−T40. 1964.
123. NAHUM, L. − Ind. Eng. Chem. Prod. Res. Devel., 4(2): 71−74. 1965.
124. RIECHE, A., L. REDINGER, and K. LINDENHAYN. − Monats. Dtsch. Akad. Wiss. Berlin, 6(6): 430−439. 1964.
125. SAKAKIBARA, A. and K. ODA. − J. Japan Wood Res. Soc., 6(6): 247−251. 1960.

126. HASEGAWA, T. — J. Chem. Soc., Japan. Ind. Chem. Sec., 63(6): 1040 −1042. 1960.

127. KRATZL, K., H. CZEPEL, and J. GRATZL. — Holz Roh− und Werkstoff, 23(6): 237 −240. 1965.

128. NAGAR, B. R. — Nature, 199(4899): 1213 −1214. 1963.

129. KRATZL, K., W. KISSER, and J. GRATZL et al. — Monatsh. Chem., 90(6): 771. 1959.

130. SEMECHKINA, A. F. and N. N. SHORYGINA. — ZhOKh, 28(12): 3265 −3269. 1958.

131. SEMECHKINA, A. F. and N. N. SHORYGINA. — Izv. AN SSSR, OKhN, No. 4: 715 −720. 1963.

132. NIYAZOV, Kh. R. and N. N. SHORYGINA. — Izv. AN SSSR, OKhN, No. 3: 563 −565. 1963.

133. SOKOLOVA, A. A., L. A. SEMAKOVA, and E. V. NAZAR'EVA. — Izv. VUZov, Lesnoi Zhurnal, No. 3: 153 −155. 1965.

134. KRATZL, K., J. ZAUNER, and P. CLAUS. — Holzforschung, 18(1−2): 47 −52. 1964.

135. GUSTAFSSON, C. and L. ANDERSEN. — Paperi ja puu, 37(1): 1−2. 1955.

136. CHUKSANOVA, A. A., L. L. SERGEEVA, and N. N. SHORYGINA. — Izv. AN SSSR, OKhN, No. 12: 2219 −2225. 1959.

137. CHUKSANOVA, A. A., O. P. GRUSHNIKOV, and N. N. SHORYGINA. — Izv. AN SSSR, OKhN, No. 10: 1810 −1812. 1961.

138. JAIN, M. R. and C. B. PURVES. — Tappi, 44(8): 592 −599. 1961.

139. GIERER, J. — Chem. Ber., 89(2): 257 −262. 1956.

140. LINDBERG, J., K. HÄSTBACKA, and T. ENKVIST. — Finska Kemists Amfundets Medd., 62(1−2): 25. 1953.

141. TANAKA, J. — J. Japan Wood Res. Soc., 7(2): 77 −81. 1961.

142. HALMEKOSKI, J. — Paperi ja puu, 43(11): 669. 1961.

143. KRATZL, K. and K. GRUBER. — Monatsh. Chem., 89(4−5): 618 −624. 1958.

144. DHOUT, J. H. — Nature, 192(4804): 747 −748. 1961.

*Chapter V*

## CHROMATOGRAPHY OF THE EXTRACTIVE SUBSTANCES OF WOOD

The previous chapters dealt with methods for the study of the components which form part of the cell walls of the plants; extractive substances, on the contrary, are not a part of the cell wall. As a rule, they can be isolated from wood more or less completely by steam distillation or by extraction with various solvents.

Depending on their method of isolation, the extractive substances may be arbitrarily divided into three main groups:

1. Extractive substances which are distilled off with steam — essential oils. This group includes hydrocarbons — monoterpenes, sesquiterpenes, diterpenes and other aliphatic and cyclic compounds; terpene alcohols, acids, some of the phenols, ethers, aldehydes, ketones and lactones.

2. Extractive substances which are extracted with organic solvents (ether, acetone or alcohol) — wood resins. These include resin acids, fatty acids, terpenyl and other esters of organic acids as well as neutral substances — alcohols, sterols, waxes, fats and resenes.

3. Water-soluble extractive substances. This group includes carbohydrates (mono-, oligo- and polysaccharides, including gums, pectins, mucilages, plant starch, etc.), tannides, mineral components, etc.

This chapter will deal with the chromatographic analysis of only the most important extractive substances, which are of importance in the chemical treatment of woods — terpene hydrocarbons, resin acids and tannides. The remaining extractive substances will be treated only superficially; for chromatographic analysis of carbohydrates the reader is referred to Chapter III.

## 1. TERPENE HYDROCARBONS AND THEIR DERIVATIVES

The extractive substances of coniferous woods include mainly monoterpene hydrocarbons $C_{10}H_{16}$ with bicyclic, monocyclic and, more rarely, aliphatic structure. Sesquiterpenes $C_{15}H_{24}$, diterpenes $C_{20}H_{32}$ and sometimes triterpenes are present in much smaller amounts.

Since the chemical wood industry manufactures large amounts of terpene mixtures as turpentine, the chromatographic analysis of multicomponent terpene mixtures has been extensively studied. This chapter will give a review of the different methods of chromatographic analysis of terpenes and the results of the application of chromatographic methods to the study of the extractive substances of wood.

Chromatographic methods are very important in terpene chemistry. According to Mayo, chromatography is "the most important and the simplest method of investigation." Bardyshev /2/, too, ascribes a major importance to chromatographic methods, especially in combination with spectroscopy.


## Column chromatography

It has already been mentioned that column chromatography was, historically, the first variant of chromatographic analysis employed in the study of mixtures of organic compounds. This technique has also been extensively employed in the chemistry of terpenes.

Early publications on column chromatography are the subject of monographs /3/ and reviews /4, 5/. The first publications on the column chromatography of terpenes include those by Winterstein and Stein /6/ and other workers /7, 8/. In terpene chemistry column chromatography is still frequently used for preparative purposes, for purification and, more rarely, in analysis.

**Chromatographic technique.** Terpenes are highly volatile, which means that the chromatographic apparatus must be tightly sealed off to prevent evaporation of material during the work. A special design of chromatographic column has been proposed /9/ for the analysis of terpenes and other volatile compounds; it is equipped with a cooling jacket, which allows the operator to work at $-40°$ column temperature without losses by evaporation.

A method for the separation of terpenes at $-78.5°$ on silica gel column has been developed /10/.

A micro-technique of displacement analysis can be employed /11, 12/ in the investigation of two-component mixtures of terpenes. The $250 \times 1.4$ mm column was filled with Davison silica gel. Liquid samples ($40 \mu l$) were introduced into the column, and the components were displaced with the more strongly sorbed absolute ethanol; in order to increase the filtration rate, an excess pressure was produced in the top of the column with the aid of nitrogen. The duration of the analysis was about 20 minutes. The elution curves were used to evaluate the homogeneity of $\Delta^3$-carene, $\alpha$-limonene, $\alpha$-pinene and $\beta$-pinene. This technique is also applicable to the study of monoterpene mixtures. A mixture of $\Delta^3$-carene and (+)-limonene has been studied /13/ by this method.

Frontal, elution and displacement techniques were all employed /14/ in the study of mixtures of terpenes of various structures. The frontal analysis technique was proposed by Claesson /15/. A study of the chromatographic behavior of individual terpenes and binary mixtures showed that better analytical conditions can be attained by the use of Norit A activated carbon (absolute ethanol as solvent) or silica gel (petroleum ether as solvent). Chloroform proved to be the best solvent in the analysis of mixtures of thymol with carvacrol on a column of silica gel. Better separation of binary mixtures is achieved in the frontal technique of analysis, which is more effective if the content of one of the components is much higher than that of the other. Systems containing limonene, pinene, cymene, pulegone, menthane, menthol, carvacrol, thymol, geraniol and linalool have been separated in this manner.

Terpenic hydrocarbons may be separated /16/ by passing their solutions through a column with carbon activated by zinc chloride. The terpenes are then separated into the following groups: a) p-cymene and limonene, myrcene; b) $\Delta^3$-carene; c) $\alpha$-pinene, $\beta$-pinene and camphene. Binary mixtures of components of different groups can be successfully separated on the activated carbons, while components of the same group are not separated. Activated carbon gave better results than silica gel.

Extensive studies on the chromatography of the terpenes which are constituents of essential oils were carried out by Kirchner and Miller. These workers began by using column chromatography and designed an original structure of the chromatographic column /17, 18/. They were not satisfied by the results obtained, however, and subsequently /19, 20/ developed a method for the separation of components of essential oils on plates with a thin layer of sorbent which they named "chromatostrips." This work, which is now classic, marked the beginning of thin layer chromatography, which is at present extensively employed.

A mixture containing turpentine, furfural, etc., has been separated /21/ on a column with active alumina. Reznikov and Khal'kin /22/ studied the adsorption of turpentine dissolved in various organic solvents on active alumina. A silica gel KSK column was employed /23/ in the chromatographic separation of menthol.


## Paper chromatography

In view of the high volatility of terpenes, these compounds are only very rarely analyzed by paper chromatography. Examples of the application of this technique include separation of sesquiterpenes on fiber glass paper impregnated with $C_{16}H_{37}$ /24/, detection of triterpenoid glycosides /25/ and the determination of a saturated terpenic ketone — thujone — as the 2,4-dinitrophenylhydrazone /26/. Terpene alcohols may be determined by this method as o-nitrophenyl- and p-phenylazophenylurethans /27/. Terpenes have also been separated in the form of addition products to mercuric acetate in methanol /28/.


## Thin layer chromatography

Thin layer chromatography was applied by Kirchner et al. /19, 20, 29/ to the analysis of terpenes. The authors proposed a special apparatus /30/ for the preparation of plates with a thin layer of sorbent and applied the technique to the study of the composition of terpenes constituting essential oils.

A better separation of terpenes was achieved on a silica gel layer bound with starch or with plaster of Paris. The chromatograms were developed with 15% ethyl acetate in hexane, and the spots were revealed by a spray of concentrated sulfuric acid or with 0.05% aqueous fluorescein, after which the chromatogram was held in bromine vapors. Fluorescent strips were prepared by mixing silica gel with starch and $ZnCdS_2$ and zinc silicate, which are fluorescing compounds.

This technique was also used by Reitsema /31/ in his analyses of different essential oils. The thin layer technique of terpene analysis has been lately improved /32 — 35/. Thin layer chromatography is now employed in the analysis of monoterpenes /36 — 38/, diterpenes /39/, triterpenes /40, 41/, tetracyclic terpenes /42/ and tetra- and pentacyclic triterpenes and related compounds /43/.

Silica gel, impregnated with silver nitrate, proved to be a satisfactory support in thin layer chromatography of terpenes /37, 42/. Oxidized terpenes are also separated on this layer /44/. Separation of different terpenic hydrocarbons was also achieved on $Al_2O_3$ /36/ which acts both as support and as sorbent during the separation /40/.

Diphenylpicrylhydrazyl has been recommended /45/ as spray reagent for the detection of terpene.

TABLE 18. $R_f$-values of monoterpenic hydrocarbons

| Compound | $R_f$-value on | |
|---|---|---|
| | silica gel | $Al_2O_3$ |
| Camphene . . . . . . . . . . . . . | 0.83 | 0.95 |
| $\triangle^3$-Carene . . . . . . . . . . . . . | 0.85 | 0.95 |
| p-Cymene . . . . . . . . . . . . . | 0.67 | 0.89 |
| p-Isopropenyltoluene . . . . . . . . | 0.62 | 0.84 |
| d-Limonene . . . . . . . . . . . . | 0.76 | 0.93 |
| 2,4(8)-Menthadiene . . . . . . . . | 0.76 | 0.93 |
| β-Myrcene . . . . . . . . . . . . | 0.74 | 0.92 |
| α-Ocimene . . . . . . . . . . . . | 0.71 | 0.91 |
| iso-β-Ocimene . . . . . . . . . . . | 0.71 | 0.91 |
| β-Phellandrene . . . . . . . . . . . | 0.79 | 0.93 |
| α-Pinene . . . . . . . . . . . . . | 0.90 | 0.96 |
| β-Pinene . . . . . . . . . . . . . | 0.88 | 0.95 |
| α-Pyronene . . . . . . . . . . . . | 0.80 | 0.94 |
| β-Pyronene . . . . . . . . . . . . | 0.80 | 0.94 |
| Sabinene . . . . . . . . . . . . | 0.75 | 0.93 |
| Terpinolene . . . . . . . . . . . . | 0.75 | 0.92 |
| α-Terpinene . . . . . . . . . . . . | 0.76 | 0.93 |
| γ-Terpinene . . . . . . . . . . . . | 0.76 | 0.93 |
| α-Thujene . . . . . . . . . . . . | 0.80 | 0.95 |
| Verbenene . . . . . . . . . . . . | 0.81 | 0.95 |

The chromatographic behavior of a number of monoterpenes, sesquiterpenes, azulenes, diterpenes, triterpenes and tetraterpenes was studied by Attaway et al. /46/. A 20 — 40 $\mu$ thick layer of silica gel G or $Al_2O_3$ G was brought onto 20×20 cm plates. Terpenes were separated by development with nonpolar solvents such as hexane. The spots were revealed by spraying with a mixture of vanillin and sulfuric acid or potassium permanganate and sulfuric acid. Table 18 shows the $R_f$-values of some of these compounds.

Thin layer chromatography may be employed in conjunction with gas-liquid chromatography in the identification of compounds which have been separated on the chromatograph by their $R_f$-values and color reactions. Highly sensitive color reactions will determine less than one nanogram of terpenes.

It has been recommended /47/ to separate tetra- and pentacyclic triterpenes on a thin layer of alumina bound with plaster of Paris. Layer thickness 0.25 mm. The plates are dried for 1 hour at room temperature and for 30 minutes at 125°. The solvent is heptane : benzene : ethanol = 50 : 50 : 0.5. The spots are revealed by spraying the chromatogram with a 20% solution of antimony trichloride or antimony pentachloride in chloroform, or with a mixture of 10% acetic anhydride and 10% sulfuric acid in absolute ethanol. After spraying the chromatograms are dried at 120° for 5 minutes.

Thin layer chromatography is also used in the analysis of terpene derivatives, in particular, to separate triterpenic acids /48/, stereo-regular menthols /49/ and other compounds.

Terpenic carbonyl compounds can be separated /50/ as 2, 4-dinitrophenyl-hydrazones on a thin layer of silica gel. The $R_f$ values obtained in different solvent systems are shown in Table 19.

TABLE 19. $R_f$-values of 2, 4-dinitrophenylhydrazones of terpenic carbonyl compounds

| Compound | $R_f$-values in | | | |
|---|---|---|---|---|
| | chloroform : CCl$_4$ | | | Petroleum ether-ben-zene 3 : 7 |
| | 1 : 19 | 1 : 9 | 3 : 17 | |
| Citral . . . . . . . . . . . . | 0.17 | 0.20 | 0.24 | 0.63 |
| Citronellal . . . . . . . . . | 0.23 | 0.37 | 0.29 | 0.30 |
| α-Thujone . . . . . . . . . | 0.17 | 0.31 | 0.23 | 0.82 |
| Menthone . . . . . . . . . . | 0.42 | 0.38 | 0.41 | 0.84 |
| Pulegone . . . . . . . . . . | 0.34 | 0.37 | 0.46 | 0.75 |
| Carvone . . . . . . . . . . | 0.29 | 0.32 | 0.36 | 0.79 |
| Dihydrocarvone . . . . . . . | 0.22 | 0.29 | 0.33 | 0.80 |
| Camphor . . . . . . . . . | 0.25 | 0.35 | 0.39 | 0.76 |
| Salicylaldehyde . . . . . . . | 0.05 | 0.07 | 0.08 | 0.44 |

Stahl and Vollmann /51/ recommended the addition of 3% silver nitrate to the thin layer of silica gel. Development with methylene chloride : chloroform : ethyl acetate : n-propanol = 50 : 50 : 5 : 5 will separate terpenic and sesquiterpenic alcohols $C_{10}$, $C_{15}$ and $C_{20}$, which are not separated on a nonimpregnated silica gel layer. The separation of these alcohols into groups with an equal number of carbon atoms is possible on a thin layer impregnated with paraffin wax.

A thin layer (0.25 mm) plate of kieselguhr G is impregnated /52/ by immersion in a 5% solution of liquid paraffin in petroleum ether (bp 40 — 60°). After evaporation of the solvent, 1—10 $\mu$l of a 0.1% solution of terpenic alcohols in benzene are brought onto the plate. The mobile phase is the lower layer of the mixture acetone : water : liquid paraffin wax = 65 : 35 : 0.5; the spraying agent is a mixture of anisaldehyde (0.5 g) and sulfuric acid (0.5 ml) in 9 ml of 90% ethanol.

Terpenic alcohols have also been separated /52/ on a layer of silica gel G, activated for 30 minutes at 110°; the chromatograms were developed with benzene : ethyl acetate = 80 : 20; the plate was then exposed to iodine vapor and sprayed with a mixture of anisaldehyde and sulfuric acid.

The $R_p$-values (relative to the path length of Sudan Red) are shown in Table 20.

TABLE 20. $R_p$-values of some terpene alcohols

| Component | $R_p$ | Color given by sprayed spot |
|---|---|---|
| Geraniol . . . . . . . . | 0.60 | Dark blue |
| trans–trans–Farnesol . . | 0.69 | Purple |
| Geranylgeraniol . . . . | 0.75 | Pinkish lilac |
| Linalool . . . . . . . . | 0.85 | Green |
| Nerolidol . . . . . . . . | 0.95 | Yellow–brown |
| Geranyllinalool . . . . | 1.01 | Yellow–brown |

It was noted by Stahl /53/ that the $R_f$-values obtained in the analysis of terpenes are not sufficiently reproducible. Additional difficulties are caused by the high volatility of terpenes; accordingly, terpene-containing mixtures are now analyzed in most cases by gas-liquid chromatography.

## Gas-liquid chromatography of terpene hydrocarbons

Gas-liquid chromatography is employed in qualitative and quantitative analysis of different mixtures of terpenes. The composition of the extractive fractions of the woods of a number of tree species, essential oils and various industrial products have been determined in this way. The analysis of the products of rosin-turpentine industries by gas-liquid chromatography is discussed in Chapter VI.

Bernhard /54/, Rudloff /55/ and other workers /56, 57/ were the first to apply gas-liquid chromatography to the study of the chemistry of terpenes. The method is best used to analyze low-boiling monoterpenes /58, 59/ and in the separation of sesquiterpenes /60, 61/, diterpenes /62/ and triterpenes /63/.

Stationary phases employed in the separation of terpenes include silicone oil /58/, tritolyl phosphate /59/, tricresyl phosphate, vaseline /64/ and other materials.

Systematic analysis of monoterpenic hydrocarbons was performed by Klouwen and Heide /65/, who also reviewed the early publications on the subject. They studied the behavior of 22 terpenes on five $300 \times 0.4$ cm columns with 17% Apiezone $L_i$; 17% silicone oil; 17% Reoplex 100; 17% Carbowax 4000 and 13% of $\beta$-,$\beta'$-oxydipropionitrile on Embacel diatomite earth $(60 - 100$ mesh); column temperatures were 120, 100, 110, 100 and 70°, respectively. The flow rate of carrier gas (hydrogen) was 75 ml/min, and 60 ml/min on the last-named column; the pressure at inlet was $133 - 182$ mm Hg. Katharometric detection; sample volume 5 $\mu$l.

Table 21 shows the values of the relative retention volumes of the terpenes studied. Using the table, the stationary phase which is most likely to ensure the optimum separation of the terpenes in question is easily found.

Merck's kieselguhr, $0.15 - 0.20$ and $0.20 - 0.25$ mm particle size, has been recommended /66/ as an effective solid support. The kieselguhr was treated for 12 hours with concentrated HCl, the acid removed by decantation, the support washed with deionized water until chloride ions were absent in the wash water (silver nitrate test), washed with acetone and dried at 150°. To prevent the terpenes from isomerizing, the kieselguhr was deactivated by soaking for one hour in a 5% solution of trimethylchlorosilane in toluene. The support was isolated by filtration, washed with toluene and methanol, in that order, and dried at 150° overnight. It was then impregnated with a solution of the stationary phase in chloroform (stationary phase: support = 4:100); the air was evacuated by pump from the pores of the support, the chloroform evaporated in vacuo at 90° and the impregnated support dried for 3 — 4 hours. Prior to the separation the filled column was stabilized at 150° during 12 hours in a stream of nitrogen.

TABLE 21. Relative retention volumes of terpenic hydrocarbons (with respect to limonene)

| Compound | Relative volumes retained on stationary phase | | | | |
|---|---|---|---|---|---|
| | Apiezone $L$ | silicone oil | Reoplex 100 | Carbowax 4000 | $\beta,\beta'$-oxy-dipropio-nitrile |
| Myrcene . . . . . . . . . . . . . . | 0.604 | 0.758 | **0.725** | 0.767 | 0.868 |
| Ocimene X . . . . . . . . . . . . . | 0.870 | 1.000 | 1.080 | **1.158** | 1.422 |
| Ocimene Y . . . . . . . . . . . . . | 0.948 | 1.080 | 1.200 | 1.292 | 1.670 |
| trans-4,5-cis-6,7-Alloocimene . . | **1.740** | 1.820 | 2.400 | 2.620 | 3.740 |
| trans-4,5-trans-6,7-Alloocimene . | **1.920** | 1.950 | 2.670 | 2.960 | 4.320 |
| α-Terpinene . . . . . . . . . . . | 0.880 | 0.930 | 0.900 | **0.900** | 1.000 |
| α-Phellandrene . . . . . . . . . . . | 0.855 | 0.860 | **0.845** | 0.830 | 0.830 |
| γ-Terpinene . . . . . . . . . . . | **1.190** | **1.170** | 1.240 | 1.286 | 1.350 |
| β-Phellandrene . . . . . . . . . . . | 1.040 | 1.050 | 1.078 | 1.070 | **1.170** |
| Limonene (Dipentene) . . . . . . . | 1.000 | 1.000 | 1.000 | **1.000** | 1.000 |
| Terpinolene . . . . . . . . . . . . | **1.425** | **1.418** | **1.485** | 1.600 | 1.630 |
| p-Cymene . . . . . . . . . . . . . | 0.930 | 0.945 | 1.308 | 1.480 | **2.400** |
| α-Pinene . . . . . . . . . . . . . | 0.508 | 0.565 | 0.410 | 0.368 | 0.276 |
| β-Pinene . . . . . . . . . . . . . | 0.718 | 0.735 | 0.640 | 0.622 | 0.560 |
| α-Thujene . . . . . . . . . . . . | **0.432** | 0.528 | 0.402 | 0.363 | 0.318 |
| Sabinene . . . . . . . . . . . . . | 0.610 | – | 0.660 | 0.650 | **0.735** |
| $\Delta^3$-Carene . . . . . . . . . . | 0.850 | 0.910 | 0.772 | 0.770 | 0.668 |
| Camphene . . . . . . . . . . . . . | 0.610 | 0.620 | 0.521 | 0.488 | 0.450 |
| β-Fenchene . . . . . . . . . . . . | 0.541 | 0.589 | 0.468 | **0.434** | 0.378 |
| α-Fenchene . . . . . . . . . . . . | 0.594 | 0.633 | 0.530 | 0.487 | 0.435 |
| Santene . . . . . . . . . . . . . | **0.320** | **0.420** | **0.292** | 0.308 | 0.242 |
| Tricyclene . . . . . . . . . . . . | 0.484 | 0.532 | 0.389 | 0.343 | 0.267 |

N o t e. The values of the retention volumes which are very different from those of the others on the same stationary phase are shown in bold type.

Satisfactory separation of terpenes was effected on two stationary phases: 1) Apiezone $L$ on kieselguhr (0.2 — 0.25 mm) in a 600×0.5 cm column, column temperature 100 — 120°, flow rate of carrier gas (helium) 90 — 140 ml/min, sample volume 0.2 μl, Perkin-Elmer 116E chromatograph, katharometric detector; 2) second column with Reoplex 400 on kieselguhr (0.15 — 0.20 mm) at 60 — 100°, flow rate of carrier gas (helium) 90 — 140 ml/min, sample volume 0.2 μl.

Analyses of numerous model mixtures of terpenes and sulfate turpentine were performed under these conditions.

Cymene isomers were separated and determined /67/ at 155° on two 600×0.5 cm columns connected in series with a mixture of 5% silicone Se-30 and 15% Bentone-34 on Chromosorb W (60 — 80 mesh) and a mixture of 10% of didecyl phthalate and 20% Bentone-34 on the same support; the inlet pressure of carrier gas (hydrogen) was 2.5 kg/cm$^2$, and the sample volume was 6 μl.

In the analysis of mixtures of terpenes and terpene alcohols it is recommended /68/ that the latter be separated by conversion to the nonvolatile borates. To do this, a column with 0.1 g fine-particled metaboric acid with impregnated support, heated to 130 — 140° is inserted in front of the column serving for the separation of the terpenes. The alcohols are quantitatively esterified, and the terpenes are separated on the main column filled with 20% saccharose acetate hexaisobutyrate on Chromosorb WS (60 — 80 mesh) in a stream of hydrogen.

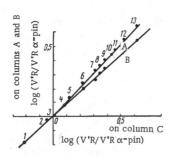

FIGURE 28. Relationship between the logarithms of the relative retention volumes of terpenes on three different columns:

1 – cyclofenchene; 2 – tricyclene; 3 – α-pinene; 4 – β-fenchene; 5 – camphene; 6 – β-pinene; 7 – Δ$^3$-carene; 8 – α-phellandrene; 9 – α-terpinene; 10 – dipentene (limonene); 11 – β-phellandrene; 12 – γ-terpinene; 13 – terpinolene.

Terpenes may be identified by the graphic method. It was found /69/ that if the relative retention times, relative retention volumes or the logarithms of relative retention volumes obtained for one column are plotted against the corresponding parameters for the second column with approximately the same selectivity, a straight line is obtained.

Figure 28 shows a plot of the relative retention volumes $\left(\log \dfrac{V'R}{V'R_{\alpha\text{-pin}}}\right)$ of 13 terpenes, obtained on three columns: A — 20% Carbowax 4000 on Embacel, length 3 meters, temperature 100°, flow rate of carrier gas (hydrogen) 75 ml/min; B— 28.5% Carbowax 4000 on Chromosorb C-44857, length 1.82 meters, temperature 130°, flow rate of carrier gas (helium) 45 ml/min; C — Carbowax 1500 on Chromosorb W, length 4 meters, temperature 100°, flow rate of carrier gas (helium) 84 ml/min.

In the absence of reference compounds required for the analysis of the components of a terpene mixture, the unknown components can be identified by the graphic method, by the use of Figure 28 and with the aid of other literature data.

Lukeš and Komers /70/ compared the separation efficiency of sesquiterpene mixtures on columns with poly(ethylene glycol) adipate, Apiezone L, poly(ethylene glycol) 4000 and tetrakis-o-(2-cyanoethyl)-pentaerythritol. It has been recommended to separate sesquiterpenes on column with 7% poly(ethylene glycol) adipate on unglazed ground tiles (0.2 — 0.3 mm). Carrier gas nitrogen, Griffin and George Co. chromatograph, katharometric detection.

Analysis of triterpenes should be preceded /71/ by the preparation of their trimethylsilyl ethers. The analysis is conducted at 240° on a 150×0.4 cm column with 1.5% of SE-30 silicone oil, 1% NGS and 1% QF-1/FS 1265 on Gasochrome P (80 — 100 mesh), flow rate of carrier gas (nitrogen) 90 ml/min, flame ionization detector, detector temperature 240°, temperature of dosing unit 270°.

## Gas chromatography of terpene derivatives

One important product which is obtained from terpenes is camphor. The method of gas-liquid chromatography is used /72/ in the analysis of alcoholic solutions of camphor. Complete resolution of (±)-camphor into optical antipodes has been achieved /73/ on a 305×0.6 cm column with 20% cyanoethoxypropane on fireproof brick (80 — 100 mesh), temperature 125°, flow rate of carrier gas (helium) 75 ml/min, retention times of the isomers 27'0'' and 28'50''.

A method of separation of mixtures of various bicyclic ketones, including camphor, has been described /74/. The analysis of technical products of the camphor industry is discussed in Chapter VI.

The method of gas-liquid chromatography is successfully employed in the separation and quantitative determination of mixtures of stereoisomers of menthol /75 — 77/. Two stationary phases have been recommended /78/ for the separation of menthol isomers: sodium alkylbenzenesulfonate and poly(ethylene glycol) 6000. A mixture of l-menthol, d-neomenthol, d,l-isomenthol, d-neoisomenthol, l-menthone, l-isomenthone, cis-d-menthoglycol, trans-l-menthoglycol, synthetic camphor and other compounds could be separated /79/ on a column with 20% Reoplex 400.

These menthol stereoisomers could also be separated /80/ at 150° on a column with octakis-(2-hydroxypropyl)-saccharose on Chromosorb W (60 — 80 mesh), flow rate of carrier gas (helium) 66 ml/minute.

Rudol'fi et al. /81/ conducted quantitative analyses of mixtures of methol, isomenthol, neomenthol, neoisomenthol, menthone and isomenthone at 130° on a 275×0.6 cm column with 10% of the polyester of diethylene glycol and adipic acid on diatomaceous earth (0.02 — 0.03 cm), flow rate of carrier gas (hydrogen) 90 ml/min, sample volume 0.005 — 0.010 ml, katharometric detection, experimental error 3%.

Good results in the analysis of stereoisomers of menthol were obtained with the aid of capillary gas-liquid chromatography, using a flame ionization detector /82/.

Gas-liquid chromatography is used in the analysis of various oxygenated terpenoid compounds /83/, in particular, geraniol, linolool and citral /84/. Oxygenated terpene derivatives (alcohols, aldehydes and esters) can be separated /85/ at 90° on a 183×0.6 cm column with a low content of liquid phase (0.125% of Hyprose SP-80 or 0.2% of Dow Corning 710) on glass beads (60 — 80 mesh), flow rate of carrier gas 40 ml/min, sample volume 0.001 ml, katharometric detector.

Triterpenic alcohols may be separated /86/ at 230° on a 200×0.2 — 0.4 cm column with 1% SE-30 on Gaschrom P 100 — 200 mesh, previously treated with hexamethyldisilazane, flow rate of carrier gas (nitrogen) 20 and 40 ml/min for columns of various diameters, evaporator temperature 280°, flame ionization detector. The analysis involved 0.5 — 2% solutions of triterpenic alcohols and their acetyl derivatives in acetone or carbon disulfide. Sample volume 1 — 3 μl.

## Transformations of terpenes and terpene derivatives in the course of chromatographic analysis

Terpene hydrocarbons are highly reactive and are readily isomerized on active surfaces. This is the principle behind the practical methods of processing of terpenes /87/.

In the chromatographic analysis isomerization is undesirable, since erroneous results may be obtained. It is accordingly necessary to ensure, when working with terpenes, that all the terpenes are stable under the conditions chosen for the chromatographic analysis.

Isomerization of terpenes has been noted for different methods of chromatographic analysis.

Arbuzov and Isaeva showed /88/ that terpenes are isomerized when passed through a silica gel column at room temperature. $\alpha$-Pinene is isomerized to camphene, dipentene and terpinolene; $\Delta^3$-carene is isomerized to dipentene and terpinolene; dipentene is converted to terpinolene which in turn undergoes further transformations.

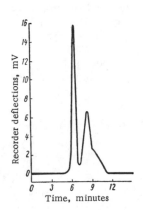

FIGURE 29. Isomerization of pure $\alpha$-pinene on a column with 25% silicone oil on celite.

d-Limonene is converted at 100° on silica gel to terpinolene, $\alpha$-terpinene, $\gamma$-terpinene and isoterpinolene, a small amount of cymene and a mixture of p-menthenes. At 150° mentadienes and disproportionation products — isomeric p-menthenes and p-cymene — are also formed. These conversions have been studied by gas-liquid chromatography /89/.

Terpenes are also isomerized on acid-washed alumina /90/ and on being separated by thin layer chromatography /91/. It was shown by Isagulyants and Fedorova /92/ that the cation exchangers KU-1 and KU-2 and sulfonated coal may act as catalysts in the dehydration of terpin hydrate to dl-$\alpha$-terpineol.

Isomeric and degradative reactions of terpenes and terpene derivatives often occur during analysis by gas-liquid chromatography /93/.

An almost complete decomposition of certain oxygenated terpenes (e.g., $\alpha$-terpineol) in the chromatograph sample inlet chamber at 205° has been noted in several cases /94/. When the temperature of the inlet chamber was 100°, there was no decomposition. The most probable reason for this effect is the contamination of the chamber with acidic materials which catalyze the decomposition of the sample compounds.

Isomerization of terpenes during gas-liquid chromatography is largely affected by the nature of the stationary phase and especially of the solid support. Isomerization of pure $\alpha$-pinene of a column with silicon oil was noted by Groth /95/. Figure 29 gives the chromatogram of $\alpha$-pinene with two peaks. The analysis was conducted at 140° on a 200 cm column with 25% silicone oil on celite; flow rate of carrier gas (helium) was 34 ml/min. These components were preparatively isolated, and neither of them was identical with $\alpha$-pinene. It was shown with the aid of IR spectra that $\alpha$-pinene had isomerized to camphene and a monocyclic terpene. This isomerization must have taken place in the initial part of the column, since the components had issued from the column separately.

It has been said above /66/ that the solid support used in the analyses of terpenes should be deactivated by hexamethyldisilazane.

The effect of the identity of the solid support on the decomposition of terpenes under conditions of gas-liquid chromatography was studied by Hayshi et al. /96/. Chromatography of monoterpenes and their derivatives (α-pinene, limonene, linalool, α-terpineol, linalyl acetate, geranyl acetate) at 140° (carrier gas helium, flow rate 60 ml/min) and of sesquiterpenic alcohols at 200° (carrier gas helium, flow rate 30 ml/min) on a copper column showed that terpenes and sesquiterpenes are totally or largely decomposed if rock crystal, quartzite, quartz sand or unglazed porcelain (particle size 28 — 48 mesh) are used as supports. Powdered glass produces a slight decomposition of linalyl acetate and α-santanol, while the other terpenes and sesquiterpenes are not affected. The decomposition of most compounds is also noted at 180° on 20% Thermol-1, at 160° on polyesters and at 140° on 5% poly(ethylene glycol) 6000 on D — M carrier.

## Chromatographic studies on the chemical conversions of terpenes and terpene derivatives

Chromatographic methods are extensively employed in the synthetic chemistry of terpenes in the purification and isolation of various products from the reaction mixtures, and in qualitative and quantitative analyses of the initial and final reaction products. This section contains only a few examples of the utilization of chromatographic methods in the studies of the various reactions given by terpenes.

Column chromatography on alumina was used /97/ in the study of the autooxidation products of $\Delta^3$-carene; the products of the autocondensation of citral have been chromatographically separated /98/. Column chromatography was also employed /99/ to separate the acids formed by the oxidation of α-pinene.

The method of gas-liquid chromatography is the technique most frequently employed in the studies of the reactions of terpenes. It was utilized /100/ in the study of the products of irreversible catalysis of monocyclic terpenes. Studies were made of the products of isomerization of α-pinene /101, 102/; the amount of polymeric substances formed during the isomerization of pinene to camphene has been determined /103/; the isomerization of linalool to geraniol has been studied /104/, as has the isomerization of the stereoisomers of dl-menthol to dl-menthol /105/.

Bardyshev and Kosnikova /106, 107/ used chromatography on a thin layer of alumina and gas-liquid chromatography to study the chemical structure of the alcohols formed during the dehydration of bornylene. The composition of gaseous and volatile liquid products of catalytic and noncatalytic isomerization of $\Delta^3$-carene has been studied by gas-liquid chromatography /108, 109/.

Gas-liquid chromatography was applied to the study of the catalytic dehydration of cis- and trans-p-menthanol-8 /110/, of the oxidation of camphene to isomeric camphene oxides by perbenzoic acid /111/, of the selectivity of the reaction between sodium sulfite and terpenes, in particular, citral /112/. The composition of the dehydration products of terpenes /113/ such as the products of pyrolysis of bornyl chloride /114/ and D-camphor /115/ and the products of irradiation of terpenes by recoil tritium atoms have been studied.

Reaction gas chromatography was used /116/ in the study of the dehydrogenation, hydrogenation and dealkylation of monoterpenes.

It will thus be seen that chromatography, especially gas-liquid chromatography is now one of the most important techniques of research in the chemistry of terpenes.

BIBLIOGRAPHY

1. DE MAYO, P. Higher Terpenoids. — Interscience Publs. 1959.
2. BARDYSHEV, I. I. — In: Sbornik "Sinteticheskie produkty iz kanifoli i skipidara," pp. 8—17. Nauka i tekhnika. Minsk. 1964.
3. LEDERER, E. and M. LEDERER. Chromatography. A Review of Principles and Applications, p. 153, 2nd ed. — Elsevier Publ. Co., NY. 1957.
4. POST, A. — J. Soc. Cosmet. Chem., Vol. 5: 23. 1954.
5. NADAL, N. G. — Am. Perfumer Essent. Oil Rev., 65(6): 17—20. 1955.
6. WINTERSTEIN, A. and G. STEIN. — Z. Physiol. Chem., Vol. 220: 247. 1933.
7. SPATH, E. and P. KAINRATH. — Ber., Vol. 70: 2272. 1937.
8. CARLSOHN, and G. MÜLLER. — Ber., Vol. 71: 858. 1938.
9. HÜCKEL, W. and W. HORNUNG. — Chem. Ber., 90(9): 2023—2024. 1957.
10. CLEMENTS, R. L. — Science, 128(3329): 899—900. 1958.
11. WIDMARK, G. and S. G. BLOHM. — Acta Chem. Scand., Vol. 9: 1296—1299. 1955.
12. BLOHM, S. G. and G. WIDMARK. — Mikrochim. Acta, Nos. 1—3: 184—190. 1956.
13. WIDMARK, G. — Acta Chem. Scand., 11(2): 391. 1957.
14. VARMA, K. C., J. B. BURT, and A. E. SCHWARTING. — J. Am. Pharm. Assoc., 41(6): 318—320. 1952.
15. CLAESSON, S. Studies on Adsorption and Adsorption Analysis. — Almaquist. 1946.
16. HEROUT, V. — Collect. Czech. Chem. Communs, Vol. 15: 381—390. 1950.
17. MILLER, J. M. and J. G. KIRCHNER. — Analyt. Chem., 23(3): 428—430. 1951.
18. KIRCHNER, J. G. and J. M. MILLER. — Ind. Eng. Chem., Vol. 44: 318—321. 1952.
19. KIRCHNER, J. G., J. M. MILLER, and G. KELLER. — J. Analyt. Chem., 23(3): 420—425. 1951.
20. MILLER, J. M. and J. G. KIRCHNER. — Analyt. Chem., Vol. 24: 1480—1482. 1952.
21. KHOL'KIN, Yu. I. and G. D. PONUROV. — Trudy Sibirskogo Tekhnologicheskogo Instituta, Vol. 23: 71—73. 1959.
22. REZNIKOV, V. M. and Yu. I. KHOL'KIN. — Trudy Sibirskogo Tekhnologicheskogo Instituta, Vol. 23: 69—70. 1959.
23. KLABUNOVSKII, E. I., A. A. BALANDIN, and L. F. GODUNOVA. — Izv. AN SSSR, OKhN, No. 12: 2243—2244. 1961.
24. WICKBERG, B. — J. Organ. Chem., 27(12): 4652—4654. 1962.
25. BELIČ, I. — Nature, 178(4532): 538. 1956.
26. JOPPIEN, P. H. — Z. Lebensmittel-Untersuch. und Forsch., 104(6): 393—401. 1956.
27. ATTAWAY, J. A. et al. — Analyt. Chem., 35(2): 234—236. 1963.
28. SYPER, L. — Dissert. Pharmac. PAN, 17(1): 33—44. 1965.
29. MILLER, J. M. and J. G. KIRCHNER. — Analyt. Chem., Vol. 25: 1107. 1953.
30. MILLER, J. M. and J. G. KIRCHNER. — Analyt. Chem., 26(12): 2002. 1954.
31. REITSEMA. — Analyt. Chem., 26(6): 960—963. 1954.
32. ITO, M., S. WAKAMATSU, and H. KAWAHARA. — J. Chem. Soc. Japan, Pure Chem. Sect., Vol. 75: 413. 1954.
33. BRYANT, L. H. — Nature, 175(4456): 556. 1955.
34. STAHL, E. — Pharmazie, 11(10): 633—637. 1956.
35. DEMOLE, E. — J. Chromatogr., 1(1): 24—34. 1958.
36. HEŘMÁNEK, S., V. SCHWARZ, and Z. ČEKAN. — Pharmazie, 16(11): 566—569. 1961.
37. SCHANTZ, M. V., S. JUVONEN, and R. HEMMING. — J. Chromatogr., 20(3): 618—620. 1965.
38. GEYER, S. and R. MAYER. — Z. Chem., 5(8): 308. 1965.

39.  VLAD, P. F.  – Izv. AN Mold. SSR, Seriya Estestvennykh i Tekhnicheskikh Nauk, No. 9: 74 – 79. 1963.
40.  HUNECK, S.  – J. Chromatogr., 7(4): 561 – 564. 1962.
41.  FURUYA, T. and H. ITOGAWA.  – J. Japan Chem., supplement No. 64, Part 2: 123 – 131. 1964.
42.  IKAH, R.  – J. Chromatogr., 17(3): 591 – 593. 1965.
43.  MURAKAMI, T., H. ITOKAWA, F. UZUKI, and N. SAWADA.  – Chem. and Pharmac. Bull., 13(11): 1346 – 1352. 1965.
44.  IKAN, R. and R. MEIR.  – Israel J. Chem., 3(3): 117 – 118. 1965.
45.  BERGSTRÖM, G. and C. LAGERKRANTZ.  – Acta Chem. Scand., 18(2): 560 – 561. 1964.
46.  ATTAWAY, J. A., L. J. BARABAS, and R. W. WOLFORD.  – Analyt. Chem., 37(10): 1289 – 1290. 1965.
47.  IKAN, R., J. KASHMAN, and E. D. BERGMANN.  – J. Chromatogr., 14(2): 275 – 279. 1964.
48.  ELGAMAL, M. H. A. and M. B. E. FAYEZ.  – Z. Analyt. Chem., 211(3): 190 – 194. 1965.
49.  PETROWITZ, H. -J.  – Angew. Chem., 72(23): 921. 1960.
50.  VASHIST, V. N. and K. L. HANDA.  – J. Chromatogr., 18(2): 412 – 413. 1965.
51.  STAHL, E. and H. VOLLMANN.  – Talanta, 12(5): 525 – 528. 1965.
52.  McSWEENEY, G. P.  – J. Chromatogr., 17(1): 183 – 185. 1965.
53.  STAHL, E., editor. Dünnschicht-Chromatographie, ein Laboratoriumshandbuch. Berlin. 1962. [Russian translation from German. 1965.]
54.  BERNHARD, R. A.  – J. Assoc. Offic. Agric. Chemists, 40(3): 915 – 921. 1957; Nature, 185(4709): 311 – 312. 1960; Analyt. Chem., 34(12): 1576 – 1579. 1962.
55.  RUDLOFF, E.  – Canad. J. Chem., 38(5): 631 – 640. 1960; 39(1): 1 – 12. 1961; No. 6: 1190 – 1199. 1961.
56.  ZUBYK, W.  – J. Analyt. Chem., 32(8): 912 – 917. 1960.
57.  MATSUARA, T., H. KOMAE, and T. AGATANI.  – J. Chem. Soc. Japan, Ind. Chem. Sec., 63(10): 1761 – 1765. 1960.
58.  PETROWITZ, H. J.  – Riechstoffe und Aromen, 12(12): 397 – 402. 1962.
59.  HASLAM, J. and A. R. JEFFS.  – Analyst, 87(1037): 658 – 663. 1962.
60.  NIGAM, I. C. and L. LEVI.  – Canad. J. Chem., 40(11): 2083 – 2087. 1962.
61.  LUKEŠ, V. and R. KOMERS.  – Abhandl. Dtsch. Akad. Wiss. Berlin. Kl. Chem. Geol. und Biol., No. 6: 147 – 150. 1964.
62.  APLIN, R. T. and R. C. CAMBIE.  – N. Z. J. Sci., 7(2): 258 – 260. 1964.
63.  IKEKAWA, N., S. NATORI, H. AGETA, K. IWATA, and M. MATSUI.  – Chem. and Pharmac. Bull., 13(3): 320 – 325. 1965.
64.  PANG LIANG-CHENG, A. BEKKER, YANG CHIH-CHEN, and A. N. NESMEYANOV.  – Izv. VUZov, Khimiya i Khimicheskaya Tekhnologiya, 6(4): 597 – 600. 1963.
65.  KLOUWEN, M. H. and R. HEIDE.  – J. Chromatogr., 7(3): 297 – 310. 1962.
66.  AHO, Y., O. HARVA, and E. IDMAN.  – Tekh., kem. aikokauslehti, 20(17 – 18): 715 – 721. 1963.
67.  RIHANI, D. N.  – J. Chromatogr., 18(1): 150 – 151. 1965.
68.  HEFENDEHL, F.  – Naturwissenschaften, 51(6): 138 – 139. 1964.
69.  VALKANAS, G. and N. ICONOMOU.  – J. Chromatogr., 12(4): 536 – 539. 1963.
70.  LUKEŠ, V. and R. KOMERS.  – Collect. Czechosl. Chem. Communs, 29(7): 1598 – 1603. 1964.
71.  IKEKAVA, N., S. NATORI, H. ITOKAWA, S. TOHINAGA, and M. MATSUI.  – Chem. and Pharmac. Bull., 13(3): 316 – 319. 1965.
72.  GLOESENER, R.  – Farmaco. Ed. prat., 13(12): 647 – 655. 1958.
73.  CASANOVA, J. Jr. and E. COREY.  – J. Chem. and Ind., No. 41: 1664 – 1665. 1961.
74.  LESHCHINER, A. S. and T. A. RUDOL'FI.  – Trudy VNII Sinteticheskikh i Natural'nykh Dushistykh Veshchestv, Vol. 7: 165 – 166. 1965.
75.  PETROWITZ, H. J., F. NERDEL, and G. OHLOFF.  – J. Chromatogr., 3(4): 351 – 358. 1960.
76.  MOORE, D. R. and A. D. KOSSOY.  – Analyt. Chem., 33(10): 1437. 1961.
77.  KLUWEN, M. H. and R. HEIDE.  – Soap. Perfum. and Cosmet., 35(12): 1082 – 1083. 1962.
78.  TERADA, H., S. TSUDA, and T. SHIONO.  – J. Chem. Soc. Japan., Ind. Chem. Sec., 65(10): 1569 – 1571. 1962.
79.  BARON, C. and B. MAUME.  – Bull. Soc. Chim. France, No. 6: 1113 – 1117. 1962.
80.  HOULIHAN, W.  – J. Analyt. Chem., 34(13): 1846. 1962.
81.  RUDOL'FI, T. A., M. M. SHCHEDRINA, and A. V. KOKHMANSKII.  – Trudy VNII Sinteticheskikh i Natural'nykh Dushistykh Veshchestv, Vol. 6: 104 – 111. 1963.
82.  KOGAMI, K., K. AOKI, T. AISAKA, T. HASEGAWA, and D. KUMANOTANI.  – J. Japan Oil Chem. Soc., 19(3): 129 – 130. 1965.
83.  KOVÁTS, E.  – Z. Analyt. Chem., Vol. 181: 357 – 364. 1961.
84.  LEETS, K. and A. ERM.  – Izv. AN EstSSR, Seriya Fiziko-Matematicheskikh i Tekhnicheskikh Nauk, 13(1): 57 – 63. 1964.

85. DATTA, P. R. and H. SUSI. — Analyt. Chem., 34(8):1028−1029. 1962; Anal. Chem. Scand., 16:1530. 1962.
86. CAPELLA, P., E. FEDELI, and M. CIRIMELE. — Chem. and Ind., No. 39:1590−1591. 1963.
87. RUDAKOV, G. A. — Khimiya i tekhnologiya kamfary (Chemistry and Technology of Camphor). — Goslesbumizdat. 1961.
88. ARBUZOV, B. A. and Z. G. ISAEVA. — Izv. AN SSSR, OKhN, No. 5:843−849. 1953.
89. HUNTER, G. L. and W. B. BROGDEN. — J. Organ. Chem., 28(6):1679−1682. 1963.
90. STEDMAN, R. L., A. P. SWAIN, and W. RUSANIWSKYJ. — J. Chromatogr., 4(3):252−253. 1960.
91. WROLSTAD, R. S. and W. G. JENNINGS. — J. Chromatogr., 18(2):318−324. 1965.
92. ISAGULYANTS, V. I. and R. I. FEDOROVA. — Trudy Moskovskogo Instituta Neftekhimii i Gazovoi Promyshlennosti, Vol. 51:108−111. 1965; ZhPKh, Vol. 38:1880−1882. 1965.
93. HESSE, G. Z. — Analyt. Chem., 211(1):5−18. 1965.
94. DAY, E. A. and P. H. MILLER. — Analyt. Chem., 34(7):869−870. 1962.
95. GROTH, A. B. — Svensk Papperstidn., 61(10):311−321. 1958.
96. HAYSHI, S., K. YANO, and N. YOKOYAMA et al. — J. Chem. Soc. Japan, Pure Chem. Sec., 85(9):553−557. 1964; Bull. Chem. Soc. Japan, 38(11):1824−1831. 1965.
97. ARBUZOV, B. A., Z. G. ISAEVA, and V. V. RATNER. — Doklady AN SSSR, 134(3):583−586. 1960.
98. BUDNITSKAYA, E. V. — Trudy Komissii po Analiticheskoi Khimii, Vol. 6:197−201. 1955.
99. BALDWIN, D. E., V. M. LOEBLICH, and R. V. LAWRENCE. — Analyt. Chem., 26(4):760−762. 1954.
100. CHUDINOV, S. V., K. P. VEDENEEV, and Yu. K. SHAPOSHNIKOV. — Gidroliznaya i Lesokhimicheskaya Promyshlennost', No. 1:13−14. 1963.
101. VALKANAS, G. and N. ICONOMOU. — Pharmac. Acta Helv., 39(7):441−449. 1964.
102. IVANOVA, L. S. and G. A. RUDAKOV. — Doklady AN SSSR, 163(1):113−115. 1965.
103. GRATSIANSKAYA, L. P., L. N. LISHTVANOVA, and M. I. GORYAEV. — Izv. AN KazSSR, Seriya Khimicheskikh Nauk, No. 1:86−88. 1964.
104. ASCOLI, F. and V. CRESCENZI. — Chimica e ind., 40(9):724−727. 1958.
105. KOLOGRIVOVA, N. E. et al. — ZhPKh, 38(8):1893−1894. 1965.
106. BARDYSHEV, I. I. and L. V. KOSNIKOVA. — In: Sbornik "Sinteticheskie produkty iz kanifoli i skipidara," pp. 213 — 222, Nauka i Tekhnika, Minsk. 1964.
107. KOSNIKOVA, L. V. — Author's Summary of Candidate's Thesis. Minsk. 1966.
108. BARDYSHEV, I. I. and V. V. BAZYL'CHIK. — Izv. AN BSSR, Seriya Khimicheskikh Nauk, No. 2:90−99. 1966; BARDYSHEV, I. I., V. V. BAZYL'CHIK, and V. I. KULIKOV. — Izv. AN BSSR, Seriya Khimicheskikh Nauk, No. 2:100−107. 1966.
109. BAZYL'CHIK, V. V. — Author's Summary of Candidate's Thesis. Minsk. 1966.
110. RUDLOFF, E. — Canad. J. Chem., 41(1):1−8. 1963.
111. HIRSJÄRVI, P., P. EENILA, J. PELTONEN, L. PIRILA, and A. PAALLYSAHO. — Suomen kem., 36(7−8):126−132. 1963.
112. TEISSEIRE, P. — Recherches, No. 10:44−47. 1960.
113. RUBLOFF, E. — Canad. J. Chem., 39(9):1860−1864. 1961.
114. BICKNELL, R. C. and A. MACCOLL. — Chem. and Ind., No. 47:1912−1913. 1961.
115. SATO, T. — Tetrahedron, 21(10):2947−2949. 1965.
116. OKAMOTO, T. and T. ONAKA. — Chem. and Pharmac. Bull., 11(8):1986−1088. 1963.

# 2. ANALYSIS OF RESIN ACIDS

Resin acids are the most important components of the extractive substances of wood. They are a constituent of both pathological resin (oleoresin) and of the physiological resin of a normally growing undamaged tree. Resin acids are the raw material in the manufacture of rosin, the analysis of which will be discussed in Chapter VI.

Since resin acids structurally resemble each other to a great extent, the analysis of their mixtures is difficult. Most chemical and physico-chemical methods merely yield overall data or approximate, rough contents of the acids in the mixture.

Column and paper chromatography are the techniques which are mostly employed in the separation of resin acids. For a review of the publications on the chromatography of resin acids, see /1/. Some of the acids can be qualitatively separated by paper chromatography /2/.

Column chromatography is the technique which is most often employed in the analysis of resin acids. Pentegova and Lisina /3/ separated resin acids and hydroxylated resin acids on columns of active carbon, silica gel and Al$_2$O$_3$ containing 6% water.

A method for quantitative analysis of resin acids by partition chromatography was developed by Bardyshev et al. /4/. The mixture of resin acids (250 — 300 mg dissolved in isooctane) was chromatogrammed on a 135×1.0 cm column with 25 grams of silicic acid (0.1 — 0.25 mm). The stationary solvent consisted of a mixture of 9 grams of α-aminopyridine with 10 grams of furfuryl alcohol. The mobile solvent was isooctane. The solvent was passed at a rate of 50 ml/hour. The eluate was analyzed with the aid of an interferometer.

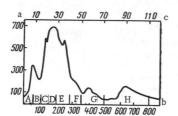

FIGURE 30. Chromatogram of a mixture of resin acids:

a — interferometer readings; b — volume of eluate, ml; c — fraction numbers; A –H – zones.

The acid fractions in individual zones (Figure 30) are combined and neutralized with cyclohexylamine (to phenolphthalein), when the salts thus formed are quantitatively precipitated from the solution. The precipitate on a Schott filter is dried at 50 — 60° to constant weight and examined in a spectrophotometer. The contents of individual acids in the zone are calculated according to formulas which comprise the differences between the specific absorption coefficients of pure salts of resin acids and their mixtures in the UV.

If the absorption coefficients $\alpha$ of the fractions are determined at several wavelengths between 230 and 300 m$\mu$ (243, 250, 266, 282 and 300 m$\mu$), the content of each component in the fraction may be calculated.

The percentage contents of the components in the mixture of salts of palustric acid $(C_{pal})$, abietic acid $(C_{ab})$ and acids not absorbing light between 230 and 300 m$\mu$ are calculated from the formulas:

$$C_{pal} = 4.53\alpha_{266};$$
$$C_{ab} = 1.67\,(\alpha_{243} - 0.5\alpha_{266}).$$

The contents of the components in mixtures of salts of levopimaric $(C^l_{lev.})$, abietic $(C_{ab})$, and neoabietic $(C_{neo})$ acids are found from the formulas:

$$C_{lev} = 10.18\alpha_{282} - \alpha_{300};$$
$$C_{ab} + C_{neo} = 1.77\alpha_{243} - 0.87\,(\alpha_{282} - \alpha_{300});$$
$$C_{neo} = 4.43\alpha_{250} + 3.00\alpha_{243} - 1.79\,(\alpha_{282} - \alpha_{300});$$
$$C_{ab} = 4.77\alpha_{243} - 4.43\alpha_{250} + 0.92\,(\alpha_{282} - \alpha_{300}).$$

Figure 30 shows an example of chromatographic separation of a mixture of resin acids. The distribution of resin acids by zones, calculated from the results of spectrophotometric measurements, is shown in Table 22.

TABLE 22. Composition of zones obtained by chromatogramming a mixture of resin acids

| Zone | Content of acids in zone, % | | | | | | | | | | | |
|---|---|---|---|---|---|---|---|---|---|---|---|---|
| | palustric | | dextropimaric | | abietic | | levopimaric | | neoabietic | | dehydroabietic | |
| | a | b | a | b | a | b | a | b | a | b | a | b |
| A | 100 | 47.3 | | | | | | | | | | |
| B | 79 | 52.7 | 21.0 | 7.2 | | | | | | | | |
| C | | | 73.9 | 27.6 | 15.2 | 5.6 | 10.9 | 3.5 | | | | |
| D | | | 48.1 | 58.4 | 47.2 | 54.4 | 4.7 | 4.9 | | | | |
| E | | | 2.6 | 3.4 | 32.0 | 40.0 | 65.4 | 73.2 | | | | |
| F | | | 13.9 | 3.4 | | | 81.1 | 17.1 | 5.0 | 6.3 | | |
| G | | | | | | | 7.8 | 1.3 | 92.2 | 93.7 | | |
| H | | | | | | | | | | | 100 | 100 |

Note. a — content of acid as % total acid content in the zone; b — content of acid as % total content of this acid eluted from the column.

This method is used in the analysis of different industrial products containing resin acids. In order to improve the separation of resin acids, it is recommended /5/ to conduct the analysis at a low temperature (+1 to +5°) on silica gel columns using the same stationary and mobile solvent phases. Partial separations of sandaracopimaric, isopimaric and pimaric acids have been attained in this manner.

## Chromatography of resin acids as derivatives

In order to facilitate the separation of resin acids, their derivatives, usually methyl esters, are frequently prepared prior to the separation. Zinkel and Rowe /7/ developed a method for the separation and identification of resin acids as methyl esters, prepared with the aid of diazomethane. The method is applicable to the analysis of pine resin. The product is developed at 30° on plates prepared by mixing 30 g alumina with a solution of 12 g $AgNO_3$ in 20 ml water and 10 ml methanol. The plates are dried at room temperature and activated for 30 minutes at 110°. The solvent system ether: petroleum ether (bp 30 — 60°) = 1:3 is employed. Spots of methyl esters of unsaturated resin acids are detected by treating the plate with a 1:4 mixture of concentrated $H_2SO_4$ and ether, heating at 110° for 15 minutes and examining in UV light; after heating at 200° for one hour, the zones of all resin acids become visible. Mixtures of methyl esters of isopimaric, levopimaric, palustric, pimaric, abietic, neoabietic and dehydroabietic acids and methyl esters of linoleic, oleic and stearic acids. Up to 0.5 — 1 γ of the esters can be detected in this way. A better separation of levopimaric and palustric acids can be attained by developing with ether: petroleum ether mixture (2:3).

The separation of resin acids as methyl esters /8/ has been achieved on Schleicher and Schüll fiberglass paper, impregnated with a 10% solution of cetane in petroleum ether (bp 60 — 71°). The mobile solvent used was a 6 M aqueous solution of $AgBF_4$ and methanol; the resin acid zones were detected with 10% $SbCl_5$ in chloroform. The separation of free fatty acids was achieved on paper impregnated with $(CH_3)_2SO_2$, petroleum ether being used as eluant.

Methyl esters of resin acids and related compounds have been separated /9/ by a successful combination of column, thin layer and gas chromatography.

Column chromatography served to achieve a preparative separation of the initial mixture of the methylation products of resin acids isolated from Pinus silvestris; the column (0.15 — 0.30 mm) contained a mixture of 125 g $AgNO_3$ with 450 g of silica gel. The components were eluted with petroleum ether (bp 40 — 60°) with increasing contents (from 2 to 10%) of diethyl ether. The separation of the components of the mixture is improved if the development is repeated.

A practically complete separation of the methyl esters of resin acids was attained on a thin silica gel layer containing silver nitrate. Benzene was employed as the mobile phase in separating methyl esters of pimaric, sandaracopimaric, isopimaric, levopimaric, palustric, dehydroabietic and neoabietic acids and also pimarinal, isopimarinal, dehydroabietinal, abietinal, pimarodiene and isopimarodiene; pimarinol, isopimarinol and abietinol were eluted with isopropanol. The spots were revealed by 10% $SbCl_5$ in chloroform.

As distinct from the free resin acids, their methyl esters are volatile, so that they can be separated by gas-liquid chromatography. Resin acid esters are separated /9/ at 150° on a 120×0.4 cm column with 1% silicone E 301 on preliminarily siliconized Gaschrome P (100 — 120 mesh), flow rate of carrier gas (nitrogen) 54 ml/min. Chromatograph manufactured by Pye Co. Evaporator temperature 200°.

TABLE 23. Results of the separation of methyl esters of resin acids by gas-liquid chromatography and by thin layer chromatography

| Type of compound | Methyl ester | Rel. retention time, min | $R_f$ | Color of spot |
|---|---|---|---|---|
| Pimaric | Pimarate | 1.00 | 0.40 | Blue |
| | Sandaracopimarate | 1.09 | 0.27 | Violet |
| | Isopimarate | 1.21 | 0.32 | Brown |
| Abietic | Levopimarate | 1.33 | 0.50 | Gray |
| | Palustrate | 1.33 | 0.60 | Yellow |
| | Dehydroabietate | 1.53 | 0.83 | Yellow brown |
| | Abietate | 1.82 | 0.75 | Gray blue |
| | Neoabietate | 2.13 | 0.73 | Gray |

Relative retention times and the $R_f$-values of the esters are shown in Table 23.

Methyl esters of resin acids were also separated under different experimental conditions /10/. One method /11/ is to work at 200° on a 182.7×0.6 cm column with 20% diethylene glycol succinate on Anachrome ABS (70 — 80 mesh), flow rate of carrier gas (helium) 150 ml/min, katharometric detector, sample volume $0.25-1.0\,\mu$l. Some of these esters were separated /12/ on a $225\times0.4$ cm column with 1% QF-1-0065 on Gaschrome P $(100-120$ mesh) at 165°, evaporator temperature 210°.

Methyl esters of resin acids can be separated /13/ at 250° on $427.5\times0.6$ cm column with 5% polyamide liquid phase (Versamide 900) on Chromosorb W or Anachrome ABS $(60-80$ mesh), flow rate of carrier gas (helium) 120 ml/min. Under these conditions methyl levopimarate is partly isomerized to methyl palustrate, methyl abietate and methyl neoabietate.

Methyl esters of resin acids can be analyzed with the use of flame ionization detectors /14/.

Gas-liquid chromatography and chromatography on silica gel columns have been used in the study of the products of the photocatalytic oxidation of levopimaric, palustric, neoabietic, dehydroabietic and pimaric acids /15/.

BIBLIOGRAPHY

1. KOMSHILOV, N.F. Kanifol' (Rosin). — Izdatel'stvo Lesnaya Promyshlennost', p. 63—71. 1965.
2. NEGORO. — J. Chem. Soc. Japan, Ind. Chem. Sec., 59 (5) : 546—547. 1956.
3. PENTEGOVA, V.A. and A.I. LISINA. — Izvestiya Vostochno-Sibirskogo Filiala AN SSSR, No. 1 : 65—69. 1957.
4. BARDYSHEV, I.I., Kh.A. CHERCHES, and L.A. MEERSON. — ZhA Kh, 18 (7) : 895—899. 1963.
5. BRUUN, H.H. and H. LEHTONEN. — Acta Chem. Scand., 17 (3) : 853—855. 1963.
6. BRUUN, H. and G. PENSAR. — Suomen Kem., 37 (9) : 143—148. 1964.
7. ZINKEL, D.F. and J.W. ROWE. — J. Chromatogr., 13 (1) : 74—77. 1964.
8. DANIELS, P. and C. ENZELL. — Acta Chem. Scand., 16 (6) : 1530—1532. 1962.
9. NORIN, T. and L. WESTFELT. — Acta Chem. Scand., 17 (6) : 1828—1830. 1963.
10. HUDY, J.A. — Analyt. Chem., 31 (11) : 1754—1756. 1959.
11. NESTLER, F.H.M. and D.F. ZINKEL. — Analyt. Chem., 35 (11) : 1747—1749. 1963.
12. TAHARA, A. and O. HOSHINO. — Scient. Papers Inst., Phys. and Chem. Res., 57 (1) : 19—24. 1963.
13. BROOKS, T.W., G.S. FISHER, and M.M. JOYE. — Analyt. Chem., 37 (8) : 1063—1064. 1965.
14. PENSOR, G. and H.H. BRUUN. — Suomen Kem., 38 (10) : 223—225. 1965.
15. SCHULLER, W.H. and R.V. LAWRENCE. — J. Organ. Chem., 28 (5) : 1386—1387. 1963.

## 3. CHROMATOGRAPHY IN THE ANALYSIS OF THE EXTRACTIVE SUBSTANCES OF WOOD

The analysis of the extractive substances of wood signifies mainly the analysis of tree sap, which is the raw material for rosin and turpentine industries. For reasons of space we shall deal mostly with the determination of terpene hydrocarbons and resin acids.

### Terpene hydrocarbons in the extractive substances of the woods of various tree species

The purpose of most of the chromatographic investigations effected was to establish the composition of the sap of the various trees. Industrial tapping mainly involves pine trees. The pinetree sap has been repeatedly analyzed by gas-liquid chromatography $/1-3/$.

In the study of the composition of sesquiterpenes from the sap of common pine (P i n u s   s i l v e s t r i s   L.) the fraction (bp 110— 125°/ 13 mm Hg) can be separated /4/ on an alkaline $Al_2O_3$ column to separate the oxygenated compounds, after which it is rectified.

Gas-liquid chromatography was employed in a study of the composition of the extractive substances in healthy and fungus-infected pinewood of P e r i d e r m i u m   p i n i, sulfate turpentine and tall oil /5/. The contents of these substances are the same in healthy and in rotten wood.

Pentegova et al. made a detailed study of the chemical composition of the sap of the cedar tree. Various chromatographic techniques applied in combination resulted in the determination of the composition of mono- and diterpenes and different oxygenated compounds. The high-boiling neutral fraction of the sap of P i n u s   s i b i r i c a   R. Mayr. was examined /6/ by column chromatography and by chromatography on a thin layer of silica gel impregnated with silver nitrate. Cembrene $C_{20}H_{32}$, mp $59-60°$, abietadiene $C_{20}H_{32}$ and dienic hydrocarbons $C_{20}H_{32}$ and $C_{20}H_{36}$ were isolated and identified in this manner.

Gas-liquid chromatography was also employed in the analysis of the sap of Siberian cedar /7/. It was found /8/, using a column with sorbitol cyanoethyl ether on INZ-600 brick (ratio 20:100), chromatograph "Khrom-1" and columns with alkaline and neutral alumina, that the oxygenated compounds of the high-boiling neutral fraction of the cedar sap include cembrol, diterpenic diol $C_{20}H_{34}O_2$ and the sesquiterpenic lactone $C_{17}H_{26}O_3$, in addition to the products mentioned above.

Chromatographic methods were employed in the study of the composition of the sap of Siberian larch (L a r i x   s i b i r i c a   Lebd.); the following technique was adopted in the investigation of the neutral components /9, 10/. The components were extracted with chloroform from the saponified solution of the sap, the ether* was evaporated and the extract distilled in vacuo; the high-boiling neutral fraction was separated into hydrocarbons and oxygenated compounds by chromatography on $Al_2O_3$; this was followed by distillation and separation of the fractions on alumina.

Cembrene /11/ was detected in the sap of Siberian larch in this manner. Another diterpenic hydrocarbon — abietadiene, which could be oxidized to abietinal and abietic acid — could also be isolated from the sap /12/.

Chromatography was applied to the study of the composition of extractive substances isolated from woods of different tree species by extracting with organic solvents.

Chromatography on $Al_2O_3$ was utilized in the separation of diterpenes isolated by petroleum ether extraction from ground wood of X y l i a   d o l o b r i f o r m i s /13/.

Terpenic alcohols in the extractive substances of the heartwood of aspen (P o p u l u s   t r e m u l o i d e s) were acetylated and then chromatogrammed on alumina columns /14/. Rao et al. /15/ studied the composition of the acetone extract of the tree S h o r e a   r o b u s t a. A triterpenic ketoester $C_{31}H_{48}O_3$, a triterpenic ketone $C_{30}H_{50}O_2$ and $\beta$-sitosterol have been isolated /16/ from the neutral fraction of the extractive substances of the wood O s t r y a   j a p o n i c a   Sarg, soluble in n-hexane.

Thin layer chromatography was employed /17/ in the study of the composition of terpenes in the ether extract of birchwood.

* [Unclear in Russian.]

126

Systematic studies of the composition of the extractive substances of various tree species were conducted by Cocker et al. /18/. The usual sequence of the operations was as follows. Shavings of the heartwood of Shorea meranti were continuously extracted for 24 hours with boiling ligroin at 60 — 80° and the extract was concentrated and left to stand overnight. A colorless precipitate of the extractive substances, mp 77 — 90°, separated out. The sample of the extractive substances was steam-distilled, the distillate extracted with ether, from which an oil was obtained. The following terpenoids were identified in the oil by the technique of gas-liquid chromatography: myrcene, 1,4- and 1,8-cineol, methyl-heptenone, $\alpha$- and $\beta$-thujone, citronellal, isopulegol, $\beta$-terpineol, $\alpha$-gurjunene, caryophyllene, piperitone, $\beta$- and $\gamma$-cadinene and 1,8-terpin. The residue of nonvolatile extractives was separated into ether-soluble and ether-insoluble fractions. The insoluble fraction was hydrolyzed with 5% KOH in diethylene glycol by boiling under reflux for 3 hours. Acidic and phenolic fractions were obtained as a result of hydrolysis. The acids, in the form of esters, were separated by gas-liquid chromatography. The normal $C_{12}$, $C_{14}$, $C_{16-18}$, $C_{20}$, $C_{22-26}$ saturated acids and the $C_{15-18}$, $C_{20-22}$. monounsaturated acids were identified. The soluble compounds yielded an acid and an ester fraction. The composition of the acids was as follows: n-dodecanoic through n-hexacosanoic (except for n-tridecanoic); normal monounsaturated tetra-, penta-, hexa-, octa- and nonadecenic, eicosenic, heneicosenic and decosenic acids; $C_{14-25}$ di-unsaturated acids. The esters were hydrolyzed for 6 hours with 5% methanolic KOH and yielded a mixture of alcohols with saturated and unsaturated acids. The ligroin extract residual after the removal of solid precipitate, yielded an acid resin fraction containing a mixture of normal acids and a neutral resin fraction, containing a mixture of triterpenoids which were not separated. The wood, which had been previously extracted with ligroin, was again extracted with acetone. Bergenin, which separated out of aqueous solution as colorless rhombic crystals, was isolated from these products.

Cocker et al. /19/ also investigated the composition of extractive substances isolated from the heartwood of the tree Cephalosphaera usambarensis with boiling ligroin. The main fraction was constituted by neutral compounds, which were found by chromatographic analysis to have the following composition (in %): terpinolene 19.6; alloocimene 12.7; limonene 11.0; $\beta$-pinene 9.1; methylheptenone 1.67; $\alpha$-pinene 3.23; it also contained ethers, hydrocarbons, $\beta$-sitosterol and a mixture of cycloeu-calenol alcohols and their methylated homologues. The extractive substances also contained a phenolic and an acidic fraction.

The composition of the extractive substances of wood, and in the first place the qualitative and quantitative composition of terpenic hydrocarbons is, in certain cases, an indication of the species to which the tree belongs. The determination of the tree species from the groundwood material is of high practical interest, since the conventional microscopic techniques and color reactions do not invariably yield correct results. A chromatographic identification of the tree species has been described /20/; it is based on the differences in the compositions of the extractive substances in trees of different species. The extractive substances were steam-distilled from pine heartwood and were examined on a gas-liquid Beckman CC-2A chromatograph. It was shown that Pinus banksiana, P.contorta, P. contorta var. latifolia and the hybrid P.banksiana contorta all have different terpene compositions and may be identified in this manner. T s u g a  h e t e r o p h y l l a may be distinguished from A b i e s a m a b i l i s by gas-liquid chromatography of the volatile products liberated by thermal treatment of the wood at 150° and thin layer chromatography of the extractive substances, which include waxes, fats, fatty acid, β-sitosterol, etc. Paper chromatography may be utilized in the study of the phenolic components of the extractive substances of wood. It is recommended that more than one chromatographic method be used in combination in order to establish the species of these trees.

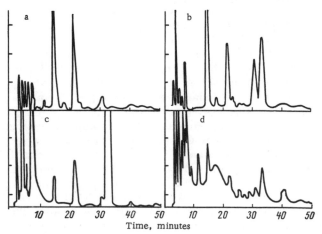

FIGURE 31. Chromatograms of products of steam distillation of trees:

a — Pinus banksiana; b — P. banksiana contorta; c — P. contorta; d — P. contorta var. latifolia.

Figure 31 illustrates the large differences in the composition of the terpenes steam-distilled from various species of trees. The contents of even the major components vary within a wide range.

## Resin acids in extractive substances of wood

For a review of the publications on the resin acids in saps of conifer trees, see /21/.

Bardyshev et al. used column chromatography in their studies of the composition of the resin acids in the sap of common pine (P i n u s s i l v e s t r i s L.) /22/, P i c e a  a j a n e n s i s Fisch. /23/ and Siberian cedar (P i n u s  s i b i r i c a Rupr.) /24/.

The quantitative technique of partition chromatography which has already been described /25/, was employed /26/ in a study of the composition of the resin acids in the sap of Crimean pine (P i n u s p a l l a s i a n a Lamb.). The composition (in %) of the resin acids was found to be: palustric 16, abietic 13, levopimaric 18, neoabietic 13, dextropimaric 28, dehydroabietic 12, etc.

The same analytical method was employed /27/ in the investigations of the resin acid composition of Pinus pithynsa, Crimean pine (Pinus pallasiana Lamb.) and of the hybrid of the two. It was shown that the compositions of the resin acids are qualitatively the same in all three species of trees. The quantitative contents of palustric, dextropimaric, isodextropimaric, abietic, levopimaric, neoabietic and dehydroabietic acids were determined in mixture with other acids; their respective proportions were markedly different in the different pine species.

In the study /28/ of the composition of the resin acids in spruce sap, 6 zones could be separated by chromatographic techniques; the quantitative composition of the acids in each zone was calculated from UV-spectrophotometric data. The sap was found to contain palustric, dextropimaric, isodextropimaric, abietic, levopimaric, neoabietic and dehydroabietic acids. Their mutual proportions in spruce and pine saps were different.

Kashtanova and Pentegova /29/ studied the composition of resin acids in the sap of Siberian cedar (Pinus sibirica R. Mayr.). The resin acid mixtures were chromatogrammed directly on silica gel or else were subjected to a preliminary reduction by lithium aluminum hydride to yield diterpenic alcohols, and then chromatogrammed on alkaline alumina.

Isopimaric acid and the products of its transformations were studied on silica and alumina columns /30/.

Paper chromatography was used /31/ in a study of the composition of the resin acids in pine and spruce; the acids had been preliminarily methylated.

Systematic investigations of the resin acids in the sap of pine and spruce by partition chromatography were effected by Bruun et al. /32/. In their most recent investigations /33/ the resin acids in wood were studied in the form of methyl esters by gas-liquid chromatography. Comparison between various stationary phases showed that the esters are best separated on poly(ethylene glycol) succinate. It has been recommended /34/ to effect the separation at 235° on a 300×0.3 cm column with poly(ethylene glycol) succinate on Chromosorb W (80 — 100 mesh); nitrogen was used as carrier gas; ionization detector; Perkin-Elmer F11 chromatograph. Under these conditions partial separation occurs of the esters of dihydropimaric, pimaric, sandaracopimaric, dihydroisopimaric and isopimaric acids.

Chromatographic methods were also employed in the study of the resin acids in the extracts obtained as a result of treating the wood with organic solvents.

It was established by gas-liquid chromatography /35/ that the acetone extract of the heartwood of Pinus resinosa Ait contained palmitic, palmitoleic, stearic, linoleic, pimaric, sandaracopimaric, abietic, neoabietic and vanillic acids, and also pinocembrin, vanillin, etc.

Skrigan /36/ employed chromatography on alumina in his study of the composition of resinous substances isolated from the deep-lying tree fossils of the interglacier era. Ether extracts of deep-lying 500,000, 300,000 and 140,000 years-old pine trunks yielded /37/ fichtelite oil, which was chromatogrammed on active alumina to give resin acids and hydrocarbons — fichtelite and retene.

## Chromatography of tannides

Wood processing involves the production of tanning extracts, which are extracted from the wood or from the bark with water. The activity of the tanning extracts is determined by the content of tannides, which are components of the extractive substances of wood.

The simplest representatives of tanning substances of the condensed series are catechins, which are found in pine, larch, willow, grapevine, tea plant and various fruits. Catechins are very unstable when isolated, are easily oxidized and condensed, and the isolation of individual components is very difficult. Accordingly, detailed studies of the composition and structure of this group of substances only became possible with the development of appropriate chromatographic investigation methods.

Catechins have been separated on silica gel /38, 39/ and cellulose /40/ columns.

A little later, catechins were qualitatively separated on paper /41, 42/ by development with n-butanol: acetic acid: water = 40:10:50 and phenol: acetic acid: water = 30:2:18. A better separation is attained by development with more acidic systems, such as n-butanol: acetic acid: water = 40:12:28 /43/, the same system with component ratio 40:10:22 or with a 2% solution of acetic acid /44/. Two-dimensional development with the two last-named solvent systems resulted in quantitative separation of seven members of the catechin complex from tea plant.

Catechins were semiquantitatively determined by paper chromatography /45/ by development with n-butanol: acetic acid: water = 5:2:6, and the spots revealed with diazotized sulfanilic acid. The amounts of the catechins were estimated from the areas occupied by the spots. Alternatively, the spots may be cut out and titrated against 0.01 N $KMnO_4$ /46/. More accurate results are obtained by radial chromatography /47/ in nitrogen, with subsequent elution of catechins from the individual zones with 96% ethanol and photometric determination of their products of reaction with vanillin.

Zaprometov /48/ developed a quantitative method for the determination of catechins eluted from the chromatogram in which they are reacted with 1% vanillin in concentrated hydrochloric acid /49/. The elution was effected with 96% ethanol at $30 - 40°$; when the eluate was treated with the reagent, a red color appeared, the intensity of which was measured on Pulfrich photometer at $\lambda_{max} = 490$ m$\mu$. l-Epigallocatechin, d, l-gallo-catechin, l-epicatechin, d, l-catechin, l-epigallocatechin gallate, l-gallocatechin gallate and l-epicatechin gallate were detected in tea plant by this method.

The spectroscopic and chromatographic properties of ellagic acid and its distribution in dicotyledonous plants have been studied /50/.

Esters of ellagic acid have been separated by paper chromatography /51/; different natural tannides have been studied by this method /52/. Tannides of the nut Areca catechu Linn., isolated by extraction with acetone and ethyl acetate /53/ were studied by two-dimensional paper chromatography. Four phenolic tannin acids have been found in the extract of myrobalans /54/.

The natural tannin acids can also be studied by column chromatography on a mixture of magnesol with celite /55/ and chromatography on a thin layer of polyamide /56/.

The composition of the acetone extract of the heartwood of R u h s j a v a n i c a Linn. has been studied /57/. Hydrolysis of the colorless, amorphous tannin powder obtained in 0.11% yield with 5% sulfuric acid yielded glucose, identified by paper chromatography and also gallic and m-digallic acids which were separated on a column of silica gel. The heartwood contains not only tannins but also free gallic acid which were isolated in a 0.17% yield.

The composition of sugars in the hydrolyzates of the tannin extracts from the barks of various species of pine was studied /58/ by paper chromatography; development was effected with $\alpha$-picoline: amyl alcohol: water $= 5:3:2$ and the spots were detected with aniline phthalate according to Partridge. Glucose and fructose were determined, and saccharose was detected in the hydrolyzate.

In addition to the analyses of terpenes, resin acids and tannides, chromatographic methods are also used in studies of hydrocarbons, phenols, saturated and unsaturated acids, amino acids and other compounds contained in wood extracts.

BIBLIOGRAPHY

1. BANNISTER, M. H., H. V. BREWERTON, and I. R. C. McDONALD. − Svensk Papperstidn., 62(16): 567−573. 1959.
2. MIROV, N. T., E. FRANK, and E. ZAVARIN. − Phytochemistry, 4(4): 563−568. 1965.
3. ICONOMOU, N. and G. VALKANAS. − Pharmac. Acta Helv., 41(1): 59−63. 1966.
4. PENTEGOVA, V. A. and O. V. LEBEDEVA. − Izv. SO AN SSSR, Seriva Khimicheskikh Nauk, 1(3): 61−64. 1964.
5. ERDTMAN, H. and L. WESTFELD. − Acta Chem. Scand., 17(6): 1826−1827. 1963.
6. PENTEGOVA, V. A. and N. K. KASHTANOVA. − Khimiya Prirodnykh Soedinenii, No. 3: 223−224. 1965.
7. PENTEGOVA, V. A., O. MOTL, and V. HEROUT. − Collect. Czechosl. Chem. Communs, 26(5): 1362−1372. 1961.
8. LISINA, A. I., A. I. REZVUKHIN, and V. A. PENTEGOVA. − Khimiya Prirodnykh Soedinenii, No. 4: 250−256. 1965.
9. SHMIDT, E. N., A. I. LISINA, and V. A. PENTEGOVA. − In: Sbornik "Sinteticheskie produkty iz kanifoli i skipidara." Nauka i tekhnika, pp. 326−329, Minsk. 1964.
10. SHMIDT, E. N., A. I. LISINA, and V. A. PENTEGOVA. − Izv. SO AN SSSR, Seriya Khimicheskikh Nauk, 1(3): 52−60. 1964.
11. LISINA, A. I. − Izv. SO AN SSSR, No. 3: 120−121. 1962.
12. LISINA, A. I. and V. A. PENTEGOVA. − Izv. SO AN SSSR, Seriya Khimicheskikh Nauk, 7(2): 96−100. 1965.
13. LAIDLAW, R. A. and J. W. W. MORGAN. − J. Chem. Soc., No. 1: 644−650. 1963.
14. ABRAMOVITCH, R. A. and R. G. MICETICH. − Can. J. Chem., 41(9): 2362−2367. 1963.
15. RAO, C. B., T. V. P. RAO, and V. VENKATESWARLU. − Current Sci., 32(12): 544−545. 1963.
16. YASUE, M. et al. − J. Japan Wood Res. Soc., 11(3): 111−113. 1965.
17. PAASONEN, P. − Suomen Kem., 38(7−8): 169−170. 1965.
18. COCKER, W., T. B. H. McMURRY, D. M. SAINSBURY, and L. E. STANLEY. − Perfum. Essent. Oil Res., 55(7): 442−445. 1964.
19. COCKER, W., T. B. H. McMURRAY, and M. S. NTAMILA. − J. Chem. Soc., pp. 1692−1699, March. 1965.
20. SWAN, E. P. − Forest Prod. J., 16(1): 51−54. 1966.
21. CHERCHES, Kh. A. and I. I. BARDYSHEV. − In Sbornik "Sinteticheskie produkty iz kanifoli i skipidara," Nauka i tekhnika, pp. 267−282. Minsk. 1964.
22. BARDYSHEV, I. I. et al. − DAN BSSR, 4(10): 421−443. 1960.

23. CHERCHES, Kh. A., I. I. BARDYSHEV, and O. T. TKACHENKO. — ZhPKh, 33(10):2381−2384. 1960.
24. BARDYSHEV, I. I., Kh. A. CHERCHES, and Zh. F. KOKHANSKAYA. — ZhPKh, 34(5):1147−1151. 1961.
25. BARDYSHEV, I. I., Kh. A. CHERCHES, and L. A. MEERSON. — ZhAKh, 28(7):896. 1963.
26. BARDYSHEV, I. I., Kh. A. CHERCHES, and Z. Yu. KOVTUNENKO. — ZhPKh, 38(2):440−442. 1965.
27. CHERCHES, Kh. A. et al. — ZhPKh, 38(11):2624−2627. 1965.
28. BARDYSHEV, I. I. et al. — Gidroliznaya i Lesokhimicheskaya Promyshlennost', No. 2:10−11. 1965.
29. KASHTANOVA, N. K. and V. A. PENTEGOVA. — Izv. SO AN SSSR, No. 3:121−123. 1962.
30. ANTKOWIAK, W., O. E. EDWARDS, R. ROWE, and J. W. APSIMON. — Can. J. Chem., 43(5):1257−1265. 1965.
31. SMIRNOV, B. P. and V. S. SIDOROV. — ZhPKh, 33(5):1192−1203. 1960.
32. BRUUN, H. H., S. GASLAND, and G. LUNDQVIST. — Acta Chem. Scand., 13(5):1039−1041. 1959.
33. PENSAR, G., and H. H. BRUUN. — Acta Acad. Aboensis., 24(6):15. 1964.
34. BRUUN, H. H. and G. PENSAR. — Acta Chem. Scand., 19(2):531−533.
35. SATO, A. and E. RUDLOFF. — Canad. J. Chem., 42(3):635−640. 1964.
36. SKRIGAN, A. I. — Sbornik nauchnykh rabot instituta fiziko-organicheskoi khimii AN BSSR, No. 7:126−140. 1959.
37. SKRIGAN, A. I. — In Sbornik "Sinteticheskie produkty iz kanifoli i skipidara," Nauka i tekhnika, pp. 108−115. Minsk. 1964.
38. BRADFIELD, A. and A. PENNEY. — J. Chem. Soc., p. 2249. London. 1948.
39. ZAPROMETOV, M. N. — Biokhimiya, Vol. 17:97. 1952.
40. FORSUTH, W. G. C. — Biochem. J., Vol. 51:511. 1952.
41. ROBERTS, E. A. H. and D. J. WOOD. — Biochem. J., Vol. 53:332. 1953.
42. ZAPROMETOV, M. N. — Trudy Komissii po Analiticheskoi Khimii, 6(9):418. 1955.
43. ZAPROMETOV, M. N. and G. A. SOBOLEVA. — DAN SSSR, Vol. 96:1205. 1954.
44. CARTWRIGHT, R. A. and E. A. H. ROBERTS. — Chem. Ind., p. 1389. 1954.
45. OSHIMA, Y., T. NAKABAYASHI, and S. NISHIDA. — J. Agric. Chem. Soc., Vol. 26:367. Japan. 1952.
46. FORSYTH, W. G. — Biochem. J., Vol. 60:108. 1955.
47. DZHEMUKHADZE, K. M. and G. A. SHAL'NEVA. — Biokhimiya, Vol. 20:336. 1955.
48. ZAPROMETOV, M. N. — In: Sbornik "Khromatografiya, ee teoriya i primenenie" (Proceedings of Conference), pp. 408−416. Izd. AN SSSR. 1960.
49. KURSANOV, A. L. — Biokhimiya, Vol. 6:120. 1941.
50. HARTWAY, D. E. — Nature, 177(4512):747−748. 1956.
51. CAIN, B. F. — N. Z. J. Sci., 5(3):390−392. 1962.
52. HADDAWAY, L. W. — Analyt. Chem., 28(10):1624−1625. 1956.
53. BANERJEE, S., S. RAJADURAI, K. N. S. SASTRY, and Y. NAYUDAMM. — Leather Sci., 10(1):6−13. 1963.
54. SANTHANAM, P. S. and S. K. BARAT. — Leather Sci., 10(4):172−174. 1963.
55. SCHMIDT, O. T. and H. REUSS. — Liebigs Ann. Chem., Vol. 649:137−148. 1961.
56. STADLER, P. and H. ENDRES. — J. Chrom., 17(3):587−591. 1965.
57. KITAO, K. and M. ARAKI. — Wood Res., No. 34:57−61. 1965.
58. GÜLBARAN, E. — J. Amer. Leather Chemists Assoc., 59(10):619−622. 1964.

*Chapter VI*

## CHROMATOGRAPHY OF PRODUCTS OF CHEMICAL PROCESSING OF WOOD

Chemical processing of wood or other vegetal material yields a large number of industrial products with different chemical structure and properties. The main products of pulp and paper industry are high molecular compounds which constitute technical pulp and pulp-based products. Wood hydrolysis and wood chemical industries mainly involve low-molecular products such as alcohols, organic acids, furfural and its derivatives, ethers and esters, phenols and other compounds.

## A. ANALYSIS OF PRODUCTS OF THE PULP AND PAPER INDUSTRY

Chromatographic methods were employed in the study of the processes which take place in the manufacture of pulp and in the analysis of the final products and side products. For reviews of early work on the applications of chromatography to production control and research in paper and pulp industry, see /1 — 3/.

### 1. Analysis of products of the sulfite pulp industry

Chromatographic methods proved very helpful in investigating the processes involved in sulfite cook, in the analysis of the final products and of the most important side product — the sulfite liquor.

Changes in the components of wood as a result of sulfite cook

The behavior of xylan /4/, glucomannan /5/, hemicelluloses and cellulose /6/ during sulfite cook has been extensively studied. For the behavior of polysaccharides during pulping, see /7/.
The first stage of decomposition of polysaccharides during sulfite cook is the formation of monosaccharides, which pass into the sulfite liquor. Many studies on the analysis of sugars in the sulfite liquor are available; they will be discussed in one of the following sections. Decomposition of

polysaccharides and monosaccharides results in the formation of organic acids, in particular, aldonic and carbohydrate sulfonic acids. These acids may be separated by ion exchange chromatography /8/. Cation exchange has been used in the study of sulfite pulping /9/.

As a step in the investigation of the behavior of polysaccharides during sulfite pulping, studies were performed /10/ on methyl-$\beta$-D-glucopyranoside as a model substance for cellulose. The glucoside was treated under conditions resembling those of neutral sulfite cook (pH 6 — 7, temperature 150 — 180°). Sodium sulfite catalyzes the decomposition of the glucoside. The reaction mixture was investigated by paper chromatography and electrophoresis. The following carboxylic acids were detected: formic, acetic, lactic and glycolic. As regards the sulfonic acids, EPR and IR spectroscopic methods revealed the presence of propane-2,2-disulfonic acid and a possible presence of 1,4-dihydroxy-3-sulfopentanoic and 1,4,5-trihydroxy-3-sulfohexanoic acids.

The structure of the products of decomposition of carbohydrates was studied in detail by ion exchange chromatography by the Chalmers Technical University in Göteborg; for a review of these studies, see /11/.

It was shown by chromatographic methods that both in sulfite and in sulfate pulping, large amounts of organic acids are formed as a result of the decomposition of carbohydrates. The identified aldonic acids include /12/ xylonic, arabonic, mannonic, gluconic and galactonic acids. The isolation and separation of hydroxy acids, in particular aldonic acids, has been attained by ion exchange chromatography /13, 14/.

Preliminary removal of cations from the liquor is effected by passing it through a column of Dowex-50 W in the H-form (0.14 — 0.29 mm) /15/.

Polymeric carbohydrates, which have dissolved during sulfite pulping, can be separated on cation exchangers in the H-form /16/. It is assumed that the reaction between hemicelluloses and bisulfite results in the oxidation of the end groups of the former, with formation of the corresponding aldonic acids by hydrolysis /17/.

We shall now discuss the analytical sequence employed /17/ in the study of the behavior of hemicelluloses in the process of sulfite cook. The sulfite liquor is deionized on a cation exchanger in the H-form, the hemicelluloses are precipitated by alcohol, and hydrolyzed for 6 hours at 100° with 1 N sulfuric acid. After neutralization of the hydrolyzate on a Dowex-1($\times$8) column the neutral carbohydrates, lignin and aldonic acids are separated. The acids are separated on an anion exchanger in the borate form /18/, using 0.1 M sodium tetraborate as eluent. The aldonic acids are then analyzed by paper chromatography /19/.

The alterations undergone by lignin in the process of sulfite cook were studied both on model compounds and on various samples of lignin and wood.

Electrophoresis has been employed /20, 21/ to separate polysaccharides formed in the early stages of the cook from sulfonated lignins.

The study of the variation in the composition of sulfite liquor during sulfite pulping is best carried out by several chromatographic techniques in combination /22/. The dissolved monosulfonic acids were separated by molecular weights by way of ion exchange and dialysis; paper chromatography was employed to study the kinetics of the dissolution and hydrolysis of polysaccharides, while gas-liquid chromatography was utilized to determine the acetic acid formed during the pulping process.

In the study of the cleavage of alkyl aryl ether bonds in lignin during pulping, methanol formed during the oxidation of lignin by periodate was determined by gas-liquid chromatography /23/.

The method of ion exchange was employed in the deionization of the liquids during a study of the sulfonation of periodate lignin /24/.

Paper chromatography was applied /25/ in a study of the solubilization of hemicelluloses and other components of wood during neutral semichemical sulfite pulping.

Paper chromatography was used in a qualitative evaluation of the sequence of hydrolysis of individual polysaccharides in wood during sulfite pulping /26/. A quantitative estimate of the yields of different sugars in the various stages of sulfite cook of spruce holocellulose was carried out by Butko /27/.

The sulfite pulping of eucalyptus wood is affected by the ellagic acid it contains, which forms complexes with metals. Their structure has been studied by chromatographic methods /28, 29/.

The chemical mechanism of sulfite pulping is as yet unclear in many of its aspects; many of these questions are susceptible of being answered with the aid of chromatographic methods of investigations.


Structure of lignosulfonates and
lignosulfonic acids

Chromatographic methods are utilized in the isolation of lignosulfonates from sulfite liquors, in their fractionation by molecular weight and in studying the products of decomposition of lignosulfonates.

**Isolation and purification of lignosulfonates.** The following procedure /30/ is recommended for the isolation of lignosulfonates from sulfite liquors. Sulfite liquor in the form of a 25% solution (10 ml) is passed through a 3×7 cm column with 10 grams of diethylaminoethylcellulose mixed with 2 grams of celite. Prior to the analysis the sorbent should be regenerated with 0.2 N NaOH. After introduction of the sample the column is washed through with 2 liters of distilled water, and the lignosulfonic acid is eluted with 0.2 N NaOH (125 ml). The alkaline solution is immediately passed through a column with Amberlite IRA-120 cation exchanger in the H-form. The lignosulfonates are obtained in the filtrate. The solution is dried at a temperature below 0°, when the lignosulfonates are obtained as a brown solid in a 1—1.3 gram yield. To prevent oxidation, the isolation of the lignosulfonates is conducted out of contact with the atmosphere, in oxygen-free nitrogen.

Lignosulfonates can be separated /31/ from hemicelluloses on cation exchangers with carboxyl groups, e.g., Amberlite IR-C-50 (0.12 — 0.30 mm). Sugars are not sorbed on the cation exchanger, and hemicelluloses are weakly retained in the presence of a 2 M solution of NaCl. Since the separation of hemicelluloses from lignosulfonates is practically quantitative, covalent bonds between hemicelluloses and lignin would seem to be absent or to be broken during the cook.

Lignosulfonates are separated from carbohydrates by successive passage over two ion exchangers /32/: Amberlite IR-120 and Duolite A-2M. The separation of sugars and lignosulfonates on ion exchange resins is accompanied /33/ by processes of ion exchange, adsorption, and molecular sieve distribution. Lignosulfonates and carbohydrates may also be separated on other ion exchangers /34/ and on diethylaminoethylcellulose /35/.

**Fractionation of lignosulfonates.** Lignosulfonic acids and lignosulfonates have the properties of polyelectrolytes; they can accordingly be fractionated by electrophoresis /36 — 38/.

We shall discuss the procedure employed in the isolation and fractionation of lignosulfonates from sulfite liquors /39/. The liquor is treated with ethyl ether and amyl alcohol. The isolated lignosulfonates are separated by chromatography on Whatman No. 1 paper and developed with n-butanol saturated with water containing acetic acid. Observations in UV light showed that lignosulfonates migrate in an irregular manner under these conditions, and 65 wt.% of the sample remain near the starting line.

Paper chromatography served in the study of the composition of lyes, in particular, lignosulfonates /40/ and the composition of the products of decomposition of lignin in the spent liquor from the pulping of aspen wood /42/.

The effect of different factors on the adsorption of lignosulfonates on kaolin and $TiO_2$ was studied by Beeckmans /42/. The adsorption of all fractions, except for the lowest molecular species, is reversible if the solution is diluted. The desorption may be induced by changing the pH.

Fractionation of lignosulfonates on ion exchange resins has become of importance. Low-molecular lignosulfonates have been separated on columns with Dowex-50 W(×2) /43/.

Lignosulfonates obtained in the first stage of sulfite cook (at 131°) of the wood of red alder tree were fractionated by Mothershead and Glennie /44/. The following substances were found in lignosulfonate fractions with a low molecular weight, isolated by column chromatography on Amberlite IR-120 or with silica gel and also by thin layer chromatography: vinyl syringyl sulfonate (more than 4% of total content of lignosulfonates); vinyl vanillyl sulfonate, coniferyl sulfonate and smaller amounts of sulfonates of coniferyl and sinapyl aldehydes; sinapyl sulfonate could not be isolated. The UV spectra of these compounds resembled those of the corresponding sulfonates obtained by synthesis from the corresponding alcohols.

Forrs and Fremer effected a successful molecular weight fractionation, using ion exchange chromatography, as well as Sephadex gel filtration. They first /45, 46/ showed that lignosulfonates may be separated from hemicelluloses of sulfite lyes and partly separated into two fractions with similar properties such as a similar content of methoxyl groups. They concluded /46/ that their lignosulfonate fractions differed in their molecular weights. The fractionation was conducted on a 400×4.2 cm column with Dowex-50(×2) resin in the H-form (100 — 200 mesh).

Lignosulfonates isolated from ion exchange resins were further fractionated by gel filtration on Sephadex G-75 /47/.

Before being introduced into the column with Sephadex, the eluate containing the lignosulfonic acids was neutralized and evaporated in vacuo. The product was introduced into a 200×4.2 cm Sephadex column and eluted with water. The separation of lignosulfonates on this column is based on different permeabilities of the swollen, gel-like dextran to molecules of different sizes. Low-molecular fractions of lignosulfonic acids were separated on a column with Sephadex G-25.

The method was then applied /48/ to the study of the solubilization of the various components of wood under different conditions of sulfite cook.

A number of low-molecular lignosulfonic acids formed during calcium sulfite cook of Norwegian spruce (P i c e a  a b i e s) was studied in detail /49/. The composition of the cooking liquor was $SO_2$ 71.5 g/l, CaO 10 g/l, final temperature of cook 130°. Oligomeric lignosulfonic acids were separated by passing the sulfite liquor through a 750×4.2 cm column with Sephadex G-25 (200—250 mesh) with water as eluent. The elution curve was plotted by determining the optical density of the filtrate at 280 m$\mu$. The acids were separated into 9 fractions. In each fraction the methoxyl group content and the elementary composition were determined. An example of chromatographic separation of the lignosulfonic acids of the sulfite liquor is shown in Figure 32.

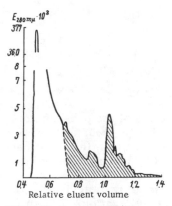

FIGURE 32. Separation of oligomeric lignosulfonic acids (shaded area) by gel filtration of Sephadex G-25.

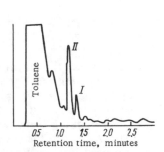

FIGURE 33. Gas chromatography of the oxidation products of lignosulfonates.

The first fractions contained the highest molecular lignosulfonic acids, the molecular size of which exceeded the distance between the macromolecules of the cross-linked dextran. Accordingly, the high-molecular lignosulfonic acids were not retained by Sephadex and emerged with the first eluent fractions. Oligomeric lignosulfonic acids penetrated inside the Sephadex layer, and the depth of the penetration increased with decreasing molecular size of the acids. When eluted with water, these components were the last to emerge into the filtrate.

The study of the properties of the isolated oligomeric lignosulfonic acids ("hemilignins," by analogy with hemicelluloses) led the authors /50/ to the conclusion that spruce lignin consists of identical repeating links. Each such link contains 16 guaiacylpropane and two p-hydroxyphenylpropane units. Each 5—10 phenylpropane unit contains 5 phenolic hydroxyls; the repeating link also contains carbonyl groups.

Molecular weight fractionation of lignosulfonates can also be effected by different methods /51/ such as dialysis /52/. Pearl et al. /53/ studied the lignanes of sulfite liquor by chromatographic methods. These methods were employed in studying the compositions of reaction mixtures obtained as a result of various chemical transformations involving lignosulfonates and lignosulfonic acids. Electrophoresis was successfully employed /54, 55/ in a study of the composition of the products of alkaline cleavage of

137

lignosulfonates. Chlorinated calcium lignosulfonates, obtained in the course of the sulfite cook, were isolated by passing the solution through a column filled with Amberlite IR-45 in the OH-form /56/.

In order to have an experimental confirmation of the presence of pyrocatechol groupings in conifer lignosulfonates, the latter were successively ethylated with diethyl sulfate, oxidized with potassium permanganate and methylated with methanol /57/. The reaction products were studied by the method of gas chromatography; length of column 2 meters, stationary phase Apiezone L, column temperature 250°, flow rate of carrier gas (hydrogen) 50 ml/min. Large peaks of methyl 3,4-diethoxybenzoate (I) and methyl 3-methoxy-4-ethoxybenzoate (II) (Figure 33) were identified in the chromatogram:

COOMe     (I)      COOMe     (II)

OEt, OEt      OMe, OEt

The formation of (I) is a direct confirmation of the presence of pyrocatechol groupings in lignosulfonates. These groupings are formed during demethylation of free guaiacyl groups of lignin in the process of sulfite cook; this was additionally confirmed by boiling vanillyl alcohol with the sulfite cooking liquor.

Glennie /58/ studied the polymerization (mainly dimerization) of monomeric model lignosulfonates during the sulfonation. The sulfonates were prepared by treating the corresponding alcohols with aqueous $NaHSO_3$. Coniferyl sulfonate, vinyl vanillyl sulfonate, coniferyl benzoate, coniferyl alcohol, vinyl syringyl sulfonate, sinapyl alcohol, vinyl veratryl sulfonate and 3,4-dimethoxycinnamyl alcohol were sulfonated by a solution of $NaHSO_3$ and/or $Na_2SO_3$ and/or hydrolyzed by a solution of NaOH. The sulfonates in the reaction mixture were separated by ion exchange chromatography on Dowex 50 W($\times$2) resin in the acid form. The size of the column was 14.7×1.7 cm; the eluate was examined by spectrophotometry. The reaction products were also analyzed by thin layer chromatography on silica gel G with two systems of solvents: n-butanol:water = 88:12 and n-butanol:n-propanol:water:acetic acid = 22:18:10:1. The fluorescing spots were detected in the UV light; the spraying agents were diazotized 2-amino-4-nitroanisole and a 5% solution of NaOH /59/. It was found that a partial dimerization and polymerization of monomeric sulfonates occurs during the sulfonation. The products thus formed could not be isolated pure, but ion exchange and thin layer chromatography was useful in classifying the products of the reaction. Alkaline hydrolysis is accompanied by desulfonation, the main reaction products being the corresponding cinnamic alcohols. A similar treatment of conifer wood also yielded monomeric and dimeric components.

Analysis of sulfite liquors

The main components of sulfite liquors are lignosulfonic acids in the form of salts, monosaccharides, oligosaccharides, water-soluble hemicelluloses, organic acids, organic and inorganic sulfur compounds, etc. For data on the composition of liquors, see /45, 60, 61/.

It has been known for a long time /62/ that lignosulfonates of sulfite liquors are adsorbed on solid surfaces.

When sulfite liquor is passed through an $Al_2O_3$ column, fluorescing zones are formed /63/, which indicates that the components of the liquor become separated. More recent analyses of sulfite liquors involved extensive use of chromatographic methods /45, 61, 64, etc./. Chromatography is also employed in the analysis of sulfur compounds in the sulfite liquor /65, 66/.

**Determination of carbohydrates in liquors.** Practical utilization of sulfite liquors mainly involves biological processing of the monosaccharides in the liquor to ethanol and to protein fodder yeast. The determination of the sugar composition of the liquor is accordingly very important /67, 68/.

It has been seen that carbohydrates may be isolated from sulfite liquor and separated from lignosulfonates by ion exchange chromatography /69, 70/. However, sugars are considerably altered /71/ on contact with ion exchange resins of the type of Dowex-1(×2) and 2(×2) in the OH-form. The eluate contained products of epimerization of arabinose /72/ and organic acids /73/ formed from the sugars on strongly basic ion exchangers. In order to obviate these difficulties, it has been recommended /71/ to use the ion exchangers in the carbonate form; paper chromatography showed that the sugars are not altered or sorbed on such resins.

Various modifications of paper chromatography are widely employed /74, 75/ in quantitative determination of sugars. Thus, it was shown as early as 1952 /76/ that sulfite liquors contain xylose, arabinose, mannose, glucose and galactose; fructose is absent. Different methods have been proposed for quantitative determination of sugars in sulfite liquors /77, 78/.

Sugars have been separated from sulfite liquor /79/ by dialysis and ion exchange and separated on paper by development with n-butanol: ethanol: water = 40:11:19.

An improved method for the determination of carbohydrates in sulfite liquors was developed by Inshakov and Sivkova /80/ who determined sugars by determining the optical densities of colored extracts from the revealed spots on an FEK-M photoelectric colorimeter. Calibration curves for the determination of galactose, glucose, mannose, arabinose and xylose in various concentrations have been plotted.

A chromatometer has been employed /81/ in a quantitative estimation of sugars after separation on paper. The contents of low-molecular fatty acids in sulfite liquor have been determined in the same manner as hydroxamic compounds and as aromatic acidic, aldehydic and phenolic compounds.

Qualitative and quantitative determination of the composition of sugars in sulfite liquors was preceded /82, 83/ by removal of all cations on a cation exchanger column, when two chromatograms were obtained. Galactose, glucose and xylose were separated by development with pyridine: ethyl acetate: water = 1:2.5:3.5, while mannose, arabinose and xylose were separated in the system acetic acid: ethyl acetate: water = 1:3:3. The spots were revealed with aniline phthalate, and the color intensity measured on a Zeiss leucometer. The following contents of individual sugars in the liquor were found (g/l): galactose 1.4 — 4.4; glucose 6.2 — 6.6; mannose 8.6 — 13.0; traces of arabinose; xylose 5.3 — 6.6. The experimental error was 5 — 13%.

Usacheva and Sapotnitskii /84/ used paper chromatographic techniques in their study of the composition of sugars in sulfite liquors, obtained during the manufacture of semichemical pulp. Good separation of sugars was obtained by developing with n-butanol: pyridine: water = 6:4:3; the system pyridine: ethyl acetate: water = 5:1:5 will also separate sugars, but since the sulfite liquor resulting from semichemical pulping contains many noninvert sugars, the spots are blurred and the chromatogram is unsuitable for quantitative work /85/.

Paper chromatography was also employed in determining the variation in the sugar composition of sulfite liquors during industrial breeding of yeast strains /86/ and mycellial fungi /87/ for protein fodder.

A method for the analysis of wastes, in particular, sulfite liquors, by paper chromatography has been developed /88/. Determinations of glucose, galactose, mannose, xylose and arabinose, and of volatile acids and other components of sulfite liquors resulting from various sulfite cooks, were performed by this method.

Chene et al. /89/ studied the variation in the composition of the liquor during the monosulfite pulping of birchwood at 170°. Samples were taken at the beginning of the cook, and 45 minutes, 2 hours and 5 hours later. The liquor was dialyzed, the dialyzate concentrated and the aldehydes, acids and phenols were extracted with organic solvents. The residue was treated with alcohol and $BaCl_2$ to precipitate lignin, the filtrate was concentrated and the sugars determined by chromatography on paper. The lignin precipitate was hydrolyzed with 72% $H_2SO_4$ and the lignin-bound sugars were determined in the hydrolyzate by the same method.

Prosinski and Pszonka /90/ developed a method for the determination of sulfonated sugars formed during sulfite pulping. They used sulfonated pentoses and hexoses as model compounds. The sulfonated sugars were successfully separated on paper by development with basic solvents.

Tsypkina and Balashova /91/ separated carbohydrate-sulfonic acids from lignosulfonic acids by precipitating the latter with complex salts. Cations were removed from the solution by passing it through an ion exchanger in the H-form.

Paper chromatography served to determine the composition of monosaccharides which had penetrated into the industrial sulfite liquor during the transport of the liquid from the boiler /92/.

A potentially important quantitative technique in the determination of sugars in sulfite liquors is gas-liquid chromatography of the sugars as trimethylsilyl derivatives. It has already been stated that this technique has lately become important in the chemistry of carbohydrates.

**Analysis of organic acids.** Samuelson /93/ was the first to show that the acids in sulfite liquors can be separated. The following sequence of operations has been recommended /94/ in the separation of these acids: a) removal of $Ca^{2+}$ ions from the liquor by passing it through a column with a sulfonated cation exchanger in the H-form; b) filtration of the liquor through a column with strongly basic anion exchanger Dowex-2 (0.2 — 0.3 mm) in the sulfate form. The column retains the low-molecular sulfonic acids, which are then eluted with dilute sulfuric acid; c) separation of weak acids from nonelectrolytes and high-molecular acids by treating the eluent with the weakly basic resin Dowex-3 (0.20 — 0.30 mm); the carboxylic acids are eluted with dilute sulfuric acids and are precipitated as barium salts by the addition of alcohol; d) separation of aldonic acids on a column of cation exchanger.

Aldonic acids are determined /18/ by passing the deionized liquor through a 2×38 cm column with Dowex-1 (×8) cation exchanger in the sulfate-bisulfate form (0.08 — 0.15 mm), when aldonic acids and sugars become adsorbed on the column. The final separation of aldonic acids is effected on a 2×148 cm column with basic anion exchanger Dowex-1(×8) (400 mesh) in the borate form. The elution of individual aldonic acids was effected with a 0.1 M solution of sodium tetraborate and the analysis of the fractions on an automatic analyzer.

The results of the separation of aldonic acids in sulfite liquor are shown in Figure 34. It is seen that satisfactory separation was achieved of all aldonic acids except for gluconic and galactonic acids. These acids can be separated using 0.07 M $Na_4B_2O_7$ as eluent. The following acids were found by this method /95/ in sulfite liquor (g/l): xylonic 1.3; arabonic 0.98; mannonic 1.15; gluconic 0.35; galactonic 1.14.

Chromatography on ion exchangers in the bisulfite form will also separate aldehydes (including furfural and hydroxymethylfurfural) which are formed during sulfite pulping of wood /96/.

**Extractive materials in sulfite liquor.** Chromatographic study /97/ of the composition of extractive substances in sulfite liquors from aspen wood pulping showed that they contain saturated fatty acids $C_{22}$ and $C_{24-26}$.

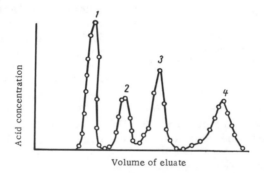

FIGURE 34. Separation of aldonic acids in sulfite liquors by ion exchange chromatography:

1 — xylonic acid; 2 — arabonic acid; 3 — mannonic acid; 4 — gluconic and galactonic acids.

A combination of paper chromatography, column chromatography, adsorption chromatography and partition chromatography established /98, 99/ the composition of the ether-soluble components in the liquor. Those identified /100/ included vanillin, syringaldehyde, benzoic, p-hydroxybenzoic, vanillic syringic, ferulic and p-coumaric acids, myristic, palmitic, stearic, oleic, linoeic,and linolenic acids, saturated aliphatic $C_{22}$-alcohols, organosilicon compounds of siloxane type and other compounds.

Compounds found as a result of subsequent investigations /101/ in the ether-soluble fraction include β-sitosterol, derivatives of flavone and flavononaringenin (5, 7, 4'-trihydroxyflavonone), morin (3, 5, 7, 2', 4'-pentahydroxyflavonone) and 4', 5, 7-trihydroxy-3'-methoxyflavone. 2, 6-Dimethoxyphenol /102/ was detected in the products of oxidation of liquors in the presence of CuO, by chromatography on paper. Sulfite liquor from the pulping of aspen wood also contains /103, 104/ sugars, glucosides, lignosulfonic and aldonic acids, which are insoluble in ether but soluble in water.

Guaiacyl propyl ketone has been isolated /105/ by the chromatographic technique from the sulfite liquors residual from the pulping of pinewood.

Hrutfiord and McCarthy /106/ studied the composition of the volatile components steam-distilled from the spent sulfite liquors from pulping western hemlock, white fir and pine wood in the presence of calcium and ammonium bases. Prior to chromatographic separation the distillate was rectified on a 120×1.8 column with glass spirals. The high-boiling components were extracted from the distillate with ether.

Volatile components were analyzed by gas-liquid chromatography on a Perkin-Elmer 154C chromatograph. The low-boiling compounds were determined on column I (200×0.6 cm) with 20% Ucon LB-550X on Chromosorb W (80 — 100 mesh) and on a similar size column II with 20% di-(2-ethylhexyl) sebacate on the same support; the respective temperatures of the columns were 50 and 60°; the flow rate of carrier gas (helium) was 70 ml/min. The components were also preparatively separated on a 200×2.5 cm column with 20% Ucon LB-550X on Chromosorb; the separated substances were trapped by freezing.

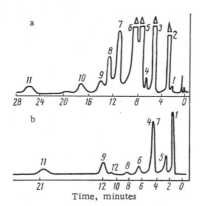

FIGURE 35. Chromatograms of volatile components of sulfite liquors:

a — column I; b — column II; 1 — acetaldehyde; 2 — sulfur dioxide; 3 — acetone; 4 — methyl acetate; 5 — methanol; 6 — dimethyl acetal; 7 — ethanol; 8 — ethyl acetate; 9 — methyl ethyl acetal; 10 — not identified; 11 — acetal; 12 — diethyl acetal.

TABLE 24. Contents of volatile components in sulfite liquors

| Component | Temperature of analysis, °C and No. of column | Retention time, min | Concentration of component, grams per liter of liquor |
|---|---|---|---|
| Acetaldehyde . . . . . . . . . . | 50 (I) | 2.0 | Traces |
| Acetone . . . . . . . . . . . . | 50 (I) | 4.9 | Traces |
| Methanol . . . . . . . . . . . | 50 (I) | 7.0 | 0.39 − 0.73 |
| Ethanol . . . . . . . . . . . . | 50 (I) | 10.9 | 0.20 |
| Methylglyoxal . . . . . . . . . . | 60 (II) | 10.6 | Traces |
| Formic acid . . . . . . . . . . . | 120 (II) | 3.7 | − |
| Acetic acid . . . . . . . . . . . | 120 (II) | 5.1 | 5.0 |
| Furfural . . . . . . . . . . . . . | 150 (I) | 7.0 | 0.23 |
| p–Cymene . . . . . . . . . . . . . | 150 (I) | 11.0 | 0.001 − 0.018 |
| 5-Methylfurfural . . . . . . . . | 150 (I) | 14.0 | 0.003 − 0.013 |

The high-boiling components were analyzed on column I at 150°, flow rate of carrier gas (helium) 66 ml/minute. Acetic and formic acids were determined on column II, 10% sebacic acid was added to the stationary phase; the analysis was carried out at 120°. The content of methanol in water was determined on a 200×0.6 cm column with Carbowax 1500 on

powdered Teflon. Furfural and acetic acid in water were determined on a
350×0.6 cm column with 10% Ucon LB-550X on powdered Teflon at 150°.
p-Cymene and 5-methylfurfural were determined on column I at 150°.

The compounds were identified by the retention times, IR spectra and
2,4-dinitrophenylhydrazones of the carbonyl compounds.

The results of the quantitative determinations of the volatile components
of sulfite liquors are shown in Table 24.

Figure 35 shows the results of the analysis of volatile components
distilled off sulfite liquor and rectified.

The composition of the sulfite liquor depends on the tree species pulped
and on the identity of the cation.


## Analysis of relief gas

The condensate of the volatile compounds in relief gas obtained in acid
sodium bisulfite cooking of the wood of Pinus radiata was studied by
chromatographic techniques; eugenol was identified in the condensate /107/.

A subsequent publication /108/ deals with the study of three fractions
of the condensate:

a) acidic fraction, soluble in sodium bicarbonate solution;

b) phenolic fraction, soluble in NaOH;

c) fraction containing terpenes and other substances.

All fractions were examined chromatographically, by column, paper,
gas-liquid and thin layer techniques.

Column chromatography on alumina was employed to achieve a partial
separation of phenolic components. The resulting fractions were then
analyzed by paper chromatography. Eugenol and isoeugenol were partly
separated on silica gel by eluting with petroleum ether. Coarse fractionation
of the neutral fraction was performed on the same column, with petroleum
ether (bp 80° — 100°) containing increasing amounts of ether.

Paper chromatography was employed in the separation of components
of various fractions. A good separation of eugenol from isoeugenol was
attained on paper impregnated with dimethylformamide; the mobile phase
was a mixture of dimethylformamide with water, cyclohexane and ethyl
acetate /109/. The solvent was prepared by mixing a 5:2 solution of
dimethylformamide with water with the system cyclohexane : ethyl acetate =
5:1. This fraction was also separated by the method of Freudenberg and
Lehmann /110/ who used the system xylene : dimethylformamide = 9:2
as the mobile phase; the paper had been preliminarily impregnated
with dimethylformamide. The spots were revealed by spraying with
diazotized sulfanilic acid.

Vanillin and acetovanillone were separated on paper impregnated with
borate /111/. Alcoholic solutions of ammonia were employed to separate
aliphatic acid, especially formic and acetic acids /112/. Terpenic
hydrocarbons were separated by chromatography on a thin layer of
kieselguhr mixed with starch; a 15% solution of ethyl acetate in hexane
was used as the mobile phase.

Gas-liquid chromatography was employed in the study of the phenolic
and neutral fractions. The components were separated on a Perkin-Elmer
154D chromatograph, with thermistor detector; helium was used as the

carrier gas. The components were sampled in vessels cooled by liquid nitrogen and were then examined by UV- and IR-spectroscopy.

The main component of the acid fraction was acetic acid; formic acid was also present. The approximate contents of a number of components were determined as follows (in g/l): eugenol and isoeugenol 0.5; guaiacol 0.04; vanillin 0.6; furfural 0.1. Neutral substances (terpenes) could be satisfactorily separated, but were not identified.

### Analysis of products of alkaline oxidation of lignosulfonates

The oxidation of lignosulfonates in alkaline medium by atmospheric oxygen at elevated temperatures is accompanied by the formation of vanillin, vanillic acid, guaiacol, acetovanillone and other compounds with a guaiacyl nucleus. This reaction forms the basis of the production of vanillin from sulfite liquors.

The reaction mixtures involved in the process of manufacture of vanillin are analyzed by chemical methods and also by chromatography /115/ and electrophoresis /114/.

The major impurity in the crude vanillin concentrate is acetovanillone, the concentration of which is 5 — 10% /116/. Acetovanillone in oxidized sulfite liquor was determined /117/ by paper chromatography. To separate vanillin and p-hydroxybenzaldehyde from acetovanillone and vanillal, the sample was applied to the paper strip and covered with 0.1 ml of a warm 41% solution of sodium metabisulfite. The components were separated with n-buranol (bp 141—143°) during $2^1/_2$ hours, the chromatogram dried, held over ammonia vapor and the acetovanillone located in UV light. The acetovanillone zone was extracted with phosphate buffer and its content determined by electrophoresis.

The separation of vanillin from acetovanillone is facilitated if the chromatographic paper has been previously treated with sodium bisulfite /118/ or with a solution of borax /119/.

A quantitative determination of vanillin and acetovanillone in sulfite liquor has been described /120/. The components are best separated on Schleicher and Schull paper No. 2043; the solvent is the top layer of the mixture of n-butanol with a solution of sodium bisulfite, adjusted to pH 9.5 with ammonia. At 20° the components can be separated in 16 hours. The spots are revealed by spraying with a 0.5% solution of diazotized p-sulfanilic acid in a 5% solution of sodium carbonate. The final determination is spectrophotometric.

This method was used in a study of the kinetics of formation of vanillin during the atmospheric oxidation of sulfite liquor, in quality control of the final product, in the analysis of the products of alkaline nitrobenzene oxidation of lignin preparations and in the quality evaluation of wood.

Other workers /121/ also reported that vanillin in sulfite liquor can be determined by chromatography.

Paper chromatography was employed in the determination of the degree of purity of technical grade vanillin obtained from lignosulfonates /122/. The purity of the vanillin obtained from the wastes of vanillin synthesis by the nitroso method is determined /123/ by chromatography on a thin layer of alumina (benzene : ethanol = 5 : 1; $R_f = 0.066$) or silica gel (hexane : ether =

1 : 5; $R_f = 0.45$). In the latter case guaiacol ($R_f = 0.71$) which is present as an impurity, is also detected.

Thin layer chromatography may be employed /124/ in the determination of vanillin and ethylvanillin in technical products.

Chromatography of vanillin and vanillin homologues has also been studied by other workers /125 — 127/. A recent development is the use of gas-liquid chromatography in these investigations /128/.

It should finally be mentioned that many of the methods described in this section may be of interest for industrial production control. In particular, the rapid quantitative analysis of sulfite liquor can be utilized in choosing the parameters of the cook, and also in the biochemical processing of the liquor. In the manufacture of protein fodder yeast it is very important to determine not only sugars, but also the organic acids in the liquor, many of which are utilized by the yeasts.

BIBLIOGRAPHY

1. DICKEY, E. E. — Tappi, 38(3): A138 — A139. 1955.
2. DICKEY, E. E. — Tappi, 39(10): 735 — 736. 1956.
3. DOSTAL, E. J. — Pulp and Paper Mag. Canada, 60(5): T141 — T147. 1959.
4. JANSON, J. and E. SJÖSTRÖM. — Svensk Papperstidn., 67(19): 764 — 771. 1964.
5. CROON, I., B. F. ENSTRÖM, and S. A. RYDHOLM. — Svensk Papperstidn., 67(5): 196 — 199. 1964.
6. RUSTEN, D. — Norsk Skogind., 16(8): 328 — 339. 1962.
7. HAMILTON, J. K. — Pure and Appl. Chem., 5(1 — 2): 197 — 217. 1962.
8. NEPENIN, N. N. and E. I. KOSILOVA. — Trudy Leningradskoi Lesotekhnicheskoi Akademii, Vol. 85: 21 — 30. 1960.
9. TSYPKINA, M. N. — In: Sbornik "Avtomatika i novaya tekhnika v proizvodstve tsellyulozy," pp. 78 — 88. Goslesbumizdat. 1957.
10. HARDELL, H. -L. and O. THEANDER. — Svensk Papperstidn., 68(14): 482 — 485. 1965.
11. SAMUELSON, O. — Das Papier, 16(10a): 512 — 518. 1962.
12. SAMUELSON, O. — Svensk Papperstidn., 61(17): 531 — 539. 1958.
13. SAMUELSON, O. and K. J. LJUNGQVIST. — Svensk Papperstidn., 61(24): 1043 — 1049. 1958.
14. ALFREDSON, B., L. GEDDA, and O. SAMUELSON. — Svensk Papperstidn., 63 (21): 758 — 761. 1960.
15. ERIKSSON, E. and O. SAMUELSON. — Svensk Papperstidn., 65(16): 600 — 605. 1962.
16. ERIKSSON, E. and O. SAMUELSON. — Svensk Papperstidn., 64(4): 138. 1961.
17. ERIKSSON, E. and O. SAMUELSON. — Svensk Papperstidn., 66(8): 298 — 300. 1963.
18. SAMUELSON, O. and R. SIMONSON. — Svensk Papperstidn., 65(9): 363 — 369. 1962.
19. SAMUELSON, O. and R. SIMONSON. — Svensk Papperstidn., Vol. 65: 685. 1962.
20. YEAN, W. Q. and D. A. I. GORING. — Tappi, 47(1): 16 — 19. 1964.
21. YEAN, W. Q. and D. A. GORING. — Pulp and Paper Mag. Canada, 65C, T127 — T132. 1964.
22. SJÖSTRÖM, E., P. HAGLUND, and J. JONSON. — Svensk Papperstidn., 65(21): 855 — 869. 1962.
23. GIERER, J., B. LENZ, I. NORES, and S. SÖDERBERG. — Tappi, 47(4): 233 — 239. 1964.
24. GORING, D. A. I. and A. REZANOWICH. — Canad. J. Chem., 36(12): 1653 — 1661. 1958.
25. QUICK, R. — Tappi, Vol. 39: 357. 1956.
26. SUNDMAN, J. Paperi ja puu, 32(9): 267. 1950.
27. BUTKO, Yu. G. — Trudy LTI TsBP, Goslesbumizdat, No. 4: 120. 1956.
28. HEWITT, D. G. and P. F. NELSON. — Holzforschung, 19(4): 97 — 101. 1965.
29. NELSON, P. F. — Holzforschung, 19(4): 102 — 105. 1965.
30. JAMES, A. N. and P. A. TICE. — Tappi, 48(4): 239 — 244. 1965.
31. ERIKSSON, E. and O. SAMUELSON. — Svensk Papperstidn., 67(5): 182 — 185. 1964.
32. PEARL, I. A. and D. L. BEYER. — Forest Prod. J., 9(10): 381 — 383. 1959.
33. FELICETTA, V. F., M. LUNG, and J. L. McCARTHY. — Tappi, 42(6): 496 — 502. 1959.
34. PEARL, I. A. and D. L. BEYER. — Forest Prod. J., 11(9): 442 — 444. 1961.
35. JAMES, A. N. and P. A. TICE. — Tappi, 47(1): 43 — 47. 1964.

36. FELICETTA, V. F., A. AHOLA, and J. L. McCARTHY. — J. Am. Chem. Soc., 78(9): 1899—1904. 1956.
37. GORING D. A. I., T. WEBB, and A. H. SEHON. — Svensk Papperstidn., 61(23): 1010—1015. 1958.
38. SAPOTNITSKII, S. A., A. K. EDOMINA, and R. M. MYASNIKOVA. — Sbornik Trudov VNIIGS, Izdatel'stvo Lesnaya Promyshlennost', No. 13: 293—297. 1965.
39. HARRIS, E. E. and D. HOGAN. — Ind. Eng. Chem., 49(9): 1393. 1957.
40. BORECKY, J. — Chem. Prumysl., 13(5): 248—249. 1963.
41. PEARL, I. A. and D. L. BEYER. — Tappi, 43(6): 568—572. 1960.
42. BEECKMANS, J. — Canad. J. Chem., 40(2): 265—274. 1962.
43. BENKO, J. — Tappi, 44(11): 766—771, 771—775. 1961.
44. MOTHERSHEAD, J. S. and D. W. GLENNIE. — Tappi, 47(8): 519—524. 1964.
45. FORSS, K. The Composition of a Spent Spruce Sulfite Liquor. — S. 1. Abo Akad., 148 pp. 1961.
46. FORSS, K. and K. E. FREMER. — Paperi ja Puu, 43(11): 676—679. 1962.
47. JENSEN, W., K. E. FREMER, and K. FORSS. — Tappi, 45(2): 122—127. 1962.
48. FORSS, K. and K. E. FREMER. — Tappi, 47(8): 485—493. 1964.
49. FORSS, K. and K. E. FREMER. — Paperi ja Puu, 47(8): 443—454. 1965.
50. FORSS, K. — Kem. Teoll., 22(11): 872—877. 1965.
51. CORO, M. and K. XATA. — J. Japan Wood Res. Soc., 10(4): 136—140. 1964.
52. SCHWABE, K. and L. HASNER. — Cellulose-Chemie, Vol. 20: 61. 1942.
53. PEARL, I. A., D. L. BEYER, and E. E. DICKEY. — J. Organ. Chem., 23(5): 705—706. 1958.
54. DEVIS, R. E., E. T. REAVILLE, Q. P. PENISTON, and J. L. McCARTHY. — J. Am. Chem. Soc., 77(9): 2405—2409. 1955.
55. GLENNIE, D. W., H. TECHLENBERG, E. T. REAVILLE, and J. L. McCARTHY. — J. Am. Chem. Soc., 77(9): 2409—2412. 1955.
56. NAKAJMA, K., M. OKUBA, and S. ONOE. — J. Japan Techn. Assoc. Pulp and Paper Ind., 18(6): 228—234. 1964.
57. HAYASHI, A. and Y. NAMURA. — Bull. Chem. Soc. Japan, 38(3): 512—513. 1965.
58. GLENNIE, D. W. — Tappi, 49(6): 237—243. 1966.
59. MOTHERSHEAD, J. S. and D. W. GLENNIE. — Tappi, 47(8): 519. 1964.
60. SAPOTNITSKII, S. A. Ispol'zevanie sul'fitnykh shchelokov (Utilization of Sulfite Liquors). — Goslesbumizdat. 1960.
61. WENZL, H. F. J. — Paper Trade J., 149(22): 47—49. 1965.
62. LYUTIN, L. V. and G. V. ZAKHAROVA. — Mineral'noe Syr'e, No. 1. 1933.
63. SCHRÖTER, G. A. — Pap. Fabr. Woch., No. 2: 50—54. 1943.
64. KVASNICKA, E. A. and R. R. McLAUGHLIN. — Can. J. Chem., 33(4): 637—645. 1955.
65. POLČIN, J. — Chem. Zvesti, 11(8) 494—497. 1957.
66. SCHÖÖN, N. -H. Svensk Papperstidn., 65(19): 729—754. 1962.
67. BUTKO, Yu. G. — Author's Summary of Candidate's Thesis. Leningrad. 1953.
68. TODA, H. and T. HAMADA. — J. Japan. Techn. Assoc. Pulp and Paper Ind., 11(7): 429—432; No. 8: 489—495. 1957.
69. SHAW, A. C. — Pulp and Paper Mag. Canada, 57(1): 95—97. 1956; 58(10): 170—171. 1957.
70. SHAW, A. C. — Canad. Pulp and Paper Ind., 10(11): 49—50. 1957.
71. SHAW, A. C. and M. DIGNAM. — Canad. J. Chem., 35(4): 322—332. 1957.
72. JERMYN, M. A. and R. R. ISHERWOOD. — Biochem. J., 44: 402. 1949.
73. PHILLIPS, J. D. and A. POLLARD. — Nature, Vol. 171: 41. 1953.
74. TODA, H. and T. HAMADA. — Bull. Inst. Pap. Chem., Vol. 28: 328. 1957.
75. SATO, K., Y. MATSUMURA, and R. MIYAKAWA. — Svensk Papperstidn., Vol. 3: 68. 1958.
76. BOGGS, L. A. — Analyt. Chem., Vol. 24: 1673—1675. 1952.
77. RENTZ, A. — Das Papier, 10(9—10): 192—200. 1956.
78. ANT-WUORINEN, O. and A. HALONEN. — Paperi ja Puu, 40(10): 481. 1958.
79. KOBAYASHI, K. — Wood Res., 9(26): 6—9. Kyoto. 1961.
80. INSHAKOV, M. D. and A. P. SIVKOVA. — Nauchno-Tekhnicheskaya Informatsiya TsBTI Bumdrevproma, No. 2: 40—48. 1961.
81. FAULHABER, M., W. FRANKE, and H. SCHRÖDER. — Materialprüfung, 4(3): 94—101. 1962.
82. PSZONKA, B. — Przegl Papiern., 17(9): 262—265. 1961.
83. PSZONKA, B. — Chem. Analit., 7(3): 667—672. Poland. 1962.
84. USACHEVA, V. T. and S. A. SAPOTNITSKII, — Sbornik Trudov NIIGS, Goslesbumizdat, Vol. 10: 215—218. 1962.
85. EMEL'YANOVA, I. Z. and T. A. BATRAKOVA. — ZhAKh, 13(1): 142. 1958.

86. SEMUSHKINA, T. N. – Sbornik Trudov VNIIGS, Izdatel'stvo Lesnaya Promyshlennost', No. 13: 69–76. 1965.
87. SEMUSHKINA, T. N. and N. I. MONAKHOVA. – Sbornik Trudov VNIIGS, Izdatel'stvo Lesnaya Promyshlennost', No. 14: 98–105. 1965.
88. ENEBO, L., J. RENNERFELT, M. STIGELL, and L. O. WILLARD. – Svensk Papperstidn., 67(1): 1–3. 1964.
89. CHÊNE, M., A. ROBERT, and R. GRANT. – Bull. Assoc. Techn. Ind. Papet., 17(3): 175–181. 1963.
90. PROSINSKI, S. and B. PSZONKA. – Przegl. Papiern., 21(5): 140–144. 1965.
91. TSYPKINA, M. N. and I. M. BALASHOVA. – ZhPKh, 32(1): 166–170. 1959.
92. SIHTOLA, H., B. ANTHONI, and E. ROSQVIST. – Paperi ja Puu, 40(10): 493–494. 1958.
93. SAMUELSON, O. – Svensk Papperstidn., Vol. 46: 583. 1943.
94. BERNTSSON, S. and O. SAMUELSON. – Svensk Papperstidn., 60(10): 389–391. 1957.
95. NORD, S. I., O. SAMUELSON, and R. SIMONSON. – Svensk Papperstidn., 65(19): 767–769. 1962.
96. CHRISTOFFERSON, K. – Analyt. Chim. Acta, 33(3): 303–310. 1965.
97. PEARL, I. A. and O. JUSTMAN. – J. Organ. Chem., 26(9): 3563–3564. 1961.
98. PEARL, I. A. and D. L. BEYER. – J. Organ. Chem., 26(2): 546–550. 1961.
99. PEARL, I. A. and P. F. McCOY. – J. Organ. Chem., 26(2): 550–552. 1961.
100. PEARL, I. A., D. L. BEYER, and O. JUSTMAN. – Tappi, 45(2): 107–113. 1962.
101. PEARL, I. A. and D. L. BEYER. – Tappi, 46(8): 502–505. 1963.
102. PEARL, I. A. and D. L. BEYER. – Forest Prod. J., 14(7): 316–318. 1964.
103. PEARL, I. A. and D. L. BEYER. – Tappi, 47(8): 458–462. 1964; 47(12): 779–782. 1964.
104. BIGGS, W. A., W. R. COOK, and I. A. PEARL. – Forest Prod. J., 13(10): 433–437. 1963.
105. KRATZL, K. and E. KLEIN. – Monatsh. Chem., 86(5): 847–852. 1955.
106. HRUTFIORD, B. F. and J. L. McCARTHY. – Tappi, 47(7): 381–386. 1964.
107. NELSON, P. F. and C. G. KALKIPSAKIS. – Holzforschung, 16(6): 189–190. 1962.
108. NELSON, P. F. and C. G. KALKIPSAKIS. – Holzforschung, 17(5): 134–138. 1963.
109. SUNDT, E. – J. Chromatogr., Vol. 6: 475. 1961.
110. FREUDENBERG, K. and B. LEHMANN. – Chem. Ber., Vol. 93: 1354. 1960.
111. BLAND, D. E. – Nature, Vol. 164: 1093. 1949.
112. KENNEDY, E. P. and H. A. BARKER. – Analyt. Chem., Vol. 23: 420. 1951.
113. KIRCHNER, J. G., J. M. MILLER, and G. KELLER. – J. Analyt. Chem., Vol. 23: 420. 1951.
114. PENISTON, Q. et al. – Analyt. Chem., Vol. 23: 994. 1951.
115. STONE, J. E. and M. BLUNDELL. – Analyt. Chem., Vol. 23: 771. 1951.
116. FOWLER, L., H. R. KLINE, and R. S. MITCHELL. – Analyt. Chem., 27(11): 1688–1690. 1955.
117. REAVILLE, E. T. and G. W. SHREVE. – Analyt. Chem., 27(4): 565–566. 1955.
118. NEWCOMBE, A. G. and S. C. REID. – Nature, Vol. 172: 455. 1953.
119. BLAND, D. E. and C. STAMP. – Pulp Paper Mag. Can., Vol. 57: 158. 1956.
120. TÖPPEL, O. – Das Papier, 15(5): 177–186. 1961.
121. FELICETTA, V. F. and J. L. McCARTHY. – Tappi, 46(6): 351–354. 1963.
122. ZUSZCZYŃSKA-FLORIAN, B. and A. ANDRELOWICZ. – Roczn. Państw. Zakl. Hig., 13(6): 541–552. 1962.
123. TERENT'EV, A. P. et al. – ZhAKh, 19(11): 1414. 1964.
124. BLANC, P., P. BERTRAND, G. SAQUI-SANNES, and R. LESCURE. – Chim. Analyt., 47(7): 354–356. 1965.
125. NIVOLI, M. – Ann. Chimica, 43(1): 38–39. 1953.
126. VONÁSEK, F. – Prumysl. Potravin., 9(6): 315–316. 1958.
127. PEARL, I. A., D. L. BEYER, and D. LASKOWSKI. – J. Organ. Chem., 24(3): 443. 1959.
128. MARTIN, G. E., F. J. FEENY, and F. P. SEARINGELLI. – J. Assoc. Offic. Agric. Chemists, 47(3): 561–562. 1964.

## 2. Analysis of products of the sulfate pulp industry

This section deals with the application of chromatographic methods to the study of the changes in polysaccharides and lignin produced by alkali cooks, to the analysis of black sulfate liquor and the side products — sulfate soap and tall oil, as well as gaseous sulfur compounds formed during the cooking and burning of the black liquor.

## Behavior of polysaccharides during alkali cooking

The yield of the pulp obtained by cooking is determined by the stability of the polysaccharides to alkaline agents; accordingly, the changes undergone by hemicelluloses /2, 3/ and individual polysaccharides during alkali cooks have been extensively studied /1/.

A number of workers /4—7/ used paper chromatography in combination with cation exchange in their studies of the transformations of hemicelluloses as a result of sulfate pulping.

Paper chromatography has been applied /8/ to the study of the delignification of larchwood by the sulfate method. The carbohydrate content was determined in the initial wood, in the residue from prehydrolysis with water, after each delignification stage and in the extract after water prehydrolysis. Prior to the chromatographic analysis the products were hydrolyzed and neutralized by passing through an AN-1 anion exchanger column until the residual sulfate content was 0.5%. The resulting solutions were evaporated in vacuo and chromatogrammed on paper. If the glucose content in the mixture is high, this sugar is separated from galactose and mannose only with difficulty. In order to improve the separation of these components, two solvent systems were used in succession: a) ethyl acetate: pyridine: water = 100:20:100, and b) benzene: n-propanol: acetic acid: water = 40:20:10:5. The sugars become separated in 3-4 days. The spots were revealed at 80° for 20 minutes, and the colored spots were extracted with methanol.

This method was used in the study of the solubilization of the various polysaccharide components of wood during the prehydrolysis with water and the sulfate cook. It was shown, for example, that the low content of mannan in sulfate pulp is explained by its more rapid solubilization as compared to xylan.

The behavior of 4-o-methyl-D-glucuronoxylan during sulfate cooking was studied by ion exchange chromatography /9/. The xylan had been isolated by extracting sulfate pulp with 5% aqueous NaOH, dissolved in 72% sulfuric acid, diluted with water and heated on the water bath. The resulting hydrolyzate was neutralized to pH 3.5 with saturated $Ba(OH)_2$, filtered through celite and treated with Amberlite IR-120 cation exchanger in the H-form.

Uronic acids were sorbed on a $40 \times 3.5$ cm column of Dowex-2 anion exchanger in the acetate form, and the acids were eluted with a solution of acetic acid of gradually increasing concentration. In this way the neutral sugars and 4-o-methyl-D-glucuronic acid were separated from the aldobiuronic acid which was obtained chromatographically pure. It was found that all fractions of xylan isolated from wood pulp contained 3—10% of the uronic acid.

Various model compounds were employed /10/ in studying the changes produced in the polysaccharides by the sulfate pulping process. Thus, the behavior of three model acids of the type of the free aldobiuronic acid, aldobiuronic acid reduced by sodium borohydride, and reduced aldotetrauronic acid in a 4% solution of NaOH at temperatures not exceeding 100°, was studied /11/. Paper chromatographic methods were employed in the preparation of the initial materials and in the study of their decomposition in alkaline medium. Acid oligosaccharides with differing degrees of

polymerization were separated by the same method /12/. It was shown
that the aldobiuronic acid was unstable under the conditions employed and
that the decomposition rate increased with the temperature. Above 60° the
acid was fully decomposed, and it was suggested that this involved the
rupture of the bond between the glucuronic acid and the xylose residue.
Other model compounds were practically stable at 100° in alkaline medium
and fully stable at room temperature. During the alkali pulping of conifer
wood the addition of borohydride or sodium polysulfide prevents the
decomposition of glucomannan, so that the yield of the pulp increases;
the yield of xylan may be expected to be higher during the pulping of
deciduous wood.


Alterations in lignin during sulfate pulping

   The main process involved in pulping is the dissolution of the lignin in
the alkaline medium under suitable working conditions. The mechanism
of solubilization of lignin during the cook was accordingly studied by many
workers and work on the subject is still continuing. The alterations
in lignin resulting from sulfate cooking have been studied on both model
compounds and on different preparations of lignin and wood.
   Sulfate cooks of vanillyl alcohol and of lignin preparations were studied
under various conditions /13/. Chromatographic analysis of the ether-
soluble substances in industrial sulfate liquors— pyrocatechol, protocatechuic
aldehyde and phenolic carboxylic acids — proved that during the sulfate
cook the methoxyl groups are demethylated, the $C-C$ bonds are broken and
redox reactions of the Canizzaro type take place.
   A number of studies were performed on model compounds in order to
study the mechanism of the rupture of the alkyl-aryl bonds by alkalis /14/.
   In order to confirm the mechanism /15/ of the transformations of lignin
during sulfate cook, the behavior of a number of synthetic model substances
acted upon by white liquor (3.5 g NaOH and 3.1 g $Na_2S \cdot 9H_2O$ in 100 ml
water) and by 2N NaOH was studied /16/. The model compounds were
identified by thin layer chromatography. It was shown that the rupture of
the aryl ether bonds is catalyzed by the sulfide groups which react with
lignin in alkaline medium. An important reaction in this process is the
formation of methylenequinone structures as a result of the action of NaOH
on lignin. Thus, sodium sulfide in white liquor assists in the solubilization
of lignin during sulfate pulping.
   Chromatographic methods were also employed /17/ in a study of the
behavior of lignin during a two-step polysulfide cook involving a preliminary
treatment of the chips with a solution of sodium polysulfide; the conventional
sulfate cook is the second stage. The behavior of vanillyl alcohol treated
with $Na_2S_x$ ($x = 2 - 4$) during $20 - 40$ minutes at 130° has been studied. It
was shown by paper and thin layer chromatography that the main products
of the reaction are vanillyl mono- and disulfides and vanillin. The same
compounds were also identified in the study of the behavior of lignin during
pulping. It has been suggested that the first cooking stage involves the
formation of the sulfide bond at the C-atom in the side chain in the
$\alpha$-position. This bond is opened in the first and second cooking stages with
the result that the carbonyl group content in the lignin increases.

Chromatographic identification of the products of hydrolysis of lignin /18/ was performed in order to identify the strong acidic groups in the lignin isolated from spruce wood during alkaline cook.

The studies of the effect of alkaline cook on lignin involved a combination of different chromatographic techniques. Paper chromatography /19/ served to detect propiovanillone in the spent liquor. Acetic acid was isolated /20/ on a column with silica gel. Chromatography was employed /21/ in a study of the origin of acetovanillone and propiovanillone; paper chromatography and gas-liquid chromatography were employed /22/ in the study of the composition of nonvolatile acids formed during the treatment of sulfate lignin with perbenzoic acid.

The cooking process may be effected by the oxidation of hydrosulfide ions in the presence of phenolic components of wood. These reactions were also studied by paper chromatography /23/.

Chromatography in the chemistry of alkali lignin and sulfate lignin

For a review of literature data on the structure of water-soluble alkali lignin see /24/. Chromatographic methods have been used for a long time in the isolation and analysis of sulfate and alkali lignins, in particular in the analysis of the phenolic components /25, 26/.

Paper chromatography and paper electrophoresis were utilized /27/ in the study of black liquors obtained by two-step sulfate and soda cooks. The black liquor was acidified with hydrochloric acid in the second stage of the cook, the lignin was filtered off and the filtrate treated with ether. The phenolic fraction was isolated /28/ from the ether extract, and was chromatogrammed on paper impregnated with phosphate buffer. When the chromatogram was viewed in UV light, 11 spots fluorescing in different colors were detected. The study of UV spectra showed that most of the compounds were aromatic. A number of components of the ether extract which are not separated by this method could be separated by paper electrophoresis at $pH > 9$.

Phenolic fractions of alkali lignin of white birch were studied by gas-liquid chromatography /29/.

Water-soluble sulfate lignin has been separated and purified in an apparatus which included chromatography on alumina and activated carbon columns /32/.

Since sulfate lignin is highly heterogeneous, even chromatographic methods do not invariably yield homogeneous fractions /30, 31/.

The products of decomposition of Bjorkman lignin, which are formed as a result of treating the lignin with solutions of NaOH or with mixtures of NaOH and $Na_2S$, were separated /33/ on columns with Sephadex C-50-P. The conditions of separation of lignin fractions with different molecular weights were established and molecular weight distribution curves of the lignin plotted. Experiments were also carried out on model substances /34/.

Chromatographic methods are employed in the study of the products of decomposition of alkali lignins. Thus, a chromatographic study of the decomposition of thiolignin on Raney nickel and other reagents was performed by Enkvist et al. /35/. The bulk of the sulfur in the thiolignin was removed by boiling under reflux with Raney nickel in alcohol. The ether-insoluble thiolignin, which constitutes about 4.9% by weight on the protolignin in the wood yields 40% of an ether-soluble product as a result of the reaction. Column chromatography and paper chromatography showed that the compounds present in the product are at least 13 in number, including guaiacylpropanol-1, guaiacylpropanol-3 and also p-propylguaiacol and p-ethylguaiacol.

Analysis of black liquor of the sulfate pulp industry

Black liquors, formed as a result of alkaline cooks, contain mainly lignins and products of alkaline degradation of hemicelluloses. The main products of degradation of polysaccharides under conditions of alkaline pulping are hydroxy acids and lactones /36/, in particular, saccharic acids /37/ and other products with acetyl groups at the ends of the molecule /38, 39/.

Chromatographic methods are widely used in the analysis of black liquors /27, 40/.

Pilyugina and Komshilov /41/ analyzed the hydroxy acids of black sulfate liquor by paper chromatography. The preparation of the black liquor for chromatographic analysis consisted in precipitating the lignin by acidifying the liquor with sulfuric acid. The solution was purified from salts on four columns with KU-1 cation exchanger, while the neutral compounds were purified on a column with AN-1 anion exchanger. The filtrate was neutralized with barium carbonate, evaporated on a water bath and treated with sulfuric acid until the $CO_2$ effervescence ceased. The precipitated barium sulfate was filtered off, and the filtrate with the free acids was chromatogrammed.

The acids were separated on "slow" chromatographic paper manufactured by the Volodarskii plant in Leningrad. Best separation of the acids was attained by development with the upper layer of the system n-butanol: water: 90% formic acid = 18:9:2. The spots were revealed with a 0.04% solution of bromophenol blue; pH 5 was produced by adding a solution of NaOH. The acids were revealed as yellow spots on a blue background.

Lactic, glycolic and levulinic acids were identified in black liquors in this way, with the aid of standard spots produced by genuine compounds. The same acids were also detected in reaction mixtures resulting from the alkaline cook of glucose, arabinose and galactose.

The composition of the volatile acids in the black liquors of the pulp industry was studied /42/ by chromatography on a silica gel column /43/. The dimensions of the column were 400×10 cm, and external pressure was applied to accelerate the filtration rate. Prior to the analysis the column was washed with chloroform saturated with water, until the eluate gave a neutral reaction. Aqueous solutions were utilized in the analysis. In order to prevent a shift in the equilibrium between the stationary and the mobile layer in the column, the moist silica gel was covered with a layer of anhydrous silica gel which had been stirred with chloroform. The amount of the added silica gel should be sufficient to absorb the water introduced with the sample. If the analysis is repeated on the same column, fresh portions of dry silica gel may be added.

The black liquor was prepared for analysis as follows /44/: a sample of the liquor was acidified to pH 1.5 with hydrochloric acid, and the precipitated lignin was filtered off and washed. The filtrate and the wash waters were combined and placed in a 10 — 20 ml pycnometer. The amount of the solution introduced into the column contained not more than 0.25 g acids. The acids are displaced with a solution of n-butanol, in chloroform: valeric acid with 1% solution; butyric acid with 4% solution; propionic acid with 12% solution; acetic acid with 20% solution; formic acid with 30% solution; lactic acid with 50% solution; glycolic acid with 70% solution; oxalic acid with 90% solution. The eluate emerged from the column at a rate of 1 drop per second; each 3 ml of the eluate were titrated against 0.01 N NaOH in methanol /42/.

This method was utilized in the analysis /42, 44/ of black liquors sampled at various stages of the cook and of the evaporation of the liquors. It was shown that as the black liquors are evaporated, their organic acid content decreases (see also /45/).

TABLE 25. Composition of the organic acids in black liquors (% on oven-dry residue of black liquor)

| Acid | Black liquor from semichemical pulping | | | | Nonevaporated liquor from the cooking of bleachable pulp |
|---|---|---|---|---|---|
| | liquor from diffusers, $(d_4^{80} = 1.13)$ | nonevaporated liquor, $(d_4^{80} = 1.13)$ | liquor, additionally heated to $170-172°$ C, $(d_4^{80} = 1.16)$ | evaporated liquor, $(d_4^{80} = 1.376)$ | |
| Valeric . . . . . . . . | 0.14 | 0.08 | 0.07 | 0.17 | 0.07 |
| Butyric . . . . . . . . | 0.35 | 0.14 | 0.06 | 0.24 | 0.18 |
| Propionic . . . . . . . | 0.53 | 0.30 | 0.07 | 0.41 | 0.28 |
| Acetic . . . . . . . . | 4.34 | 2.69 | 2.09 | 2.92 | 2.90 |
| Formic . . . . . . . . | 4.56 | 3.41 | 3.10 | 2.84 | 4.41 |
| Lactic . . . . . . . . | 1.71 | 2.77 | 2.12 | 2.08 | 1.79 |
| Glycolic . . . . . . . | 1.16 | 0.84 | 0.86 | 1.54 | 1.27 |
| Oxalic . . . . . . . . | 0.77 | 0.88 | 0.85 | 1.05 | 0.32 |
| Total . . . . . . | 13.56 | 11.11 | 9.22 | 11.25 | 11.22 |

Table 25 shows the results of analyses of black liquors obtained by cooking pinewood to a semichemical pulp, and of the nonevaporated liquor obtained in cooking the pinewood to a bleachable pulp.

It is seen from the data given in the table that the main organic acids present in black liquors are formic, acetic, lactic and glycolic. An additional heat treatment of black liquor at 170 — 172° during one hour results in a decrease in its content of acids.

The hydroxy acids in black sulfate liquors are separated /46/ by ion exchange chromatography. Saccharic and aldonic acids in mixture with glycolic and lactic acids are determined by this method.

According to a number of workers /38, 39, 47/, black liquors contain a small amount of free sugars. The individual composition of the sugars was established /48/ by paper chromatography.

Prior to the chromatographic analysis, lignin was precipitated from the black liquor by adding a 30% solution of sulfuric acid to pH 3.0— 3.5. The filtrate was neutralized, evaporated, passed through a KU-1 cation exchanger column and analyzed chromatographically. The solvent was a mixture of 100 ml n-butanol, 19 ml glacial acetic acid and 40 ml water, to which water was then added drop by drop until first turbidity, which disappeared after 15 — 20 minutes shaking.

Sugars were separated by the ascending method; 200 — 1000 $\gamma$ of each sugar were applied to the starting line. The chromatogram was dried and sprayed with aniline phthalate to detect the aldoses; ketoses were detected with the aid of a mixture of 90 ml of 96% alcohol, 10 ml of 1% HCl and 1 gram of urea /49/. The sugars were identified by the $R_f$ values of genuine sugar samples.

It was found that black liquors contain small amounts of glucose and arabinose; other sugars were not detected.

Sulfides, thiosulfates and polysulfides in black liquors can be determined /50/ by ion exchange chromatography on columns with the strongly basic resin Dowex-1($\times$8). Thiosulfates and most of the sulfides are eluted with 1 M $NaNO_3$ at 70 — 80°, while the polysulfide sulfur ($S_{k-1}$ in $Na_2S_k$) and the remainder of the sulfides are eluted with a mixture of 1 M $Na_2SO_3$ and $NaNO_3$ at 70 — 80°. The polysulfides in the eluate pass into the thiosulfate; the sulfides and the thiosulfates are determined by potentiometric titration at pH 7.6 and addition of formaldehyde to bind the sulfites.

Ion exchange chromatography is also employed /51/ to determine the iodine-reducing substances in black liquors.

Since the composition of sulfate liquors is complex, a combination of different chromatographic techniques is expediently employed. It is recommended to purify and fractionate the sulfate lignin by ion exchange chromatography and gel filtration; organic acids can be separated by paper or column chromatography, while the volatile components are best determined by gas-liquid chromatography.

**Analysis of products of processing of alkali lignin.** A recent development /52/ is the manufacture of dimethyl sulfide and dimethyl sulfoxide from lignin; these are excellent solvents.

Dimethyl sulfide is analyzed by gas-liquid chromatography /53, 54/. In the preparation of dimethyl sulfide /55/ the alkali lignin was treated with $Na_2S$ in an alkaline medium at 270 — 300°. According to the data yielded by gas-liquid chromatography, the dimethyl sulfide thus obtained contained 87.5% of the main product, while methyl mercaptan was present as impurity. Depending on the experimental conditions (amount of $Na_2S$ in NaOH, pH), the yield of crude dimethyl sulfide was 1.84 — 4.82% on the dry lignin. The crude product was purified by shaking with a solution of NaOH in a separating funnel and subsequent fractional distillation in the presence of granulated NaOH.


Analysis of turpentine and tall oil


Sulfate pulping yields terpenic hydrocarbons and resin acids of the wood in the form of a side product— sulfate turpentine and sulfate soap, from which tall oil is obtained. Distillation of the crude tall oil yields technical grade tall oil and tall resin. These products are valuable and many pulp mills have special units in which sulfate turpentine and sulfate soap are trapped and refined.

The composition of the side products of sulfate pulp industry, in particular of tall oil and tall rosin, has been the subject of numerous studies These products are often analyzed by chromatographic techniques. Thus, in studying the fatty acids of pinewood and tall oil, the techniques employed were chromatography on silica gel /56/ and magnetite /57/. Paper chromatography was employed in qualitative and quantitative analysis of phytosterol in the nonsaponifiable matter of tall rosin /58/; vanillin was detected in the neutral fraction of tall oil /59/.

The compositions of sulfate turpentines produced industrially in different countries were compared /60/. The head fractions of turpentine were separated by chromatography on activated alumina column, with subsequent elution with anhydrous methanol, when heptanone-2 and heptanol-2 in azeotropic mixture with $\alpha$-pinene were obtained. In tree sap and extractive turpentines these products were absent.

The most complete data on the composition of sulfate turpentine were obtained by gas-liquid chromatography.

Systematic investigations of the composition of monocyclic terpenes in Swedish sulfate turpentine were carried out by Groth /61/, who recommended the following conditions for the separation of turpentine components: a $200 \times 0.5$ cm column is charged with 25% dibenzylpyridine or 25% microcrystalline wax with 5% dibenzylpyridine on celite (60—80 mesh). The first stationary phase is recommended for the separation of components which follow $\Delta^3$-carene, while the second is to be used for the analysis of fractions between $\alpha$-pinene and $\Delta^3$-carene. Microcrystalline wax consists of higher naphthenes, its average molecular weight is 590 and its melting point is 73—76°. The analysis was conducted at column temperature of 140°, the flow rate of carrier gas (helium) was 25—50 ml/minute, sample volume 5 $\mu$l; the instrument used was a Perkin-Elmer 154 chromatograph.

Figure 36 shows an example of a chromatographic separation of the components of sulfate turpentine from Pinus sylvestris. The separation was conducted on a column with 25% dibenzylpyridine; the flow rate of carrier gas (helium) was 40 ml/minute. Components were identified by preparative gas-liquid chromatography, followed by IP-spectroscopy of the isolated compounds.

For the sake of comparison, the composition of monocyclic terpenes isolated by steam distillation from ground pine and spruce woods was investigated. It was shown that sulfate turpentine and turpentine of freshly felled trees contain the same components (except for sulfur compounds which are found in sulfate turpentine only). The proportions of the individual components show considerable variation.

Gas-liquid chromatography was employed /62/ in the study of the composition of sulfate (technical, purified from sulfurous impurities), tree sap and extractive turpentines from various countries and of artefact mixtures of pure terpenes. A column (1.15 m long) with poly(propylene glycol) (or di-n-decyl phthalate, poly(ethylene glycol) etc.) on celite was used. The sample volume was 5 $\mu$l, and the analysis took 45 minutes. The results were close to the data obtained by IR spectroscopy.

It was established /63/ by gas-liquid chromatography that sulfate turpentine produced in Finnish mills contains 67% $\alpha$-pinene, 16% $\Delta^3$-carene, 6.5% dipentene, 3.8% $\beta$-pinene, 3.5% ocimene, 0.6% $\beta$-phellandrene, 0.8% camphene, less than 0.1% terpinolene and 0.8% p-cymene.

The chromatographic method is widely used in the analysis of sulfate soap, crude tall oil, purified tall oil and tall rosin.

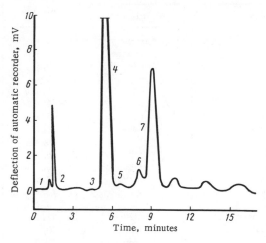

FIGURE 36. Chromatogram of sulfate turpentine:

1 – methyl mercaptan; 2 – dimethyl sulfide; 3 – dimethyl disulfide; 4 – α – pinene; 5 – camphene; 6 – β – pinene; 7 – △³ – carene.

Lawrence /66/ compared the data of chromatographic analyses /64, 65 and noted major differences in the compositions of different kinds of rosins (Table 26).

TABLE 26. Comparison of the compositions of different kinds of rosin

| Components | Content of components, % | | |
| --- | --- | --- | --- |
| | in tree sap rosin | in sulfate soap | in tall rosin |
| Levopimaric acid . . . . . | 26 | 0 | 0 |
| Abietic acid . . . . . . . | 10 | 27 | 40 |
| Palustric acid . . . . . . | 11 | 7 | 6 |
| Neoabietic acid . . . . . | 11 | 9 | 4 |
| Dehydroabietic acid . . . | 3 | 3 | 18 |
| Hydroxy acids . . . . . . | 11 | 25 | 3 |

The composition of the fatty acids of tall oil was studied by gas-liquid chromatography after preliminary methylation /67/. The esterification reduced the risk of isomerization and other chemical alterations of the acids during the chromatographic analysis. To methylate, 100 – 200 mg of the acids were placed in a 20 × 150 mm tube and 3 ml of the methylating agent (125 g $BF_3$ in 1 liter methanol) was added; the mixture was then heated on a steam bath for 2 minutes. The resulting methyl esters of the fatty acids were extracted with petroleum ether (bp 30 – 60°) and filtered, after which the petroleum ether was expelled on a water bath.

155

TABLE 27. Retention times of a number of methyl esters of fatty acids

| Name of acid | | Number of C atoms | Relative retention time |
|---|---|---|---|
| chemical | trivial | | |
| Octanoic . . . . . . . . | Caprylic | 8, s | 0.074 |
| Nonanoic . . . . . . . . | Pelargonic | 9, s | 0.088 |
| Decanoic . . . . . . . . | Capric | 10, s | 0.114 |
| Undecanoic . . . . . . . | – | 11, s | 0.146 |
| 10-Undecenoic . . . . . | – | 11, 1–u | 0.169 |
| Dodecanoic . . . . . . . | Lauric | 12, s | 0.184 |
| Tridecanoic. . . . . . . | – | 13, s | 0.228 |
| Tetradecanoic . . . . . | Myristic | 14, s | 0.324 |
| Pentadecanoic . . . . . | – | 15, s | 0.405 |
| Hexadecanoic . . . . . | Palmitic | 16, s | 0.544 |
| Hexadecanoic . . . . . | Palmitoleic | 16, 1–u | 0.609 |
| Heptadecanoic . . . . . | Margaric | 17, s | 1.745 |
| Octadecanoic . . . . . | Stearic | 18, s | 1.0 |
| Octadecenoic . . . . . | Oleic | 18, 1–u | 1.08 |
| Octadecadienoic . . . . | Linoleic | 18, 2–u | 1.27 |
| Nonadecanoic . . . . . | – | 19, s | 1.37 |
| Octadecatrienoic . . . . | Linolenic | 18, 3–u | 1.67 |
| Bicosanoic . . . . . . . | Arachidic | 20, s | 1.90 |
| Heneicosanoic . . . . . | – | 21, s | 2.64 |
| Eicosatetraenoic . . . . | Arachidonic | 20, 4–u | 3.10 |
| Octadecatrienic . . . . | – | 18, 3–u, c | 3.14 |
| Docosanoic . . . . . . . | Behenic | 22, s | 3.64 |
| Tricosanoic . . . . . . . | – | 23, s | 4.95 |

Note. s – saturated; c – conjugated; 1–u, 2–u, 3–u, 4–u – number of unsaturated bonds.

The resulting esters were separated on a $200 \times 0.6$ cm column with 20% poly(ethylene glycol succinate) on Chromosorb R; column temperature 200°, evaporator temperature $350 - 400°$, flow rate of carrier gas (helium) 180 ml/minute. Katharometric detection, Perkin-Elmer 154 C chromatograph.

The relative retention times of methyl esters of fatty acids which may be contained in tall oil are shown in Table 27.

Gas-liquid chromatography was also employed /68/ in the analysis of the fatty acids of tall oil, fractionated in countercurrent installations.

The distillate of the tall oil studied contained 1% resin acids and 2% neutral substances. The countercurrent fractionation apparatus consisted of 200 tubes: n-heptane and a mixture of equal amounts of methanol, formamide and glacial acetic acid was employed. The separated fractions were esterified with diazomethane, and the resulting methyl esters separated on a nonpolar (Apiezone L) and a polar (poly(ethylene glycol succinate)) phase. The compounds were identified by their relative retention volumes.

Preliminary methylation technique was also utilized /69/ in a study of the composition of the fatty acids and resin acids of crude sulfate soap. The methylation was effected as follows: a sample of the sulfate soap floating at the top was blended with a mixture of a 5% solution of NaCl with ether (1:1) and acidified to methyl red. The free acids were extracted with ether, the ether was evaporated, and the residual acids dissolved in a methanol: ether mixture. The methylation was effected with diazomethane /70/, when both fatty and resin acids of the sulfate soap were fully methylated.

156

The esterification products were separated on a 3.05 meter column with poly(ethyl succinate); column temperature 215°, evaporator temperature 310°, flow rate of carrier gas 67 ml/minute, sample volume 5 μl, katharometric detection.

TABLE 28. Retention times of methyl esters of a number of fatty acids and resin acids

| Acid | Relative retention time | Acid | Relative retention time |
|---|---|---|---|
| Palmitic . . . . . . . . . . . . . | 1.0 | Pimaric . . . . . . . . . . . . | 5.4 |
| Palmitoleic. . . . . . . . . . . | 1.2 | Dihydroabietic . . . . . . . . | 6.0 |
| Stearic . . . . . . . . . . . . . | 1.6 | Palustric . . . . . . . . . . . . | 6.8 |
| Oleic . . . . . . . . . . . . . . . | 1.9 | △8a-, 8-Isopimaric . . . . . . | 7.9 |
| Linoleic . . . . . . . . . . . . | 2.3 | Abietic + dehydroabietic . . . | 10.5 |
| Eicosanoic . . . . . . . . . . . | 2.9 | Neoabietic . . . . . . . . . . | 11.1 |
| Linoleic (with conjugated bonds) | 3.3 | | |

The relative retention times (with respect to methyl palmitate) of a number of esters are shown in Table 28.

An example of the separation of the products of methylation of sulfate soap acids is shown in Figure 37. It is seen that the esters of both fatty acids and resin acids are separated under the experimental conditions employed.

Gas-liquid chromatography was also employed in the analysis of phenolic components contained in the light fractions of tall oil /71/. The analysis was conducted at 180 – 225° on a column 200 or 600 cm long; the stationary phases included apiezone, poly(propylene glycol) or silicone on kieselguhr; the flow rate of carrier gas (helium) was 45 – 50 ml/minute. The head fraction of tall oil distillate is saponified by KOH, the neutral compounds are extracted with ether, the acids are extracted with a solution of sodium carbonate and the phenols with a 7% solution of KOH. The phenols obtained are redistilled under a pressure of 1 mm Hg on a column with a headpiece

FIGURE 37. Chromatographic separation of methyl esters of fatty acids and resin acids in sulfate soap. Esters of:

1 – palmitic acid; 2 – stearic acid; 3 – oleic acid; 4 – linoleic acid; 5 – pimaric acid; 6 – dihydroabietic acid; 7 – palustric acid; 8 – dehydro-abietic acid and abietic acid.

and the fractions are collected at 94 – 104, 104 – 145, 145 – 160 and 160 – 175°. The first three fractions are chromatogrammed. Phenols with a high boiling point are etherified by shaking a solution of 1 gram of the phenol in 5.5 ml of 2 N NaOH with 1.5 gram of dimethyl sulfate for 25 minutes, after which 2 ml of 2 N NaOH are added. The mixture is heated on a water bath for 30 minutes, extracted with ether and the ether extract is successively washed with a solution of alkali and with water. The identified phenols included phenol, guaiacol, ethylguaiacol, propylguaiacol, eugenol, cis- and trans-isoeugenols and acetovanillone. Phenols not forming internal hydrogen bonds and not containing heavy substituents ortho to the hydroxyl group display a linear relationship between the logarithm of the relative retention time and the boiling point of the substance.

In a microdetermination /72/ of resin acids and fatty acids, a tall oil sample of about 75 mg is used for the analysis, whereas a 9 gram sample of tall oil is required in the standard ASTM D-803 determination. The total acid number 'of the tall oil is determined by potentiometric titration. Prior to the determination, the fatty acids in tall oil are methylated by the reagent $CH_3OH - BF_3$; the unreacted resin acids are titrated against 0.2 N methanolic KOH and the acid number and the content of resin acids (as abietic acid) are calculated. Fatty acids (as oleic acid) are found by difference between the total acid content and the content of the resin acids. The completeness of the methylation of fatty acids in this determination was studied by gas-liquid chromatography. The reaction mixtures were separated on a $213.4 \times 0.65$ cm column with 12% ethylene glycol succinate on Gaschrome Z at 195°, flow rate of carrier gas (helium) 150 ml/min, katharometric detection. It was demonstrated that the $CH_3OH - BF_3$ reagent selectively methylates fatty acids, while the resin acids remain free.

Analysis of blow gases of the sulfate pulp industry

Gas chromatography is successfully employed in the analysis of gaseous sulfides formed during sulfate cooks and in the burning of sulfate liquors /80/.

These gases include hydrogen sulfide, sulfur dioxide, mercaptans, alkyl sulfides and alkyl disulfides. Model mixtures of these components were separated /73/ on a $183 \times 0.79$ cm column with 30% stationary phase on Chromosorb (30 − 60 mesh). The recommended stationary phases are Triton X-100, X-305, X-45 and other alkyl aryl polyether alcohols. The working temperatures were 50 and 100°, the flow rate of carrier gas (helium) was 50 ml/minute, katharometric detection, Podbielniak Chromacon 9400-3A chromatograph.

Nine-component mixtures containing air, $CH_3SH$, $C_2H_5SH$, $(CH_3)_2S$, $SO_2$, $(C_2H_5)_2S$, n-$C_4H_9SH$; $(CH_3S)_2$, $(C_2H_5S)_2$ have been separated in this manner. The presence of water in the mixture interferes with the separation of the components; accordingly, water is best preliminarily removed.

Since the katharometric detector employed was not very sensitive, the analysis of industrial samples had to be preceded by their concentration. The sampling of industrial gas was conducted /74/ by adsorbing the components on a silica gel column; this was followed by their desorption and quantitative chromatographic determination. Water vapor was preliminarily removed from the gas by cooling to 0°; the uncondensed vapor was adsorbed at 55° on anhydrous calcium sulfate; sulfurous compounds are not sorbed under these conditions.

Sulfurous compounds were concentrated on a U-shaped silica gel column (28 − 60 mesh) at −78.5° (mixture of dry ice with acetone). A fairly complete (95% on the average) desorption of the component was attained by heating the column to 115° under a residual pressure of 0.2 mm Hg. For quantitative determinations, the desorbate was condensed at −195.8° (cooling with liquid nitrogen), after which it was introduced into the chromatograph.

This procedure for preliminary concentration of industrial sulfurous gases is quite involved and is difficult to use for industrial routine control of the composition of the blow gas. Direct analysis of such samples became possible when flame ionization detectors were employed /76/. The instrument used was the Perkin-Elmer 154D chromatograph with a flame ionization detector, which is highly sensitive to hydrocarbons while being insensitive to water. Components of various industrial gases were separated on a 2 meter long column with two stationary phases — poly-(propylene glycol) Ucon LB-550-X or Triton X-100 on diatomite; the flow rate of carrier gas (helium) was 50 ml/min, the column temperature was 70°, and the sample volume was 5 ml.

Table 29 shows the retention times of a number of compounds which are used as standards.

TABLE 29. Retention times of hydrocarbon sulfides (minutes)

| Sulfides | Stationary phase | |
| --- | --- | --- |
| | Ucon LB-550-X | Triton X-100 |
| $CH_2SH$ | 2.0 | 1.9 |
| $C_2H_5SH$ | 3.0 | 4.0 |
| $(CH_3)_2S$ | 3.4 | 4.4 |
| iso-$C_3H_7SH$ | 4.0 | – |
| n-$C_3H_7SH$ | 6.6 | – |
| iso-$C_4H_9SH$ | 10.5 | – |
| $(C_2H_5)S$ | 11.3 | 17.4 |
| $(CH_3S)_2$ | 21.4 | 31.5 |
| n-$(C_3H_7)_2S$ | 45.7 | 81.0 |
| $(C_2H_5S)_2$ | 76.3 | 118.0 |

The method is suitable for use in the analysis of different industrial gases formed during the burning of black liquors, in the chlorine oxidation tower and in other technological units.

The sulfur-containing compounds may be identified /78/ by a simultaneous use of electron capture and flame ionization detectors. Chromatographic separation is performed at 110 and 140° on 305.0×0.3 cm columns filled with Carbowax 20M or silicone DC-710 and on Chromosorb W (60 — 80 mesh) at a flow rate of the carrier gas (nitrogen) of 50 ml/minute. The gas stream issuing from the column was divided into two equal parts, one of which was passed through the flame ionization detector (hydrogen flow rate 25 ml/min, flow rate of air 30 ml/minute), while the other half was passed through an electron capture detector (potential 90 V). The peaks are identified by their relative retention times on the polar and nonpolar phases and by the signal ratio of the two detectors.

The sampling of the gases is a major factor in the accuracy and reproducibility of the results of the chromatographic analysis of the sulfides in the Kraft liquor.

A study of the various sampling and sample storage techniques showed that reproducible and accurate results are obtained if the samples are withdrawn into a pear-shaped 500-ml glass flask equipped with a device for passing through the sample gas /79/. The sample should be analyzed not later than 48 hours after withdrawal. The sample for the chromatographic analysis was withdrawn from the flask with a medicinal type syringe by piercing the rubber stopper of the flask. The analysis was performed on a 200×0.65 cm column with 20% tri-m-tolyl phosphate on Chromosorb W (60 — 80 mesh) or with 25% didecyl phthalate on Chromosorb P (60—80 mesh);

column temperature 90°, flow rate of carrier gas (nitrogen) 50 ml/min, Perkin-Elmer 154D chromatograph.

Under these conditions the corrected retention times of dimethyl sulfide $(CH_3)_2S$, dimethyl disulfide $(CH_3)_2S_2$ and methyl mercaptan $CH_3SH$ are, respectively, 1.04, 7.40 and 0.54 on the first column and 2.26, 15.10 and 1.04 minutes on the second column. Quantitative determination of the components is made with the aid of calibration curves. The following equation has been deduced for the correction of analytical results for the temperature and the water content in the sample:

$$C_c = C_f(1 + vd_t/V - v),$$

where $C_c$ is the corrected concentration, $C_f$ the experimentally found concentration, $v$ is the volume of water, $d_t$ is the distribution coefficient at t°C and $V$ is the volume of the sampler (250 ml).

It is recommended to use a gas chromatograph rather than an Orsat apparatus for the analysis of blow gases in routine control of recovery of chemicals during Kraft pulping. This results in an improved accuracy and the time of the analysis is reduced by one half /80/.

Three possible combinations of different columns were tested. Good separation of components of industrial gases is attained by connecting three columns in series. The first column (46 × 0.8 cm) was filled with silica gel (42 — 60 mesh), the second (720 × 0.8 cm) with 30% tetraethylene glycol dimethyl ether on fireproof brick C-22 (42 — 60 mesh) washed with acid, the third (180 × 0.8 cm) with zeolite 5A (42 — 60 mesh). Column temperature 40°, flow rate of carrier gas (helium) 100 ml/minute, katharometric detector.

An example of the chromatographic analysis of blow gases of a sulfate pulp mill is shown in Figure 38. The gas composition in % was: $CO_2 - 17$, $H_2 - 6$, $O_2 - 2$, $N_2 - 70$, $CH_4 - 0.5$, $CO - 3.5$. The sensitivity of the potentiometer with respect to these components varied considerably. In order to improve the sensitivity, nitrogen may be used as carrier gas in the determination of hydrogen in the mixture.

A method for the identification of dialkyl and alkyl aryl sulfides has been described /81/. The method involved desulfidization of the samples over Raney nickel, followed by analysis of the mixture of alkanes and aromatic hydrocarbons by gas-liquid chromatography.

In a method for the analysis of mercaptan mixtures /82/ the mercaptans are oxidized by iodine to the corresponding disulfides and chromatogrammed at 60, 100 and 150° on a column (122 × 0.6 or 183 × 0.6 cm) with 20% silicone or 23% silicone oil 200 on Chromosorb P (60 — 80 mesh), carrier gas argon at 1.4 atm gage pressure, $Sr^{90}$ ionization detector, sample volume 0.001 ml.

Gas-liquid chromatography is employed /83/ in the analysis of mercaptans contained in aqueous alkaline solutions. The method may be employed in the analysis of waste waters of sulfate pulp mills /84/.

Sulfides and mercaptans are also analyzed by partition and adsorption chromatography in thin layers /85/, but these techniques are less convenient than gas-liquid chromatography.

Of the methods discussed above, those involving the use of chromatographs with flame ionization detector, e.g., [Soviet] chromatographs KhT-63, "Tsvet," LKhM-7a and others, can be recommended for use in sulfate pulp industry. The various brands of poly(ethylene glycol), silicone oils and polyether phases just mentioned may be used as liquid stationary phases.

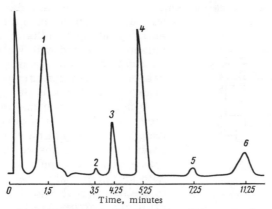

Time, minutes

FIGURE 38. Chromatographic separation of blow gases of sulfate pulp industry:

$1 - CO_2$; $2 - H_2$; $3 - O_2$; $4 - N_2$; $5 - CH_4$; $6 - CO$.


## 3. Analysis of pulp and paper

Analysis of pulp

Chromatographic methods are utilized in the determination of the content of different impurities /86/ in pulp. The most important in this connection is the determination of the carbohydrate components, which is effected by paper chromatographic techniques /87/. In studying cellulosic materials, paper chromatography may occasionally be combined with electrophoresis /88, 89/.

Paper chromatography was utilized in the study of the carbohydrate composition of sulfite and sulfate pulps from beechwood /90, 91/. Column chromatography followed by paper chromatography was used in the determination of methylglucuronoxylan in pulp and wood /92/. It was shown by paper chromatography that the hydrolyzates of cotton and wood pulp contain mannose /93 — 95/. Hydrolysis followed by paper chromatography was used in the study of four morphologically different fractions of bleached straw pulp. The fractions were very similar chemically. Chromatography was employed in the study of the polysaccharide composition of sulfite pulp /97/ from beech /98/ and red pine /99/ in order to determine the content of 4- o- methyl- D- glucuronic acid in Kraft pulp xylan./100/ and in the analysis of hemicelluloses of annual plants /101/.

We shall discuss one method for determining the carbohydrate composition of pulp /102/. The pulp is hydrolyzed with 72% $H_2SO_4$, diluted with water 35 $^1/_2$ times and boiled under reflux for 6 hours, the reaction mixture filtered, an aliquot part of the filtrate shaken with Duolite A- 7 anion

161

exchanger, filtered again and the pH of the solution is adjusted to 2 — 3 by adding 6 N NaOH.  The solution (50 ml) is concentrated to 2 ml and chromatogrammed on Whatman No. 1 paper, using butanol: glacial acetic acid: water = 4:1:5 as solvent.  The compounds are detected by spraying with a solution of aniline phthalate (930 ml aniline and 1.6 g phthalic acid in 100 ml butanol saturated with water).  Zones of a duplicate chromatogram not treated with the reagent are cut out, ground and used in microdeterminations of sugars /103/.

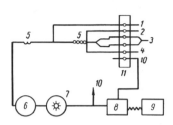

FIGURE 39.  Block diagram of apparatus for automatic determination of sugars:

1 — air feed at 0.60 ml/min; 2 — sample feed at 0.32 ml/min; 3 — feed of 60% $H_2SO_4$ at 2×119 ml/min; 4 — 16% orcinol feed at 0.096 ml/min; 5 — mixing vessels; 6 — thermostat, 80°C; 7 — lamp, 200 W; 8 — colorimeter, 420 mμ; 9 — automatic recorder; 10 — outlet of mixture after analysis; 11 — dosimeter.

A semiautomatic method was proposed /104/ (see also /105/) for a quantitative chromatographic determination of the carbohydrate composition of pulps and woods.  The hydrolyzate of wood or pulp sample was treated with an ion exchange resin, e.g., Dowex-1(×4) in the bicarbonate form, in order to raise the pH of the hydrolyzate to 4.  The ion exchangers were washed with water (400 ml water per 25 ml resin).  The wash waters were mixed with the filtered hydrolyzate, evaporated to a residual volume of 10 ml and diluted with alcohol.

In purifying the hydrolyzate it is desirable to test it for the presence of organic acids.  To do this, a fraction of the hydrolyzate 15 times as large as that used in chromatographic analysis is placed in an anion exchanger column filled with an acetate resin, washed with water and eluted with sodium acetate /106/.

The chromatographic analysis was carried out on a sample with a monosaccharide content corresponding to about 700 μg of the initial wood or pulp.  The analysis was conducted on a 450×6 cm column filled with a large-pore anion exchanger in the sulfate form, grain size 10 — 25 μ, exchange capacity 3.8 eq/g (Cl-form).  The eluent employed was 92% ethanol and the elution was effected at 75%; disaccharides may also be eluted under these conditions /107/.

The eluate was analyzed on a continuous automatic analyzer /108/ by determining the intensity of the color which appeared when the monosaccharides were reacted with orcinol and 60% solution of sulfuric acid. The block scheme of the different units of the analyzer is shown in Figure 39.  The optical density of the filtrate at 420 mμ was continuously measured with the aid of a colorimeter and was automatically recorded. The following emergence sequence of monosaccharides was noted in the filtrate from chromatographic analysis of a sample of pulp withdrawn in the initial stage of polysulfide cook: ribose (internal standard), arabinose, xylose, mannose, galactose, glucose.  Figure 40 shows an example of the elution of individual sugars from the hydrolyzate of a pulp.  The filtration rate was 0.5 ml/min.

The deviation from the mean of the results obtained for the contents of xylose, mannose and glucose are 2 — 5 rel.%, and in the determination of other sugars 10 rel.%.

This method may prove of interest in the studies of the variation in the composition of the wood during the cook and in evaluating the quality of pulps.

Chromatographic methods for the determination of carboxyl groups in filter paper /109/ and cellulose /110/ have been described.

A description of the terminal carboxyl groups in alkali pulp, based on the amount of levulinic and $\alpha$- and $\beta$-glucometasaccharinic acids isolated by chromatography from pulp hydrolyzates, has been given /111/.

Resins which appear in technical grade pulp of deciduous trees may be analyzed by thin layer chromatography /112/.

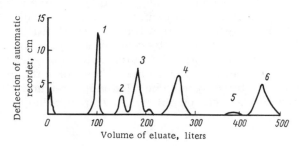

FIGURE 40. Chromatographic separation of sugars contained in the hydrolyzate of technical grade pulp:

1 – ribose (internal standard); 2 – arabinose; 3 – xylose; 4 – mannose; 5 – galactose; 6 – glucose.

Studies of pulp purification processes

The quality of technical grade pulp is determined to a large extent by its purification, in which bleaching is an important stage. In the technological processes involved in pulp purification, routine quality control is an important factor.

Kozmal et al. /113/ studied the composition of spent liquors obtained during hot purification of unbleached sulfite pulp. The composition of the saccharinic acids thus formed was compared with the products of decomposition of monosaccharides by boiling 8 N NaOH.

The separation of the reaction products was conducted by paper chromatography. The solvent used was ethyl acetate : acetic acid : water = 10 : 1.3 : 1 or n-butanol : acetic acid : water = 4 : 1 : 5. The chromatograms were sprayed with solutions of periodate, benzidine and hydrochloric acid in a mixture of methanol with acetone; a part of the chromatogram was sprayed with bromophenol blue reagent in order to determine the lactic acid which was used as standard. In this way saccharinic acids, detected in the products of alkaline decomposition of cellulose — by other authors as well — were identified /114, 115/.

Saccharinic acids can also be separated /113/ by gas-liquid chromatography after their conversion to volatile esters. In addition, electrophoresis can be performed on salts of saccharinic acids.

Sato et al. /116/, in their study of the pulp bleaching mechanism, used electrophoresis in separating the products of beating of unbleached sulfite pulp. They showed that lignosulfonic acids are not chemically bound to carbohydrates. They have been separated by zone electrophoresis on cellulose powder.

A successful combination of different chromatographic techniques was applied /117/ in a study of pulp bleaching by chlorine dioxide. The experimental technique involved will now be discussed.

The study of the reactions involved in pulp bleaching is difficult owing to the heterogeneity of the process. Soluble oligosaccharides, such as cellotetraose, cellotetritol and methyl β-cellotetraoside are more conveniently employed for experimental purposes. The oligosaccharides were obtained by hydrolysis of cotton linters by 85% $H_3PO_4$ at 60°. Higher polysaccharides were precipitated by diluting the hydrolyzate with water and filtering; further fractionation of water-soluble oligosaccharides was attained by concentrating the hydrolyzate, after which the desired fraction (DP 3-10) was precipitated by acetone. Individual compounds were obtained by the separation of fractions on a chromatographic column with a mixture of celite and activated carbon.

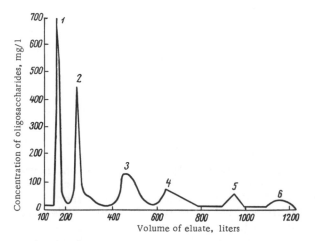

FIGURE 41. Separation of oligosaccharides in pulp on a chromato-graphic column:

1 – cellotriose; 2 – cellotetraose; 3 – cellopentaose; 4 – cello-hexaose; 5 – celloheptaose; 6 – cellooctaose.

The charge in the column was prepared from 1.2 kg carbon (Darco G-60) and 1.2 kg celite. The sorbent mixture was filled into the column as suspension in aqueous alcohol. The oligosaccharide mixture (65 kg) was dissolved in water (4 liters) and fed into the column. The oligosaccharides were successively eluted from the column with water containing progressively increasing amounts of butanol-1. It was found that in order to elute each oligosaccharide with DP 3 — 8 the butanol concentration in the solution must be gradually increased between 1.3 and 5.0%.

The filtrate was withdrawn in 2 liter portions, concentrated and analyzed by paper chromatography, using the system ethyl acetate : acetic acid : water (6:3:3, 6:3:4 or 6:3:5) as solvent. The eluates with the individual oligosaccharides were concentrated to one liter volumes, filtered through carbon and again concentrated to a residual volume of 100 ml. When methanol and acetone were added and the mixture cooled, the sugars crystallized out. The results of this fractionation are shown in Figure 41.

The oligosaccharide fractions were also analyzed by thin layer chromatography on kieselguhr G (250 $\mu$); the solvent was butanol-1 : ethanol : water = 50:30:20. The results of the analysis are shown in Figure 42.

The oxidation of the oligosaccharides and their derivatives was conducted at various concentrations of $ClO_2$, pH 3 (phosphate buffer), 56°, time of oxidation 2 — 24 hours. The reaction products were hydrolyzed or reduced by sodium borohydride, with subsequent hydrolysis; the resulting mixture was analyzed. The acidic reaction products were determined by thin layer chromatography, while the monosaccharides were determined by gas-liquid chromatography as trimethylsilyl ethers. Eluates of some of the chromatograms were evaporated to dryness and finally dried by evaporation from benzene. These residues were analyzed by gas-liquid chromatography /118/. The residue was dissolved in 1 ml of pyridine, 0.2 ml hexamethyldisilazane was added and then 0.1 ml of trimethylchlorosilane. The mixture was shaken for 30 seconds and the precipitate formed was allowed to settle.

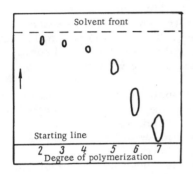

FIGURE 42. Separation of oligosaccharides from pulp by thin layer chromatography.

The samples were analyzed on a Perkin-Elmer 800 gas chromatograph with hydrogen flame ionization detector, using a $180 \times 0.8$ cm column filled with 15% poly(ethylene glycol succinate) on Chromosorb W (45 — 60 mesh). The working temperature was 150°, with helium as the carrier gas. Peak identification was effected by comparing the retention times of the reaction products with those of model compounds.

Kinetic studies showed that the oxidation of oligosaccharides (and probably also of pulp) by $ClO_2$ is a zero order reaction. It was found that two kinds of oxidation reactions may take place: direct oxidation of glucosidic bonds before or after hydrolysis with the formation of gluconic and arabonic acids and other products; oxidation of 2, 3-dihydroxyls to dicarboxylic acids via 2-ketoglucose and 2, 3-diketoglucose as intermediate products of the reaction.

The purpose of this chromatographic analysis was to elucidate the mechanism of pulp bleaching. Similar techniques may obviously be employed in routine control of technological purification of pulps.

Analysis of paper

Chromatographic methods employed in the analysis of carbohydrate components of woods and pulps can be successfully applied to the analysis of paper. They have been discussed in some detail in Chapter III and in the preceding section.

**Chromatographic determination of synthetic resins in paper.** The pulp and paper industry now produces several hundred brands of paper, many of which are impregnated with synthetic resins. The analyst frequently has to identify the kind of the resin employed as well as its content in the paper.

This can be successfully accomplished by chromatographic methods. Luciani /120/ developed a method for the determination of the synthetic resins present in paper as impregnating substances and as size. Urea-formaldehyde and melamine-formaldehyde resins are first saponified by dilute hydrochloric acid and the resulting solution is chromatogrammed on paper. The solvent is a mixture of ethanol with butanol, acetic acid and water, and the spots are revealed by p-dimethylaminobenzaldehyde (for urea) and picric acid (for melamine).

Styrene resin is nitrated by concentrated nitric acid prior to chromatographic analysis, the resulting p-nitrobenzoic acid is extracted with ether and the extract separated on paper. The chromatogram is eluted with a mixture of propanol-2 with ammonia and water, and the chromatograms revealed with p-dimethylaminobenzaldehyde with subsequent determination by UV-spectroscopy.

Chene et al. /121/ proposed a chromatographic determination of urea-formaldehyde and melamine-formaldehyde resins in paper and cardboard, which is suitable for industrial laboratories. Solutions with carbamide resins are pre-hydrolyzed with concentrated HCl with the addition of a few drops of $H_2O_2$ ($2 - 3$ ml acid for $5 - 10$ mg resin) and the solution is applied to the paper. The chromatogram is then developed with butanol: distilled water: acetic acid = 4:5:1 and the spots are revealed with Ehrlich's solution (0.5 g p-dimethylaminobenzaldehyde, 1 ml concentrated HCl, 100 ml 96% alcohol). In the presence of urea bright yellow spots are formed; melamine gives lemon yellow spots. The spots may also be revealed by spraying with a solution of $I_2$ in KI. Quantitative determination is carried out on a few ml of solution containing $1 - 2$ mg resin. The accuracy of such determinations (weight of spot) is about 7%. These resins can also be determined by chromatography on a thin layer of silica gel; the analysis is then faster, but less accurate.

Paper chromatography served to determine /122/ ethylene-urea-formaldehyde, urea-formaldehyde and melamine-formaldehyde resins in paper, especially in moisture-proof papers. The chromatograms were developed with n-butanol: alcohol: water = 3:1:1 and with a mixture of 30% formalin: 10% ammonium nitrate: 10% sodium acetate = 2:1:1. The chromatograms are dyed with a 0.2% solution of Acylanchromotrope RR and 0.12% acetic acid at 60° during 2 minutes, after which they are rinsed with cold water and dried in the air.

The content of synthetic resins in paper and cardboard may be determined by pyrolytic gas-liquid chromatography. The potentialities of this method in the determination of polysaccharides and polysaccharide esters were discussed in Chapter III.

The method may be used to determine urea-formaldehyde resins present in the paper in about 1% /123/. For such low resin contents the Kjeldahl method and IR spectroscopy are not accurate enough. Pyrolytic chromatography will determine the resin content to within ± 10%.

Samples of paper with different resin contents were slowly pyrolyzed at a temperature high enough to ensure full decomposition of all the components of the paper. The reaction products were separated on two columns: the first column, in which the organic substances were separated, operated at an elevated temperature, while the second, molecular sieve column operated at room temperature to separate $H_2$, $O_2$ and $N_2$. Pyrolysis was usually carried out on 0.0030 g samples of paper of different brands. An example of the chromatographic separation of the products of pyrolysis on the molecular sieve column is shown in Figure 43. The amount of the resin in the paper is determined by determining the area of the nitrogen peak.

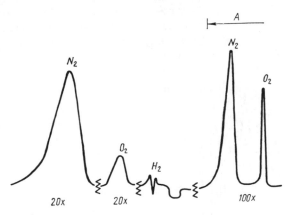

FIGURE 43. Chromatogram of pyrolysis products of paper containing urea–formaldehyde resin (A − air in paper sample).

Papers and cardboards sized with rubber latexes display altogether new, valuable properties. In the past few years the preparation of these substances has evoked major interest. Gridyushko, Khol'kin and Kolesnikov /124/ developed a method for a quantitative determination of chloroprene rubber in paper by pyrolytic gas-liquid chromatography. Latex-sized paper was analyzed on a KhL-7 chromatograph with katharometric detector.

The low-temperature pyrolysis block provided with the instrument was replaced by a pyrolytic cell constructed in the laboratory, in which the pyrolysis temperature could be raised to 900°. The cell consisted of a quartz tube 7 mm in diameter on which was wound a nichrome spiral, 0.4 mm thick, with a resistance of 7.3 ohms. The cell temperature was measured with a thermocouple. In choosing the experimental conditions of pyrolysis, the cell temperature was studied as a function of the duration of heating and of the voltage applied to the spiral. The reproducibility of the conditions of pyrolysis was attained with the aid of a special press-button unit.

Comparison was effected between the chromatograms of the pyrolysis products of pulp, paper, rubber, nonionic surfactant W-OP-100 (size regulator) at different temperatures of pyrolysis. The following conditions of pyrolysis were found to be best: time of pyrolysis 10 seconds, voltage 50 V, cell temperature 500°. At this temperature the most characteristic chromatographic spectra of the hydrolysis products are obtained.

Separation of hydrolysis products was tested on the following polar phases and mixtures of polar and nonpolar phases introduced into a 200×0.6 cm stainless steel column: 10% poly(ethylene glycol) 1540 on Chromosorb P (60 — 80 mesh), 5% poly(ethylene glycol succinate) on celite 545 (60 — 80 mesh), 10% of a mixture of poly(ethylene glycol) and dibutyl phthalate (1:2) on Chromosorb P (60 — 80 mesh), 10% mixture of poly (ethylene glycol) and dibutyl phthalate (9:1) on celite 545 (60 — 80 mesh). Another liquid stationary phase which was tested was W-OF-100, on which the products of thermal decomposition of paper are satisfactorily separated.

It was found that the pyrolysis products of latex-sized paper are best separated on 10% of a 1:2 mixture of poly(ethylene glycol) 1540 with dibutyl phthalate on Chromosorb P (60 — 80 mesh). A comparison of chromatograms obtained at 70 — 100° showed that the optimum temperature is 90°, at which the separation of the mixture components is best. Detector temperature 100°, sensitivity of potentiometer 1 mV for the entire scale range.

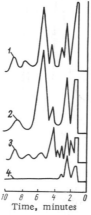

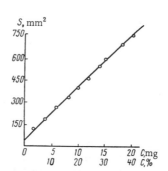

10  8  6  4  2  0
Time, minutes

FIGURE 44. Chroma-
tograms of pyrolysis
products:

1 — paper; 2 — rubber;
3 — cellulose; 4 —
surfactant.

FIGURE 45. Calibration curve for
the determination of rubber in
paper sized with latex:

C — content of rubber; S — area
of characteristic peak.

Figure 44 shows the chromatograms of the pyrolysis products of latex-sized paper and its components — cellulose, rubber and surfactant. It is seen that about 10 major peaks are formed under these conditions. Synthetic chloroprene rubber gives a characteristic peak with retention time of 5'35". This peak is practically absent in other components of the paper, so that it can be employed in the determination of the rubber content in the sheet.

In order to establish the relationship between the relative rubber content and the area of the characteristic peak, chromatograms of artefact mixtures of rubber and cellulose have been prepared. The artefact mixtures were so prepared that the sum of the weights of the latex and cellulose in the samples always remained constant at 50 mg. The rubber content in the samples varied between 0 and 40%.

It is seen from Figure 45 that there is a linear relationship between the content of the rubber in the mixture and the area of the characteristic peak, so that the calibration curve can be employed in the determination of the rubber content in the composition of the paper.

The method was employed in the study of the effects of different parameters on the size and sizing quality, and latex-sized paper could be quantitatively analyzed.

Gorskii, Khol'kin and Kirpich /125/ applied pyrolytic gas-liquid chromatography in the analysis of paper containing synthetic fibers. The manufacture of such kinds of paper is only a few years old, and the sheets display valuable properties. The content of synthetic fibers is found from the areas under the characteristic peaks which are formed as a result of pyrolysis of the samples.

The optimum pyrolysis temperature is 500°; the pyrolysis takes place in a modified pyrolysis block of chromatograph KhL-7, katharometric DT-5 detector. Comparison of different phases showed that the optimum conditions for the separation of pyrolysis products are: 20% poly(propylene glycol) 425 on celite 545, column temperature 80°, detector temperature 90°.

Paper containing between 10 and 75% added nitron, fiber length 4—5 mm, fiber thickness 14 $\mu$, was analyzed under these conditions. In the comparison between the chromatograms of pure cellulose and nitron (Figure 46), the characteristic peak with a retention time of 13'20" was chosen, and the nitron content in the paper was found from this peak with the aid of the calibration curve in Figure 47.

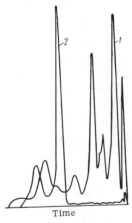

Time

FIGURE 46. Chromatograms of pyrolysis products:

1 — cellulose; 2 — nitron.

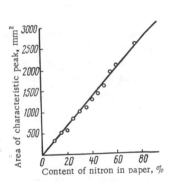

FIGURE 47. Calibration curve for the determination of the content of nitron in paper from the area of the characteristic peak.

Pyrolytic gas-liquid chromatography may be utilized in the analysis of paper with different synthetic fibers by selecting suitable characteristic peaks.

Adcock /119/ compiled a review of the publications dealing with gas-liquid chromatographic analysis of the volatile substances in wrapping paper which are liable to impart an unpleasant odor to foodstuffs.

**Determination of the mineral components of paper.** This can be accomplished by paper chromatography /126, 127/. Thus, fillers and mineral constituents of paper coatings have been determined in this way /128/. Ascending and descending chromatography and separations on circles of filter paper resulted in the separation of a mixture of Al, Ba, Ca, Ti and Zn; quantitative determinations are accurate to within ± 10%. The spots of the cations are observed in UV-light or after dying with various reagents, including 1% solution of alizarin in 95% ethanol, 0.2% aqueous solution of the sodium salt of tetrahydroxyquinone, etc.

A rapid and accurate identification of fillers and coating materials can be made /129/ by thin layer chromatography. The sample is ignited, the ash is dissolved and Ba, Ca, Mg, Al, Ti, Fe and Zn determined. To detect the spots of the cations, the plates are treated with alcoholic solutions of alizarinsulfonic acid and ammonia, when different cations assume different colors. This method is more rapid than paper chromatography.

**Chromatographic control of paper production.** Chromatographic methods are employed in the control of the different production stages of paper, in particular, the sizing process /130/, and in the determination of carbohydrates in the recycled water of the pulp industry /131/. Column chromatography and paper chromatography were applied in the study of the polysaccharides from the slime of Pseudomonas aeruginosa formed during the production of paper /132/.

Chromatography was employed in a study of the distribution of abietic acid /133/ which is mainly responsible for the difficulties encountered in the production of paper from sulfite pulp, due to the presence of resins /134/.

Thus, chromatographic methods may be used in controlling the technological processes involved in paper and cardboard manufacture as well as in the quality control of the finished products. Pyrolytic gas-liquid chromatography is to be recommended for the detection and determination of the individual components of the new kinds of paper, in particular, synthetic sizes and fiber materials.

BIBLIOGRAPHY

1. MAYAT, N.S. and O.P.GOLOVA. — Uspekhi Khimii, 28(9):1114−1133. 1959.
2. HAMILTON, J.K., E.V.PARTLOW, and N.S.THOMPSON. — Tappi, 41(12):803−816. 1958.
3. AXELSSON, S., I.CROON, and B.ENSTRÖM. — Svensk Papperstidn., 65(18):692−697. 1962.
4. SIMONSON, R. — Svensk Papperstidn., 65(20):817−818. 1962.
5. SIMONSON, R. — Svensk Papperstidn., 66(20):839−845. 1963.
6. SIMONSON, R. — Svensk Papperstidn., 67(18):721−727. 1964.
7. SIMONSON, R. — Svensk Papperstidn., 68(15):500−505. 1965.
8. YUR'EVA, M.K. and N.S.TROSTYANSKAYA. — ZhPKh, 38(10):2303−2308. 1965.
9. CROON, I. and B.F.ENSTRÖM. — Tappi, 44(12):370−374. 1961.
10. AURELL, R., N.HARTLER, and G.PERSSON. — Acta Chem.Scand., Vol.17:545. 1963.
11. HARTLER, N. and I.-L.SVENSSON. — Ind.Eng.Chem.Prod.Res. and Devel, 4(2):80−82. 1965.
12. TIMELL, T.E. — Svensk Papperstidn., Vol.65:435. 1962.
13. ENKVIST, T., T.ASHORN, and K.HÄSTBACKA. — Paperi ja Puu, 44(8):395−404. 1962.
14. GIERER, J. and I.NORÉN. — Acta Chem.Scand., 16(7):1713−1729. 1962.

15. GIERER, J. et al. − Acta Chem. Scand., Vol. 18 : 1469. 1964.

16. GIERER, J. and L.-A. SMEDMAN. − Acta Chem. Scand., 19(5) : 1103−1112. 1965.

17. NAKANO, J., S. MIYAO, K. OKUDA, and N. MIGITA. − J. Japan Wood Res. Soc., 12(1) : 51−63. 1966.

18. EKMAN, K. H. − Soc. Sci. Fennica, Comment. Phys.-Math., 23(1) : 63. 1958.

19. ISHIZU, A., C. TAKATSUKA, and N. MIGITA. − J. Japan Wood Res. Soc., 7(3) : 121−125. 1961.

20. ISHIZU, A., J. NAKANO, and N. MIGITA. − J. Japan Wood. Res. Soc., 7(6) : 247−251. 1961.

21. ISHIZU, A., J. NAKANO, and N. MIGITA. − J. Japan Wood Res. Soc., 8(4) : 139−144. 1962.

22. KAGINO, T., J. NAKANO, A. ISHIZU, T. OGINO, et al. − J. Japan Wood Res. Soc., 9(3) : 85−89. 1963.

23. LINDBERG, J. J. and C. -G. NORDSTRÖM. − Paperi ja Puu, 41(2) : 43−44. 1959.

24. STRUNNIKOV, V. N. and D. V. TISHCHENKO. − ZhPKh, 38(11) : 2545−2549. 1965.

25. LINDBERG, J. J. and T. ENKVIST. − Soc. Sci. Fennica, Comment. Phys.-Math., 17(4) : 1−23. 1953.

26. FIELD, L., P. E. DRUMMOND, P. H. RIGGINS, and E. A. JONES. − Tappi, 41(12) : 721−727. 1958.

27. LINDBERG, J. J., K. HÄSTBACKA, and T. ENKVIST. − Finska Kem. Medd., Vol. 62 : 25−32. 1953.

28. PEARL, I. A. − J. Am. Chem. Soc., Vol. 71 : 2196. 1949.

29. SOBOLEV, I. and C. SCHUERCH. − Tappi, 41(8) : 447−452. 1958.

30. ENKVIST, T. − Paperi ja Puu, 45(11) : 649−656. 1963.

31. PEARL, I. A. − Forest Products J., 13(9) : 373−385. 1963.

32. STRUNNIKOV, V. N. and D. V. TISHCHENKO. − ZhPKh, 39(2) : 427−432. 1966.

33. ADLER, E. and B. WESSLÉN. − Acta Chem. Scand., 18(5) : 1314−1316. 1964.

34. ADLER, E., I. FALKEHAG, J. MARTON, and H. HALVARSON. − Acta Chem. Scand., 15(5) : 1313−1314. 1964.

35. ENKVIST, T., K. HÄSTBACKA, and S. KANTELE. − Suomen Kemistiseuran Tiedonantoja, 73(2) : 35−58. 1964.

36. RADĚJ, Z. and Z. KRIŠTOFOVA. − Papir a celul., 19(6) : 152−153. 1964.

37. GREEN, J. W. − Tappi, 39(7) : 472−477. 1956.

38. LETONMYAKI, M. N. and N. F. KOMSHILOV. − Izv. Karel'skogo i Kol'skogo Filialov AN SSSR, No. 2 : 158. 1958.

39. LETONMYAKI, M. N., N. F. KOMSHILOV, and N. G. DZHURINSKAYA. − Izv. Karel'skogo i Kol'skogo Filialov AN SSSR, No. 4 : 140. 1958.

40. HERRLINGER, R. and C. O. WARRELL. − Tappi, 46(2) : A132−A136. 1963.

41. PILYUGINA, L. G. and N. F. KOMSHILOV. − Trudy Karel'skogo Filiala AN SSSR, Vol. 38 : 45−52. 1963.

42. KOMSHILOV, N. F. et al. − ZhPKh, 38(3) : 650−657. 1965.

43. TURGEL', E. O. and T. V. KASHTANOVA. − Gidroliz* naya i Lesokhimicheskaya Promyshlennost', No. 1 : 16. 1961.

44. KOMSHILOV, N. F., L. G. PILYUGINA, and T. A. SELIVANOVA. − ZhPKh, 38(6) : 1337−1339. 1965.

45. LETONMYAKI, M. N. et al. − Bumazhnaya Promyshlennost', No. 1 : 9−11. 1964.

46. ALFREDSON, B., L. GEDDA, and O. SAMUELSON. − Svensk Papperstidn., 63(21) : 758−761. 1960.

47. KOMSHILOV, N. F. and M. N. LETONMYAKI. − Bumazhnaya Promyshlennost', No. 3 : 5. 1955.

48. KOMSHILOV, N. F. and L. G. PILYUGINA. − Trudy Karel'skogo Filiala AN SSSR, Vol. 38 : 39−44. 1963.

49. BOYARKIN, A. I. − Fiziologiya Rastenii, 2(6) : 1035. 1955.

50. OLSSON, J. E. and O. SAMUELSON. − Svensk Papperstidn., 68(6) : 179−185. 1965.

51. YORSTON, F. H. − Pulp and Paper Mag. Canada, 63C : T102−T106. 1962.

52. BOGOMOLOV, B. M. et al. − Izv. VUZov, Lesnoi Zhurnal, No. 1 : 128−140. 1962.

53. AKAMATSU, I., T. FUJI, and Y. KIMURA. − Bull. Govt Ind. Res. Inst., Osaka, 15(4) : 320−323. 1964.

54. FUJI, T., I. AKAMATSU, and Y. KIMURA. − Bull. Govt Ind. Res. Inst., Osaka, 15(4) : 324−328. 1964.

55. FUJI, T., I. AKAMATSU, and Y. KIMURA. − J. Japan Techn. Assoc. Pulp and Paper Ind., 18(9) : 381−384. 1964.

56. KAJANNE, P. Paperi ja Puu, 39(9) : 417−422. 1957.

57. KAJANNE, P. − Suomen Kem., 31(4) : B199−B203. 1958.

58. DANDA, J. and J. HANOUSEK. − Papir a celul., 17(3) : 57−59. 1962.

59. LUNDQVIST, R. − Arkiv Kemi, 21(6) : 497−501. 1964.

60. WITEK S. and M. BUKALA. − Svensk Papperstidn., 68(3) : 69−71. 1965.

61. GROTH, A. B. − Svensk Papperstidn., 61(10) : 311−321. 1958.

62. MILTENBERGER, K. H. and G. KEICHER. − Farbe und Lack, 69(9) : 677−684. 1963.

63. HIRSJÄRVI, P. − Suomen Kem., 37(1) : A21−A28. 1964.

64. BALDWIN, D. E., V. M. LOEBLICH, and R. V. LAWRENCE. − Chem. and Eng. Data Series, Vol. 3 : 342. 1958.

65. LOEBLICH, V. M. and R. V. LAWRENCE. − J. Am. Oil. Chem. Soc., Vol. 33 : 320. 1956.

66. LAWRENCE, V. − Tappi, 45(8) : 654−656. 1962.

67. STINE, I. A. and J. B. DOUGHTY. − Forest Prod. J., 11(11) : 530−535. 1961.

68. AHO, Y., O. HARVA, and S. NIKKILÄ. – Tekn Kem. Aikauslehti, 19(9–10):390–392. 1962.

69. ABRAMS, E. – Tappi, 46(2)II:136A–139A. 1963.

70. SCHLENK and GELLERMAN. – Analyt. Chem., Vol. 32:1412. 1960.

71. SANDERMANN, W. and G. Z. WEISSMANN. – Analyt. Chem., 189(1):137–148. 1962.

72. CROWELL, E. P. and B. B. BURNETT. – Tappi, 49(7):327–328. 1966.

73. ADAMS, D. F. and R. K. KOPPE. – Tappi, 42(7):601–605. 1959.

74. ADAMS, D. F., R. K. KOPPE, and D. M. JUNGROTH. – Tappi, 43(6):602–608. 1960.

75. CAVE, G. C. B. – Tappi, Vol. 46:11. 1963.

76. ADAMS, D. F., R. K. KOPPE, and W. U. TUTTLE. – J. A. P. C. A., Vol. 15:31. 1965.

77. THOMAS, E. W. – Tappi, 47(9):587–588. 1964.

78. OAKS, D. M., H. HARTMANN, and P. DIMICK. – Analyt. Chem., 36(8):1560–1565. 1964.

79. WILLIAMS, I. H. and F. E. MURRAY. – Pulp and Paper Mag.(Canada), 67(8):T347–T355. 1966.

80. RHOAD, F. – N. South. Pulp and Paper Manufacturer, 28(3):60, 62, 64. 1965.

81. FRANC, J., J. DVOŘÁČEK, and V. KOLOUŠKOVÁ. – Mikrochim. Acta, No. 1:4–9. 1965.

82. SPOREK, K. F. and M. D. DANYI. – Analyt. Chem., 35(8):956–958. 1963.

83. LeROSEN, H. D. – Analyt. Chem., 33(7):973–974. 1961.

84. WERNER, A. E. – Can. Pulp and Paper Ind., 16(3):35–43. 1963.

85. PRINZLER, H. W., D. PAPE, and M. TEPPKE. – J. Chromatogr., 19(2):375–381. 1965.

86. HATANO, A. and H. SOBUE. – Bull. Chem. Soc. Japan, 26(7):403–406. 1953.

87. SAEMAN, J. E., W. E. MOORE, R. Z. MITCHELL, and M. A. MILLETT. – Tappi, 37(8):336–343. 1954.

88. DERMINOT, J. – Bull. Inst. Text. France, No. 80:71–77. 1959.

89. DERMINOT, J. and M. MAURES. – Bull. Inst. Text. France, 17(108):985–993. 1963.

90. KARÁCSONYI, S. and M. MAHDALIK. – Svensk Papperstidn., 64(13):500–504. 1961.

91. KARÁCSONYI, S. and M. MAHDALIK. – Papir a celul., 17(9):195–197. 1962.

92. TODA, H. – J. Soc. Text. and Cellulose Inds, Japan, 16(9):725–729. 1960.

93. ADAMS, G. A. and C. T. BISHOP. – Tappi, Vol. 38:672. 1955.

94. MATSUZAKI, K., K. WARD, and M. MURRAY. – Tappi, 42(6):474–476. 1959.

95. SOBUE, MATSUDSAKI, and HATANO. – J. Soc. Text. and Cellulose Ind., 9(11):556–567. Japan. 1953.

96. CHIAVERINA, J. and A. RONDIER. – Bull. Assoc. Techn. Ind. Papet., 18(3):146–150. 1964.

97. TODA, H. and T. HAMADA. – J. Japan Techn. Assoc. Pulp. and Paper Ind., 12(5):324–334. 1958.

98. BANDEL, W. – Das Papier, 7(15–16):306–309. 1953.

99. MORITA, E. – J. Chem. Soc. Japan, Ind. Chem. Sec., 65(4):566–568. 1962.

100. AURELL, R. and K. KARLSSON. – Svensk Papperstidn., 67(5):167–169. 1964.

101. CHI CH'ING-HUI, et al. – Sbornik Trudov Instituta Prikladnoi Khimii AN KNR, Vol. 2:49–54. 1959.

102. PALOHEIMO, L., E. HERKOLA, and M. L. KERO. – Maataloustietell. Aikakauskirja, 34(2):57–65. 1962.

103. SOMOGYI, M. – J. Biol. Chem., Vol. 160:61. 1945.

104. ARWIDI, B. and O. SAMUELSON. – Svensk Papperstidn., 68(9):330–333. 1965.

105. ARWIDI, B. and O. SAMUELSON. – Svensk Kem. Tidskr., Vol. 77:84. 1965.

106. ALFREDSSON, B., S. BERGDAHL, and O. SAMUELSON. – Anal. Chim. Acta, Vol. 28:371. 1963.

107. SAMUELSON, O. and B. SWENSON. – Anal. Chim. Acta, Vol. 28:426. 1963.

108. ARWIDI, B. and O. SAMUELSON. – Anal. Chim. Acta, Vol. 31:462. 1964.

109. ULTES, A. J. and J. HARTEL. – Analyt. Chem., 27(4):557–560. 1955.

110. FLEURY, J. P. and E. SCHNEIDER. – Bull. Inst. text. France, No. 75:43–54. 1958.

111. ALFREDSSON, B. and O. SAMUELSON. – Tappi, 46(6):379–381. 1963.

112. NISIGA, T., M. TANAKA, and T. KONDO. – J. Japan Techn. Assoc. Pulp and Paper Ind., 18(10):429–434. 1964.

113. KOZMAL, F., J. HOSTOMSKI, and M. KOŠIK. – Zeszyty Problemowe Postepów Nauk Rolniczych, Zes., 52:311–323. 1965.

114. RICHARDS, G. N. and H. H. SEPHTON. – J. Chem. Soc., p. 4492. 1957.

115. GREEN, J. W. – J. Am. Chem. Soc., Vol. 78:1894. 1956.

116. SATO, K., A. KOBAYASHI, and H. MIKAWA. – Bull. Soc. Japan, 35(3):483–486. 1962.

117. BECKER, E. S., J. K. HAMILTON, and W. E. LUCKE. – Tappi, 48(1):60–64. 1965.

118. SWEELEY, C. C., R. BENTLEY, M. MAKITA, and W. W. WELLS. – J. Am. Chem. Soc., Vol. 85:2497. 1963.

119. ADCOCK, L. H. Penrose Annual, Vol. 57:265–315. – London, Lund Humphries. 1964.

120. LUCIANI, M. – Cellul. e carta, 15(5):9–12. 1964.

121. CHENE, M., D. MOREL, and M. DUBOURGEAT. – Papeterie, 87(3):264–269. 1965.

122. HOC, S. – Allgem. Papier–Rundschau, No. 12:650–653. 1962.

123. SZYMANSKI, H. A., C. A. SALINIS, and N. WAGNER. – Progr. Industr. Gas Chromatogr., Vol. 1:201–207. New York, Plenum Press. 1961.

124. GRIDYUSHKO, G. S., Yu. I. KHOLINA, and V. L. KOLESNIKOV. – Obshchaya i Prikladnaya Khimiya, Vol. 1, No. 2. 1968.
125. GORSKII, G. M., Yu. I. KHOL'KIN, and E. G. KIRPICH. – Bumazhnaya Promyshlennost'. (In press).
126. LUCIANI, M. – Cellul. e Carta, 12(8): 7–13. 1961.
127. LUCIANI, M. Metodo cromatografico su carta per l'identificazione delle sostanze minerali costituenti la patinatura e la carica della carta. Roma, Tip. A. Palombi, 17 p.
128. Wochenbl. Papierfabr., 91(2): 53–57. 1963.
129. HAMMERSCHMIDT, H. and M. MÜLLER. – Papier (BRD), 17(9): 448–450. 1963.
130. KLINGELHOFFER, H. – Z. Angew. Phys., 8(4): 171–175. 1956.
131. ROSCHIER, R. H. – Suomen Kem., 31(1): B106–B110. 1958.
132. BOUVENG, H. O., I. BROMNER, and B. LINDBERG. – Acta Chem. Scand., 19(4): 1003–1004. 1965.
133. KUROGI, K. and T. MIWA. – J. Japan Wood Res. Soc., 5(4): 121–124. 1959.
134. KUROGI, K. – Bull. Kyuschu Univ. Forests, No. 30: 1–102. 1958.

# B. CHROMATOGRAPHY OF PRODUCTS OF THE HYDROLYSIS INDUSTRIES

The main products of hydrolytic processing of vegetal raw materials are monosaccharides which are either isolated pure or else are subjected to further biochemical or chemical processing. Accordingly, the processes employed in the hydrolysis industries are numerous and, as a result, there are major differences in the chemical composition and structure of components forming part of the intermediate products, by-products and final products.

Chromatographic methods now begin to be employed in industrial laboratories. Even though in principle all products of the hydrolysis industries can be analyzed by chromatographic methods, sufficiently rapid and accurate methods have not yet been developed for a large number of the products.

This section will deal mainly with the analysis of hydrolyzates, products of rectification of alcohol, products of furfural industry, etc.

## 1. Analysis of hydrolyzates and their processing products

The major components of hydrolyzates are monosaccharides, products of incomplete hydrolysis of polysaccharides (dextrins) and volatile compounds which include organic acids, aldehydes, alcohols, ketones, esters and other compounds.

### Determination of carbohydrates

Paper chromatography is extensively employed in the quantitative and qualitative analysis of sugars in the hydrolyzate, neutralizate and in the mash.

Emel'yanova and Batrakova /1/ developed a method for the detection of pentoses and hexoses (without separation into individual sugars) in alcoholic and yeast mash of hydrolysis and sulfite waste alcohol industries.

In the analysis, a 0.005 ml sample of the mash is placed on the chromatographic paper (Figure 48), the narrow end is dipped into ethyl acetate : pyridine : water = 5:1:5, and the system is kept in a sealed desiccator for 30 — 50 minutes. The resulting chromatogram is revealed with a mixture of 0.92 ml aniline and 1.66 g phthalic acid in 100 ml ethanol and dried at 70 — 100°. Pentoses and hexoses give two spots; a visual estimation of their color intensity serves as the criterion for the completeness of their utilization by the yeast. The method is rapid and simple (an analysis takes 40 — 60 minutes) and may accordingly be employed in factories for routine production control.

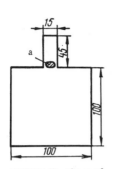

FIGURE 48. Shape of the sheet of chromatographic paper (a — spot at which sample is applied).

In quantitative work a method previously described /2/ is employed. In order to improve the accuracy of the chromatographic determination it has been recommended /3/ to apply a larger sample to the starting line. The hydrolyzate need not be neutralized prior to the chromatographic determination /4/.

A quantitative paper chromatographic method /2/ was utilized in a study /5/ of the composition of the semi-products of the manufacture of crystalline glucose from wood. The method served to determine the composition of the invert sugar, syrup, massecuite and other half-products obtained at the different stages of pilot scale production of glucose from wood.

Sharkov et al. /6/ used paper chromatography in their investigation of the carbohydrate composition of aqueous prehydrolyzates of pine. The total analytical scheme of the prehydrolyzate is shown in Figure 49. Xylose, arabinose, mannose, glucose, galactose and uronic acids were determined in the aqueous prehydrolyzate. After inversion of prehydrolyzate (boiling for $2\,^1/_2$ hrs in 2.0% HCl) it was noted that the content of reducing substances had increased considerably, which indicated the presence of dissolved oligosaccharides in the prehydrolyzate. To separate the oligosaccharides the system butanol : pyridine : water = 6:4:3 was employed; monosaccharides were separated with ethyl acetate : pyridine : water = 5:1:5; quantitative determination was performed by eluting the sugars and making a potentiometric titration /2/. The composition of the isolated oligosaccharides was not uniform; they consisted mainly of mannoglucolactan and araboxylouronide.

Antonovskii et al. /7/ studied the composition of the aqueous prehydrolyzate in the manufacture of sulfate viscose pulp from the wood of Siberian larch.

The sugars of the pentose hydrolyzate and neutralizate mainly consist of xylose; glucose is present in negligible amounts /8/. The hydrolyzate and neutralizate were analyzed by paper chromatography, using water-saturated phenol or n-butanol : acetic acid : water = 4:1:5 as the mobile solvent. The spots were revealed with ammoniacal silver nitrate or with alcoholic resorcinol solution.

Krayanskii et al. /9/ studied the pentose and hexose hydrolyzates of millet husks; the solvent was butanol : acetic acid : water = 4:1:5, and the sugars were revealed by their color reaction with p-anisidine hydrochloride, prepared as follows: 1 g crystalline p-anisidine hydrochloride is dissolved in 10 ml absolute methanol, the solution is made up to 100 ml with n-butanol and 0.1 g sodium hydrosulfite is then added. In quantitative work the unrevealed spots were cut out, and the water eluate was analyzed by the orcinol method. Hexoses were determined in the eluates by the reaction with sulfuric acid followed by spectrophotometric determination at 320 m$\mu$ (SF-4 spectrophotometer). The experimental error is not more than 10%. The method may be used to analyze carbohydrate mixtures in hydrolyzates; it is simple and the reagents are readily available.

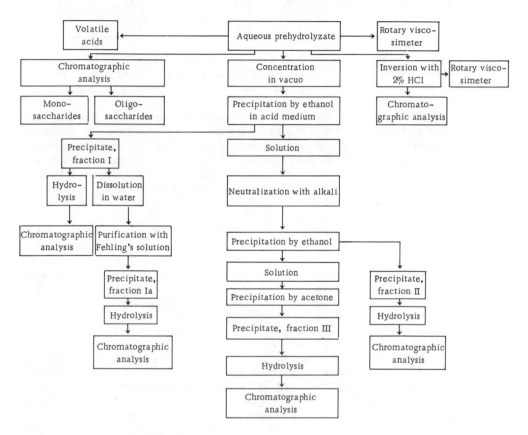

FIGURE 49. Analytical scheme for aqueous prehydrolyzate.

In his study of the composition of monosaccharides in the hydrolyzates of seed glumes of millet and seed coating of buckwheat, Dudkin /10/ compared a number of solvent systems: I - butanol: acetic acid: water = 4:1:1; II - ethyl acetate: pyridine: water = 5:1:5; III - butanol: ethanol: water = 10:1:2; IV - benzene: n-butanol: pyridine: water = 1:5:3:3. The last named solvent system proved to be the best (Table 30).

The system phenol: n-butanol: acetic acid: water = 20:40:8:40 has been recommended /11/ for the separation of mannose, arabinose and fructose.

TABLE 30. $R_f$-values during chromatographic separation of sugars in different solvent systems

| Monosaccharide | Solvent system | | | |
|---|---|---|---|---|
| | I | II | III | IV |
| Galactose | | | | 0.25 |
| Glucose | 0.12 | 0.03 | 0.03 | 0.27 |
| Fructose | | | | 0.30 |
| Arabinose | 0.17 | 0.08 | 0.08 | 0.34 |
| Xylose | 0.22 | 0.12 | 0.10 | 0.41 |
| Rhamnose | 0.33 | 0.23 | 0.19 | 0.53 |

Paper chromatography was used in the study of prehydrolyzates /12/, pentose and hexose hydrolyzates of the wood of different trees /13 — 16/, hydrolyzates of cotton stalks /17/ and other agricultural wastes /18/ and in a study of the kinetics of percolation hydrolysis /19/.

Korol'kov and Likhonos /20/ used paper chromatography in the study of the reducing nonsugars of the hydrolyzate, which can be separated from the sugars by adsorption on activated carbon brand A. The total dextrin content may be found by the difference between the amount of the dissolved polysaccharides and the amount of the sugar found in the hydrolyzate.

Paper chromatography was also employed in studying the composition of a mixture of oligosaccharides, hydroxymethylfurfural and glucose contained in acid hydrolyzates /21/.

A new, very interesting, gas-liquid chromatographic technique was recently utilized /22/ in the analysis of sugars in wood hydrolyzates. With paper chromatography, which is most widely employed to determine the carbohydrate composition of hydrolyzates, more than 24 hours are required to complete one analysis, and the relative error in the determination of sugars is not less than 10%. Gas-liquid chromatographic analysis takes only 1 — 2 hours, and its accuracy may be considerably higher.

Sugars in wood hydrolyzates /23/ are determined in the form of trimethylsilyl derivatives (p. 71).

**Synthesis of derivatives.** A 0.5 ml sample of the neutralized hydrolyzate (or any other aqueous solution containing not more than 100 mg/ml total sugars) and 0.25 ml of a 10 mg/ml solution of isoinositol are withdrawn with the aid of a graduated micropipet. The solutions are placed in a 14.5×45 mm ampoule. Four ampoules are mounted on a rotating evaporator, in which the sample mixture and the standard are evaporated to dryness on a water bath at 40° during 10 — 15 minutes.

The residue is dissolved in 1.4 ml dry pyridine. When analyzing products containing glucose and galactose, the solubilization should be conducted rapidly and without heating, or new anomeric forms of sugars may be formed. Hexamethyldisilazane (0.4 ml, 2.0 mmoles) is then introduced into the ampoule, which is then stoppered and vigorously shaken. After adding 0.2 ml (1.6 mmole) of trimethylchlorosilane the ampoule is again shaken for one minute. It is then closed with a stopper which should be made of polypropylene to prevent any reaction between the stopper and trimethylchlorosilane. Hexamethyldisilazane and trimethylchlorosilane may be added immediately or 2 — 3 minutes after the sample mixture has dissolved in pyridine.

In the course of the silylation a fine suspension of ammonium chloride is formed, which eventually settles to the bottom. It does not interfere with the immediate analysis of the mixture on the chromatograph, for which a 2 μl sample is taken.

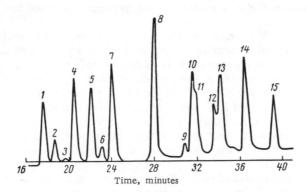

FIGURE 50. Chromatogram of a model mixture of sugars as trimethylsilyl derivatives:

1 − β-arabinose; 2 − arabinose; 3 − xylose (traces); 4 −α-arabinose; 5 −α-xylose; 6 − arabinose; 7 − β-xylose; 8 −α-mannose; 9 −γ-galactose; 10 −α-glucose; 11 −α-galactose; 12 − β-mannose; 13 − β-galactose; 14 − β-glucose; 15 − isoinositol (internal standard).

**Chromatographic procedure.** Trimethylsilyl sugar ethers were separated on a 205×0.5 cm column with 14% ethylene glycol succinate on Chromosorb W, previously washed with acid. The flow rate of the carrier gas (helium) was 140 ml/min, flame ionization detector ($H_2$ velocity 35 ml/min, air velocity 310 ml/min), evaporator temperature 300°; the temperature of the column was raised from 110 to 190° at 2°/min. In quantitative work isoinositol was employed as an internal standard. Figure 50 shows an example of chromatographic separation of a mixture of five sugars as their trimethylsilyl derivatives. This method was employed /22/ in the determination of xylose and mannose in hydrolyzates of wood cellulose.

Silicon derivatives of sugars can also be separated on other stationary phases. Thus, Stepovaya and Khol'kin accomplished a satisfactory separation of trimethylsilyl derivatives of arabinose, xylose, α-methylmannoside, galactose, glucose and mannose on a column with 10% silicone oil on celite 545 (Figure 20).

This analytical procedure may in time replace paper chromatography in the analysis of hydrolyzates and other carbohydrate-containing products.

Gas chromatography was recently employed /24/ in the determination of dissolved $O_2$ and $CO_2$ in media fermented by Saccharomyces cerevisiae yeast.

Determination of organic impurities in hydrolyzates

The hydrolyzates of wood and agricultural plant residues contain a large number of volatile and nonvolatile organic compounds formed as a result of the hydrolysis of the raw material and decomposition of the monosaccharides.

Usmanov et al. /25/ employed the method of paper chromatography to study the composition of organic acids in the hydrolyzates of cottonseed hulls. The mixture was separated in 24 hours on a $42 \times 40$ cm sheet of paper, with water-saturated n-butanol containing 5% formic acid. The spots were revealed with a 0.04% alcoholic solution of bromocresol blue. The $R_f$-values were calculated for model solutions containing oxalic, succinic, citric, tartaric, malic and lactic acids. As a result, oxalic acid was detected in the pentose hydrolyzate of the cotton hulls and in the syrup prior to the ion exchange; no acids were found in the syrup after purification on ion exchangers.

The composition of dehydration hydrolyzates, obtained as wastes in the production of furfural, was also studied by paper chromatography /26/. Citric, acetic, formic, malic, malonic and levulinic acids were detected.

Dudkin and Shkantova /27/ studied the composition of steam-distilled acids which are formed on treating grain husks with boiling $0.2 N H_2SO_4$ or on successive treatment with 4% NaOH and $0.2 N H_2SO_4$. Paper chromatographic development with n-butanol saturated with an equal volume of $1.5 N$ ammonia showed that propionic acid was not present in the distillate; acetic and formic acids were not separated. These acids were separated on a column with KSK silica gel, previously treated with $0.5 N H_2SO_4$ to reduce the degree of ionization of organic acids.

Volatile and nonvolatile acids in hydrolyzed substrates were determined by combining chromatographic with chemical methods /28/. The neutralized hydrolyzate, slops and mash were taken for the analysis. The hydrolyzed substrates contained large amounts of organic acids. Volatile acids are mainly accounted for by acetic acid with a minor admixture of HCOOH. Nonvolatile acids include levulinic acid as the major component; succinic, fumaric, malic and citric acids are also present. The spent mash contained much smaller amounts of organic acids than the neutralizate and the slops which indicates that organic acids, in particular, levulinic acid, are consumed by the yeast growing in the neutralizate and slops.

The application of gas-liquid chromatography to the analysis of volatile components of the hydrolyzate is very promising.

Khol'kin, Morozov et al. studied the potentialities of the analysis of volatile components of the hydrolyzate without their preliminary concentration on an LKhM-7a chromatograph with a flame ionization detector. The samples introduced into the chromatograph had been taken from the vapor phase in equilibrium with the liquid phase. It was shown that the minimum concentrations of volatile components in the liquid phase which can be determined with this instrument are, %: acetaldehyde 0.002, formaldehyde 0.5, propionaldehyde 0.01, acetone 0.005, ethanol 0.01, methanol 0.01, furfural 0.2, acetic acid 0.1, formic acid 0.1, propionic acid 0.01. The sensitivity of the method can be considerably increased.

Determination of cations

The iron cations contained in the pentose hydrolyzate of vegetal material were determined /29/ by the method of ion exchange.

The analysis was based on the absorption of cations when the hydrolyzate was passed through columns of KU-1 and KU-2 exchangers in the H-form. After the hydrolyzate had been passed, the columns were washed with distilled water. The cations bound to sulfate and to organic anions were determined by following the variations in the acidity of the hydrolyzate after the cation exchange. To determine iron, the column was regenerated by passing through 4N HCl and distilled water in succession. To the washings thus obtained 2M sodium acetate solution was added to adjust the pH to 3.5—4, then a 10% solution of hydroxylamine and a 0.2% solution of $\alpha, \alpha'$-dipyridyl were added, the solution was left to stand until the iron was fully reduced and a colorimetric determination carried out.

The total cation content in pentose hydrolyzates of maize cobs, sunflower seed husks and tan wastes varies /32/ between 71.5 and 111.6 meq/l; 80 — 87% of the cations are bound as sulfates, while 13 — 20% are bound to organic anions.

## 2. Analysis of products of ethanol rectification

The rectification of ethanol yields a number of intermediate products, side products and final products. Of interest for practical purposes is the analysis of industrial alcohol and crude alcohol, and, of the side products, the analysis of methanol-ether-aldehyde (MEAF) or the methanolic fraction.

The processing of the methanolic fraction to standard products has lately been extensively studied.

Chemical processing of the methanolic fraction is difficult, mainly owing to the fact that it contains numerous components and its exact composition is not known. Analytical laboratories have so far utilized only chemical methods of analysis which, besides being laborious, yield merely approximate values for the overall contents of ethers, aldehydes and other groups of organic compounds. The composition of this fraction varies, moreover, with the processing conditions employed.

Up till now no rapid method for the determination of the composition of these products has been available. Khol'kin et al. /31/ developed a rapid method for the determination of all major components in MEAF and in other nonaqueous half-products of rectification of ethanol. Optimum conditions were established for the separation of multicomponent systems and determination of individual components on UKh-1 chromatograph.

Since the industrial products concerned are complex mixtures of alcohols, ethers, aldehydes and other compounds, it was of interest to test the separating power of a number of liquid phases. The following liquid phases were tested on model mixtures: transformer oil, silicone oil, dinonyl phthalate, glycerol, tricresyl phosphate, poly(ethylene glycol), dimethyl phthalate, dibutyl phthalate and many others. The best proved to be 45% poly(ethylene glycol) on Zikeev Tripoli earth and 30% tricresyl phosphate on diatomite brick.

The experiments established the optimum conditions for the separation of the mixture under study: column temperature $77 - 78°$; flow rate of carrier gas (helium) 40 ml/min; gas pressure at column inlet 1.2 atm; length of column 4 meters, its internal diameter 6 mm. The sensitivity of the potentiometer was adjusted in accordance with the concentration of the compound sought in the mixture.

TABLE 31. Times of retention (minutes) of a number of components at different experimental temperatures

| Compound | Temperature of analysis, °C | | |
|---|---|---|---|
| | 48 | 77 | 100 |
| Propanol . . . . . . . . . . . . . | 39.0 | 16.1 | 12.5 |
| Ethanol . . . . . . . . . . . . . | 24.5 | 13.5 | 5.6 |
| Acetone . . . . . . . . . . . . | 15.5 | 7.5 | 5.6 |
| Methanol . . . . . . . . . . . . . | 15.2 | 11.0 | 6.1 |
| Methyl acetate . . . . . . . . . . | 15.0 | 5.2 | 4.0 |
| Ethyl acetate . . . . . . . . . . . | 12.0 | 9.5 | 6.0 |
| Methyl ethyl ketone . . . . . . . | 9.8 | 7.5 | 4.6 |
| Ethyl formate . . . . . . . . . . | 8.2 | 6.1 | 4.5 |
| Acetaldehyde . . . . . . . . . . | 7.7 | 3.7 | 2.5 |
| Diethyl ether . . . . . . . . . . | 4.0 | 2.6 | 2.0 |

Table 31 shows the results of a chromatographic separation of a model mixture of 10 components, which may be expected to be present in industrial products. The experiments were performed at three temperatures to ascertain the optimum temperature values. At 48 and 77° the separation is fairly satisfactory; at 100° the peaks of some of the components merge. The optimum temperature proved to be 77° which corresponds to a complete separation of the mixture within a fairly short time.

These results ensured a successful separation of the methanolic fraction of hydrolysis alcohol industry. Methanol, ethanol, ethyl acetate, acetone, methyl acetate, ethyl formate, acetaldehyde and two unidentified components were found in the fraction. The identification of the compounds was effected by comparing the times of retention of the components of the sample with those of model compounds and by the method of addition of known compounds into the sample product.

For purposes of quantitative determinations, calibration curves were plotted for each compound, which gave the relationship between the amount of the substance introduced into the chromatograph and the area under the peak on the elution curve. The peak areas were found from the formula:

$$S = h d_{1/2} \eta,$$

where $S$ is the peak area, $cm^2$; $h$ is the peak height, cm; $d_{1/2}$ is the width of the peak at mid-height, cm, and $\eta$ is the sensitivity of the potentiometer in the chromatograph.

The amount of the sample introduced was measured with the aid of a graduated microsyringe to within $\pm$ 0.0002 ml.

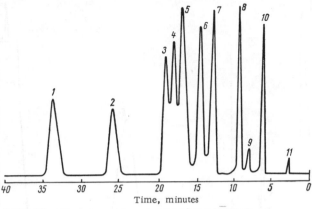

FIGURE 51. Chromatographic separation of model mixture:

1 – methyl ethyl ketone; 2 – ethyl acetate; 3 – acetone; 4 – isopropyl
formate; 5 – ethanol; 6 – ethyl formate; 7 – methanol; 8 – methyl
formate; 9 – acetaldehyde; 10 – diethyl ether; 11 – air.

Samples of the methanolic fraction obtained in a hydrolysis plant were
withdrawn in a systematic manner. Analyses of these samples showed that
the composition of the product is not constant and that the contents of
individual components vary within the following limits (%): methanol
83.6 — 92.2; ethanol 2.12 — 5.0; ethyl acetate 0.19 — 0.42; acetone 0.015 —
0.93; methyl acetate 0.23 — 0.96; ethyl formate 0.38 — 2.08; acetaldehyde
0.14 — 1.27; other compounds 0.35 — 2.5. These differences become much
larger for samples taken in different plants. It was shown that a large
amount of ethanol is lost in the methanolic fraction. Thus, the ethanol
content in the methanolic fractions of the hydrolysis plants varied between
5.7 and 22.8%.

Samples of crude alcohol and industrial ethanol were also analyzed by
the chromatographic method. The former contained methyl acetate, ethyl
acetate and methanol, while the latter contained methyl acetate.

We continued our study of the products of rectification of alcohol /32/
using UKh-1 and KhL-4 chromatographs of Soviet manufacture, and the
argon chromatograph manufactured by Pye Co. in England. We could
identify all the components of MEAF as well as analyze crude and industrial
alcohols in this manner.

Figure 51 represents a successful separation of a 10-component model
mixture containing the ethers, alcohols, ketones and aldehydes which are
present in the products of rectification of ethanol. Mixture separation was
conducted at 50° on two 450×0.4 cm columns connected in series: the first
contained 20% of $\beta, \beta'$-dicyanodiethyl sulfide on celite 545 (30 — 60 mesh).
The flow rate of carrier gas (hydrogen) was 52 ml/minute, the current
intensity of the detector of 195 mA, evaporator temperature 200°,
katharometric detector, UKh-1 chromatograph.

Figure 52 shows a chromatogram of the separation of the components
of industrial MEAF obtained at 22.5° on a 120×0.4 cm column with 10%
poly(ethylene glycol) 400 on celite 545 (100 — 120 mesh), flow rate of carrier
gas (argon) 50 ml/minute, argon detector with Sr[90] ionization, Pye
chromatograph. Nine components could be identified under these conditions.

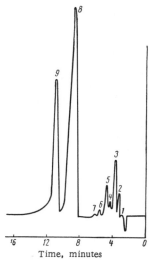

FIGURE 52. Chromatographic separation of MEAF on poly (ethylene glycol) 400:

1 – acetaldehyde; 2 – methyl formate; 3 – acetone; 4 – ethyl formate; 5 – methyl acetate; 6 – ethyl acetate; 7 – methyl ethyl ketone; 8 – methanol; 9 – ethanol.

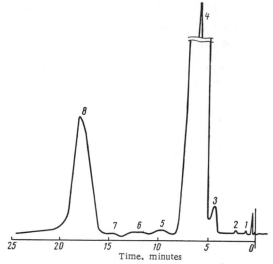

FIGURE 53. Chromatogram showing the separation of the components of hydrolysis alcohol on poly(ethylene glycol) 1540:

1 – ethyl acetate; 2 – methyl ethyl ketone; 3 – methanol; 4 – ethanol; 5 – isopropanol; 6 – isobutanol; 7 – n-pentanol; 8 – water.

The same components were found when the separation of MEAF was conducted at 50° on a $450 \times 0.4$ cm column with 15% poly(ethylene glycol) 1540 on celite 545 (30 — 60 mesh), flow rate of carrier gas (hydrogen) 46 ml/minute, current intensity of detector 195 mA, katharometric detection, UKh-1 chromatograph.

The succession of the emergence of MEAF components becomes altogether different when a $450 \times 0.4$ cm column with 10% benzyldiphenyl on celite 545 (30 — 60 mesh) is employed. The separation was conducted on this column at 56°, the flow rate of carrier gas (hydrogen) was 89 ml/ minute, current intensity of detector 190 mA, UKh-1 chromatograph. Under these conditions two new components of the MEAF were detected — isopropanol and propionaldehyde.

The crude ethanol and industrial ethanol manufactured by a hydrolysis plant were analyzed on a $240 \times 0.4$ cm column with 15% poly(ethylene glycol) 1540 on celite 545 (30 — 60 mesh) at 60°, the flow rate of carrier gas (hydrogen) was 117 ml/minute. Chromatograph KhL-4, katharometric detection, current intensity of detector 90 mA.

It is seen from the chromatogram in Figure 53 that the hydrolysis alcohol contains methanol, ethyl acetate, methyl ethyl ketone, isopropanol, isobutanol, n-pentanol and water as impurities.

The method is suitable not only for quality control of industrial products but also for current control of technological processes, in particular, rectification.

182

Gas-liquid chromatography can also be employed in the analysis of the rectification products of sulfite waste alcohol industry. Jensen et al. /33/ studied the composition of fusel oils from sulfite alcohol. Kamibayasi et al. /34/ studied the distribution of low-boiling acetals, acetaldehyde, methanol and paraldehyde during the distillation of alcohol from the spent sulfite liquor. They showed that dimethyl acetate* and paraldehyde are formed when the alcohol is distilled in a column.

Brännland /35/ developed a method for the determination of alcohol in sulfate fermentation mixture (mash) and condensate in the presence of aldehydes, methanol and higher alcohols. The analyses were conducted on a chromatograph with a katharometric detector.

## 3. Analysis of products of the furfural industry

General methods of chromatographic analysis of furfural and furfural derivatives

Furfural is the main product of the hydrolytic furfural industry, which is extensively developed outside the Soviet Union and is now rapidly growing in the Soviet Union as well. Chromatographic methods may be utilized in the production control of furfural, mainly in the determination of furfural in aqueous furfural-containing condensates, in the intermediate products of furfural manufacture and in the commercial product.

Furfural as a side product is formed in many processes of hydrolysis, wood-chemical, and pulp and paper industries. It is found as a rule in hydrolyzates, lyes, pyroligneous distillate and in other products, its analytical determination being complicated by the presence of numerous impurities — alcohols, aldehydes, ketones, ethers, terpenes, etc.

Recently, catalytic conversions of furfural have been the object of intensive studies. These reactions are now frequently investigated with the aid of chromatographic methods.

In the separation of mixtures which contain not only furfural but also its derivatives, as well as other carbonyl compounds, ethers, alcohols, etc., column chromatography, thin layer chromatography and (recently) gas-liquid chromatography are all employed.

**Column chromatography.** Successful chromatographic separation of furfural, methylfurfural and hydroxymethylfurfural as 2,4-dinitrophenyl-hydrazones (DNPH) was carried out by Wahhab /36/. The mixture of the three hydrazones is dissolved in $CS_2$ and passed through a column with anhydrous $MgSO_4$, when two zones are obtained. The first zone is eluted from the column with carbon disulfide, after which $CS_2$ is displaced from the column with petroleum ether and the chromatogram is eluted with anhydrous benzene when the second zone is split into two. The lower zone is extracted with benzene, while the upper is extracted with a mixture of 30% ethyl acetate and benzene. A complete separation is obtained in 25 minutes in a $10 \times 2$ cm column. In order to identify the components in each zone, genuine DNPH of furfural, methylfurfural and hydroxymethyl-furfural were added to the eluate and the eluate again passed through the column.

* [Sic in Russian, original paper not available.]

The degree of separation of the mixture and the extraction of the zones are effected /37/ by the identities of the sorbent and of the solvent.  The sorbents tested included talcum, calcium carbonate, magnesium sulfate, magnesium oxide, silica gel, and a 1:1 mixture of talcum with silica gel.  The adsorption of DNPH on the sorbent decreased in the following sequence of solvents: petroleum ether, benzene, acetoacetic ester, ethanol.  Satisfactory results were obtained with columns $8-10$ cm long and $2-3$ cm in diameter filled with magnesium sulfate.  Successive elution of dinitrophenylhydrazones with different solvents was conducted in the sequence of increasing eluting powers.

In a study of the products of decomposition of carbohydrates /38/ a mixture of furfural, 5-hydroxymethylfurfural, furyl alcohol, fumaric acid and other compounds was separated on an alumina column.

Preparative separation of the mixture was conducted on a $33\times4$ cm column with alkaline $Al_2O_3$.  Elution with acetone resulted in the simultaneous emergence of furfural, 5-hydroxymethylfurfural, furylic alcohol and fumaric acid; mesityl oxide was eluted with ethyl acetate and carbohydrates with methanol and water.  The acetone eluate was concentrated and rechromatogrammed on a $70\times4$ cm column with 925 g neutral $Al_2O_3$.  Elution with toluene resulted in the appearance in the eluate of furfural, mixture of furfural and furyl alcohol and pure furyl alcohol, in that order.  Hydroxy-methylfurfural was eluted from the column with chloroform, and fumaric acid with 95% ethanol.  The degree of separation was checked by chromato-graphic analysis of the eluate on paper, using toluene as solvent (in the analysis of furfural and furyl alcohol fractions).  Fractions containing hydroxymethylfurfural and fumaric acid were developed with butanol: acetic acid: water = 4:1:1 and with a mixture of acetone with methanol.

Khol'kin and Ponurov /39/ separated a mixture of furfural, acetone, acetic acid and turpentine (1:1:0.5:0.5 by volume) on a $15\times1$ cm column with $Al_2O_3$ of activity II.  The terpenes in the turpentine are not separated in this way; the eluent was benzyl acetate.

Cortis-Jones /40/ described the separation of furfural from cholesterol by gel filtration on a copolymer of styrene and divinylbenzene.

A mixture of carbonyl compounds containing furfural was separated /41/ on a column of Amberlite IRA-400, previously treated with sodium bisulfite or sodium bicarbonate solution.

The reaction mixture obtained in catalytic synthesis of maleic anhydride from furfural was purified from cations on KU-1 and KU-2 cation exchangers /42/.

The presence of hydroxymethylfurfural in starch hydrolyzates has been demonstrated /43/ by chromatographic and spectrophotometric techniques.

Bird and Stevens /44/ described a determination of 5-nitro-2-furfural-dazine in nitrofurazone on an alumina column, in which a photometric determination is carried out on the eluate at 378 m$\mu$; chloroform serves as the eluent.  Kemula et al. /45/ developed a chromatographic method for the analysis of a mixture of anti- and synoximes of 5-nitrofurfural and furazole.

Column chromatography on KGS silica gel ($30-50$ mesh) was employed /46/ in the analysis of the acid products of oxidation of furfural in the gaseous phase.  The silica gel was preliminarily washed with the eluent — chloroform: n-butanol = 80:20 — to which 0.5N sulfuric acid had been added, as the stationary phase.  Samples of the eluate were titrated against

0.025 N alcoholic NaOH. The contents of maleic and fumaric acids were determined in the oxidation products.

The chromatographic method was applied /47/ in a study of the resinous products of autooxidation of furfural. It had been previously established /48/ that the resinous substances formed in the process are heterogeneous. It was accordingly necessary /47/ to find sorbents on which the resinous substances could be fractionated and to find the conditions under which the individual fractions of these substances would emerge into the filtrate for the sake of further study. Frontal, elution and elution-displacement techniques were applied, as a result of which the resinous substances could be successfully fractionated and the individual zones separated in the filtrate.

These studies showed that when a partly resinous sample of furfural is passed through a chromatographic column filled with alumina, the resinous substances form three zones, each of a different color. However, these zones could not be quantitatively transferred to the filtrate. The incomplete displacement of the resinous furfural fractions is due to the high absorbent power of active alumina. In addition, the highly active alumina is often responsible for secondary reactions, as a result of which the adsorbent turns pink when wetted with the solvent.

Resinous substances are best separated on starch. The first zone is fully eluted with benzene, the second is partly displaced by water and, more completely, by ethanol. A narrow zone of resinous substances which could not be displaced into the filtrate was noted in the top part of the columns. The following optimum conditions were established: furfural sample volume 0.5 ml (for a 1 — 2% content of resinous substances). Volume of solvent to wet the sorbent 7 ml; volume of solvent for elution 10.0 ml; volume of solvent for displacement 10.0 ml. Internal diameter of column 11 mm, height of adsorbent column 20 cm.

The area under each peak on the elution curve of the elution-displacement analysis is proportional to the amount of resinous substances taken for the analysis. As the content of resinous substances in furfural increases, the heights and areas of the peaks increase, so that the contents of individual resinous components in the furfural can be determined.

The use of two successive displacing solvents was tried out. The results shown in Figure 54 indicate that all three zones of the resinous substances can be eluted into the filtrate. On comparing the optical densities and the acidity values of the different fractions it is seen that the faintly colored zone which can be displaced with water is the most strongly acidic, i. e., it consists mainly of low-molecular organic acids. The high acidity of the remaining zones is due in the first place to the acidity of the high-molecular products of autooxidation of furfural.

It seemed of interest to follow the sequence of formation of the individual fractions of resinous substances during the autooxidation of furfural. To do this, a chromatographic analysis was performed on the resinous substances formed by the autooxidation of furfural at 100°, in free contact with atmospheric oxygen. The emergence curves of the elution-displacement analysis (ethanol was the displacing solvent) of a few samples of furfural are shown in Figure 55.

These data show that both the first and the second fractions of resinous substances are formed at the same time in the very first stages of the reaction. As the reaction proceeds, the concentration of resinous substances

185

increases, as indicated by the increased surface area of the first and second peaks on the emergence curves. The optical properties of the individual fractions of resinous substances in the visible light were compared.

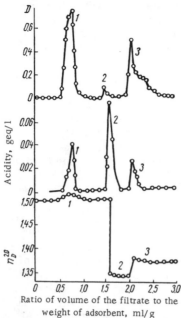

FIGURE 54. Chromatographic fractionation of resinous substances of furfural into three zones (adsorbent: starch):

1 — elution with benzene; 2 — displacement with water; 3 — displacement with ethanol.

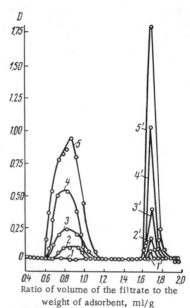

FIGURE 55. Emergence curves of elution-displacement analysis of furfural samples taken during the autooxidation at 100°C (adsorbent: starch).

To purify furfural from impurities /50/, it may be passed through an adsorption column with active alumina. This method was employed /51/ in the preparative purification of furfural. The purpose of the purification of furfural was to obtain a neutral product /52/ with parameters fully identical with the standard values. As a preliminary step, a relative evaluation of the effectiveness of the different methods of furfural purification formerly employed was conducted, when it was found that none of the methods yielded a neutral pure furfural.

Good results were obtained by using active alumina, which reduces the acidity of furfural to practically zero and has a high sorption capacity. Accordingly, the following procedure for the preparative purification of furfural was adopted:

a) preliminary vacuum distillation of furfural;

b) neutralization of the distillate by passing it through an aluminum oxide column;

c) final vacuum distillation of furfural on a fractionation column at 1 — 2 mm Hg residual pressure.

The parameters of the product thus obtained are practically identical with those of perfectly pure furfural.

**Paper chromatography.** Since furfural is quite volatile, its derivatives are employed in paper chromatography. Shimanskaya and Slavinskaya /53/ gave methods for the chromatographic analysis of mixtures of furfural with other carbonyl compounds as 2, 4-dinitrophenylhydrazones /54/, Girard reagent derivatives /55/ and as hydroxamic acids /56/.

Conditions for the separation of carbonyl compounds containing furfural by paper chromatography are shown in Table 32.

TABLE 32. Separation of furfural-containing mixtures of carbonyl compounds by paper chromatography

| Reagent for the preparation of derivatives | Chromatographic paper brand | Solvent | Spray reagent | References |
|---|---|---|---|---|
| Girard T and Girard P reagents | Whatman No. 1 | Butanol : ethanol : water = 27 : 3 : 10 | None | 55 |
| 2, 4-Dinitrophenyl-hydrazine | Whatman No. 1, previously held in N, N-dimethyl-formamide | n-Hexane | Spots visible in UV light | 54 |
| Benzenesulfohydroxamic acid | | Butanol : acetic acid : water = 4 : 1 : 5 | 2% solution of $FeCl_3$ | 56 |

A qualitative detection method for aldehydes and ketones by paper chromatography has been described. The most sensitive reagent for the detection of aldehydes is Schiff's reagent containing 0.15% $H_2SO_4$; furfural is best detected by Nessler's reagent.

Paper chromatography is also employed in the analysis of other compounds of the furane series, such as the mixture of 5-hydroxymethyl-furfural and levulinic acid formed by the decomposition of hexoses /58/, and in a study /59/ of the connection between the structure and chromatographic behavior of monocarboxylic and dicarboxylic acids of furane, pyrrole and thiophene series. Paper chromatography served /60/ to identify derivatives of furane and dibasic aliphatic acids and also /61/ acids contained in the products of the catalytic oxidation of furfural to maleic anhydride. The separation was conducted by the ascending method on Whatman No. 1, treated with a 1% solution of oxalic acid and washed with water. The acids were applied to the paper as ammonium salts; the solvent employed was the system 95% ethanol : 25% solution of ammonia = 100 : 1, and the spots given by the acids were detected by bromophenol blue. The catalysis product contained furfural, maleic and tartaric acids. Condensation products of furyl alcohol may also be studied by paper chromatography /62/.

**Thin layer chromatography.** The applications of thin layer chromatography in the determination of furfural and its derivatives are limited. In a study of the composition of essential oils /63/, terpenes as well as furfural were detected in this manner. Furfural is detected by thin layer chromatography using 2, 4-dinitrophenylhydrazine /64/. $\alpha$-Methylfurfural, as well as furfural were found /65/ in essential oils by thin layer chromatography.

**Gas chromatography of furanes.** Most compounds of the furane series are highly volatile, owing to which complex mixtures can be separated by this technique. Hanneman et al. /66/ reported the times of retention of different compounds, including a number of compounds in the furane series, by using molten salts as the stationary phase in gas-liquid chromatography. Shuikin et al. /67/ described the analysis of mixtures of furane and tetrahydrofurane homologs by gas-liquid chromatography.

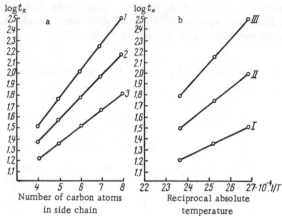

FIGURE 56. Dependence of log $t_\kappa$ on the number of carbon atoms in the molecule (a) and on the reciprocal absolute temperature (b) (stationary phase: silicone elastomer E-301):

1 — 100°C; 2 — 120°C; 3 — 150°C; I — furane; II — ethylfurane; III — butylfurane.

Sylvane, furfural and furyl alcohol /68/ can be determined on a 200×0.6 cm column with 5% poly(p-isooctylphenol ether) on NaCl; column temperature 140°, hydrogen flow rate 85 ml/min. If this technique is employed, the qualitative and quantitative analysis of the mixture takes only 45 minutes.

Major gas-liquid chromatographic studies on furanes are now carried out in the Institute for Organic Synthesis of the Academy of Sciences of the Latvian SSR. Gas-liquid chromatography was employed /69/ in quantitative analyses of mixtures containing furane, its alkyl derivatives, tetrahydrofurane, tetrahydropyran, dihydropyran, butanol-1, furfural, furyl and tetrahydrofuryl alcohols and water. The elastomer E-301, dinonyl phthalate and tricresyl phosphate were used as stationary phases.

The following are the optimum analytical conditions: the column is charged with 25% of silicone elastomer E-301 on celite 545 (kieselguhr), column temperature 100° in the separation of furane derivatives and 120° in the separation of mixtures containing high-boiling alcohols and furfural; rate of flow of carrier gas (helium) 1.5 liter/hour, pressure drop in column 160 — 1200 mm Hg, Griffin GV chromatograph, experimental error in the analysis of alkylfuranes ± 25%.

It was shown that there was a linear relationship between the logarithm of the retention time and the number of carbon atoms in the alkylfuranes to be separated at 100 and 150°; this is in agreement with the findings of Shuikin et al. /67/, and also with earlier results /70/. Andersons et al. /71/ also showed that there is a linear relationship between the logarithm of the retention time of furane, ethylfurane and butylfurane and the reciprocal absolute temperature of the analysis (Figure 56).

An example of the separation of a mixture containing several components is shown in Figure 57, while the analysis of a more complex mixture is shown in Figure 58. Table 33 shows the values of the relative retention volumes of a number of furane derivatives /69/.

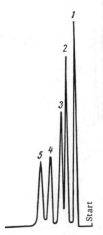

This method was applied to the study of low-boiling (below 120°) products of catalytic conversion of tetra-hydrofurylic alcohol, which included furane, methyl-furane, tetrahydrofurane, butanol-1 and dihydropropan.

Andersons et al. /72/ also developed a method for the determination of furane in mixture with methylfurane, toluene and air. When the silicone elastomer E-301 is used as the stationary phase, mixtures of furane and toluene can be analyzed to within 2 — 5 rel.% at column temperatures of 100 and 150°. Furane present in air in concentrations of 75 — 150 mg/l can be fairly accurately determined at 100°. Experimental conditions for the determination of methylfurane present as impurity in furane have also been established.

FIGURE 57. Separation of a mixture of furane, methylfurane, tetrahydrofurane, dihydropyran, and butanol-1 at 100°C:

1 – furane; 2 – methylfurane; 3 – tetrahydrofurane; 4 – butanol-1; 5 – dihydropyran.

Giller et al. /73/ used an earlier method /69/ to study the products of alkylation of furane by olefins which included the initial furane, methylfurane, ethyl-furane, isopropylfurane, n-propylfurane, isobutylfurane and n-butylfurane — by gas-liquid chromatography. The interpretation of the chromatograms was verified by comparison with those given by model compounds.

Polyakova et al. /74/ described a method for the determination of furane and carbon dioxide in the products of decarbonylation of furfural. The analysis is conducted on a two-step, three-section column at 34°, flow rate of carrier gas (nitrogen) 13.8 ml/min, katharometric detector, total duration of analysis 25 minutes, experimental error 1 — 7 rel.%. The analysis is begun by separating the zone common to hydrogen and carbon dioxide from furane on a 150×0.5 cm column with 10% tricresyl phosphate on Inzen diatomite (0.025 — 0.050 cm); $H_2$ and $CO_2$ are then separated on an 80×0.5cm column with silica gel KSK (0.025 — 0.050 cm). Furane is determined on an 80×0.5 cm column with 5% tricresyl phosphate on diatomite. This may be done by the combustion of furane to $CO_2$ which is then determined.

Gas chromatography was employed /75, 76/ to determine furane and n-butanol in the tetrahydrofurane obtained by the hydrogenation of furane. The experimental conditions were as follows: a 250×0.3 cm column with 30% tricresyl phosphate on Inzen diatomite (0.025 — 0.050 cm), temperature 68°, flow rate of carrier gas (nitrogen) 16.3 ml/minute, pressure at entry 0.75 atm, katharometric detection; relative errors 2.4% and 3.2% in the determination of furane and n-butanol respectively, time of determination about 50 minutes.

α-Methylfurane and α-methyltetrahydrofurane were separated /76/ by gas-liquid chromatography on a 300×1.6 cm column with 20% dibutyl sebacate on Inzen brick; they were identified by IR spectroscopy.

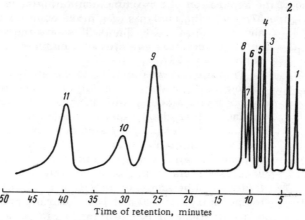

FIGURE 58. Separation of a mixture of furane derivatives at 100°C
(stationary phase: silicone elastomer E-301):

1 – water; 2 – furane; 3 – methylfurane; 4 – tetrahydrofurane; 5 –
butanol; 6 – methyltetrahydrofurane; 7 – tetrahydropyran; 8 – dihydropyran; 9 – furfural; 10 – furylic alcohol; 11 – tetrahydrofurylic
alcohol.

Janak et al. /77/ developed a method for the identification of tetrahydrofurane acetals by gas chromatographic analysis on a column with 25% high-
vacuum silicon grease on celite (0.025 – 0.03 cm) treated with hexamethyldisilazane at 170°; hydrogen was employed as the carrier gas.

TABLE 33. Relative retention volumes of furane derivatives (internal standard: furane)

| Furane derivative | Stationary phase | | | | | | | | |
|---|---|---|---|---|---|---|---|---|---|
| | silicone elastomer E-301 | | | dinonyl phthalate | | | tricresyl phosphate | | |
| | temperature, °C | | | | | | | | |
| | 100 | 120 | 150 | 100 | 120 | 150 | 100 | 120 | 150 |
| Furane . . . . . . . . . | 1.00 | 1.00 | 1.00 | 1.00 | 1.00 | 1.00 | 1.00 | 1.00 | 1.00 |
| Methylfurane . . . . . . | 1.72 | 1.52 | 1.31 | 1.72 | 1.56 | 1.35 | 1.72 | 1.51 | 1.33 |
| Ethylfurane . . . . . . . | 3.15 | 2.10 | 1.72 | 3.53 | 2.87 | – | 2.89 | 2.33 | – |
| Propylfurane . . . . . . | 5.12 | 3.85 | 2.62 | 6.00 | 5.04 | 2.90 | 5.62 | 4.03 | 2.81 |
| Butylfurane . . . . . . . | 9.60 | 6.26 | 3.84 | 12.29 | 9.39 | 4.90 | 10.82 | 7.30 | 4.19 |
| Tetrahydrofurane . . . . | 2.00 | 1.72 | 1.48 | 2.19 | 1.89 | 1.50 | 2.28 | 1.91 | 1.56 |
| Tetrahydropyran . . . . | – | 2.06 | 1.95 | – | 2.42 | – | 2.90 | 2.45 | 1.93 |
| Dihydropyran . . . . . . | 2.85 | 2.36 | 1.85 | 3.12 | 2.58 | 1.92 | 3.21 | 2.56 | 1.93 |
| Butanol-1 . . . . . . . | 2.25 | 1.85 | 1.45 | 4.39 | 3.26 | 1.92 | 5.74 | 3.97 | 2.62 |
| Furfural . . . . . . . . | – | 4.40 | 3.14 | – | 12.65 | – | – | – | 10.90 |
| Furyl alcohol . . . . . . | – | 5.02 | 3.31 | – | – | – | – | – | – |
| Tetrahydrofuryl alcohol. | – | 5.72 | 4.25 | – | 17.36 | – | – | – | 13.12 |

The behavior of 13 furane sulfides and furylthienylmethane derivatives
was studied by gas-liquid chromatography on 20% poly(ethylene glycol
adipate) on diatomite brick at different temperatures /78/.

Gas-liquid chromatography was also employed /79/ in a study of the decomposition products of cool flame combustion, when cis- and trans-2, 5-dimethyltetrahydrofurane, 2-ethyltetrahydrofurane and other products were identified by IR spectroscopy, and in a study of the base-catalyzed condensation products of mesityl oxide under homogeneous and heterogeneous conditions /80/, as well as in studies of other reactions.

Gas chromatography was employed /81/ in the study of the mechanism of conversion of fructose to hydroxymethylfurfural. Gas chromatography of the acetylated reaction mixture demonstrated the presence of glucose.

Gas-liquid chromatography was utilized to determine /82/ tetrahydrofurane in the reaction mixture obtained during the synthesis of cyclooctatriene from ethylene, which also contained acetone, benzene and dioxane. The separation was effected at 130° on a 245 cm long column with 30% silicone A on Zeolite A (60 mesh). The flow rate of nitrogen carrier gas was 15 ml/min, that of carrier hydrogen was 30 ml/min, volume of sample 1.47 $\mu$l, falem ionization detector.

Up to $2 \cdot 10^{-5}\%$ furfural can be identified in gasoil /83/ by gas-liquid chromatography. The analysis is conducted at 50° on a column with 0.4% of 2, 2'-iminodipropionitrile on glass beads (100 — 120 mesh) for a sample volume corresponding to 0.25 — 0.50 ml of the dry ether extract. If the inlet pressure of the carrier gas (argon) is 0.84 — 1.06 atm, the furfural peak appears in 40 minutes.

Stevens /84/ developed a method for the determination of acrolein and furfural in phenol-acrolein and phenol-furfural resins. Phenol and furfural were separated on a 366×0.6 cm column with 10% SF-96 silicone on Fluoropak; flow rate of carrier gas (helium) 105 ml/min; m-cresol was used as the internal standard.

Analysis of intermediate products of
furfural manufacture by gas-liquid
chromatography

Gas-liquid chromatography was recently successfully employed in the analysis of different technical furfural-containing products. It was applied /85/ to the study of the composition of the condensate of vent steam obtained during the prehydrolysis of hardwoods. To do this, the products were fractionally distilled on a packed column and the components of each fraction were separated by gas chromatography. The condensate proved to have the following composition (in relative units): furfural 200, acetic acid 60, methanol 12, 5-methylfurfural 4.9, diacetyl 2.8, methyl acetate 1.2, acetaldehyde and dimethylacetal 0.6, acetone 0.1, acetaldehyde below 0.1; methyl formate and formic acid were absent. The variations in the contents of these components during the process of prehydrolysis were studied.

It must be stressed that gas-liquid chromatography is a very promising method in the analysis of the different intermediate, side and final products of furfural industry. A particularly interesting application of the method is the control of the processes involved in the rectification of furfural.

That such analyses are in principle feasible was shown by Ibraev and Goryaev /86/, who separated model systems containing furfural, methylfurfural, methanol, acetic acid and ethyl acetate. These compounds are also present in the industrial products of furfural manufacture.

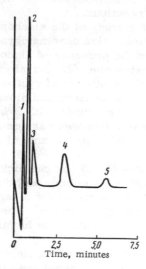

FIGURE 59. Chromatogram of a model mixture:

1 – methanol; 2 – ethyl acetate; 3 – acetic acid; 4 – furfural; 5 – methylfurfural.

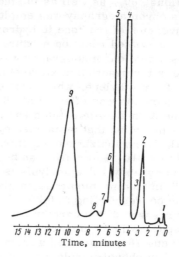

FIGURE 60. Chromatogram of the head fraction in the fractionation of furfural:

1 – air; 2 – acetaldehyde; 3 – methyl formate; 4 – propionic aldehyde; 5 – methyl acetate; 6 – acetone; 7, 8 – not identified; 9 – methanol.

The analytical conditions were as follows: a 120×0.4 cm column with 25% dinonyl phthalate on celite (kieselguhr), 160 – 170°, flow rate of carrier gas (hydrogen) 12 – 30 ml/min, inlet overpressure 0.7 – 1.2 atm, Shandon chromatography with flame ionization detector. The volume of the sample 1 μl, time of analysis 10 minutes.

Figure 59 shows an example of the separation of a model mixture. Silicone oil and glycerol were also tried out as stationary phases in the separation of model mixtures, but acetic acid could not be separated from ethyl acetate in this manner.

Aqueous, furfural-containing solutions can be analyzed by this technique; furfural is then extracted with ethyl acetate.

Fedotova and Tsirlin /87/ used gas-liquid chromatography in their study of the composition of the head fraction from the main furfural column in the rectification of furfural-containing condensates obtained as a result of processing husks of sunflower seeds, cottonseed hulls and oakwood tan waste.

The head fractions were first rectified on a laboratory column and were then analyzed on columns 0.8 cm in diameter; the columns contained poly(ethylene glycol) 1000 on diatomite brick INZ-600 (0.5 – 0.25 mm); the stationary phase: solid support ratio was 30:100 by weight. Column temperature $60-65°$, flow rate of carrier gas (hydrogen) $110-120$ ml/min, katharometric detector, UKh-1 chromatograph. Mixtures can also be separated on diethylene glycol succinate and on dioctyl sebacate with sebacic acid as the stationary phase.

TABLE 34. Retention times $\tau_{sp}$ and retention volumes $V_R^°$

| Component | Bp, °C | Stationary phase | | | | | |
|---|---|---|---|---|---|---|---|
| | | diethylene glycol succinate | | dioctyl sebacate with sebacic acid | | poly(ethylene glycol) 1000 | |
| | | $\tau_{sp}$ | $V_R^°$ | $\tau_{sp}$ | $V_R^°$ | $\tau_{sp}$ | $V_R^°$ |
| Acetaldehyde . . . . . | 20.7 | 175 | 89 | 130 | 90 | 150 | 165 |
| Methyl formate . . . . | 31.5 | 190 | 110 | – | – | 175 | 174 |
| Propionic aldehyde . . | 48.8 | 255 | 150 | – | – | 195 | 230 |
| Acetone . . . . . . . | 56.5 | 320 | 190 | 240 | 223 | 300 | 384 |
| Methyl acetate . . . . | 57.0 | 325 | 182 | 310 | 314 | 265 | 374 |
| Methanol . . . . . . . | 64.7 | 410 | 220 | 215 | 206 | 455 | 712 |

Satisfactory separation of an artefact mixture containing acetaldehyde, methyl formate, propionic aldehyde, methyl acetate, acetone and methanol could be achieved in this manner.

Table 34 shows the retention times and retention volumes of a number of components present in the products of furfural manufacture.

Figure 60 shows the chromatogram of the head fraction (bp $50-60°$) of the distillate of the hydrolytic furfural obtained from tan waste.

Gas-liquid chromatography was also employed in the production control of Defoliant E which is based on furfural /89/.

In addition to the analysis of the intermediate products of the furfural industry, chromatographic methods are also used in quality control of technical grade furfural.

Chromatographic analysis of technical grade furfural

The analysis of technical grade furfural manufactured by hydrolysis plants presents serious difficulties. Conventional analytical methods give erroneous results owing to the presence of impurities.

The main impurities present in technical grade furfural obtained from the steam condensates of autovaporization of the hydrolyzate are water, turpentine and organic acids. Furfural obtained from hardwoods and from agricultural residues contains the same kind of impurities, except for turpentine. In industrial practice furfural is determined by the bromide-bromate method which, as a rule, gives high results. More accurate results are obtained if furfural is determined by barbituric acid, but such determinations are very long (about one day) and are not used in production control for this reason.

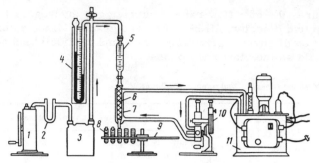

FIGURE 61. Diagram of apparatus for chromatographic analysis:

1 — pump; 2 — U-shaped filter; 3 — receiver; 4 — mercury manometer; 5 — funnel; 6 — chromatographic column; 7 — water jacket; 8 — graduated tubes; 9 — rotating disk stand; 10 — refractometer; 11 — water thermostat.

The chromatographic method for the analysis of furfural developed by Khol'kin et al. /90/ involves selective adsorption on a solid sorbent of the different components of technical grade furfural.

In developing the method the authors clarified the relationship between the amounts of impurities in the furfural and the shape of the elution curve; the effect of organic impurities on the accuracy of the determination; the effect of the temperature, geometry of chromatographic column and other experimental parameters. A thorough check of the method showed that it yields accurate results in the analysis of furfural and that it may be employed both in research and in industrial laboratories /91/. For a brief description of the method, see also /92/, p. 144.

A diagram of the apparatus employed is shown in Figure 61. Chromatographic column 6 is filled with the dry granulated adsorbent — alumina, activity grade II (TU MKhP 2962-54). The column is filled dry, without previously wetting the adsorbent with the solvent. To do this, the alumina is poured into the column through a narrow stem funnel, and the column is continually tapped against the laboratory bench to ensure a uniform density of the adsorbent. Internal diameter of column 11 mm; height of adsorbent layer 100 mm; volume of adsorbent 9.5 cm$^3$, weight 10.38±0.002 g, bulk density 1.09 — 1.10 g/cm$^3$. The amount of the adsorbent poured in is measured by weighing or by measuring the volume occupied by the adsorbent in the column. The column should always be filled in the same manner, as the results may be distorted if the density of the adsorbent is not uniform.

The water jacket 7 serves to keep the column at a constant temperature of 25°. The furfural sample is introduced into the column with the aid of funnel 5, and the filtrate obtained is collected in graduated tubes 8 afixed to the rotating disc stand 9.

The volume of the first portion of the filtrate is 0.1 ml, those of the following portions are 0.3, 0.5 ml and so on, to 1 ml. The number of portions thus collected is 25 — 35. In order to accelerate the rate of filtration of the furfural, an excess pressure is applied with the aid of pump 1. The air from the pump enters funnel 5 through a cotton plug 2 and receiver 3. The magnitude of the excess pressure (250 — 350 mm Hg)

194

is controlled with the aid of mercury manometer 4. Under a pressure of this magnitude the filtration time is $15-20$ minutes.

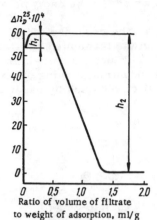

FIGURE 62. General shape of the chromatographic elution curve of crude furfural ($\Delta n_D^{25} \cdot 10^4$ is the difference between $n_D^{25}$ of the filtrate and of the initial sample).

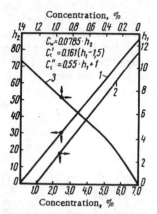

FIGURE 63. Calibration curves for the analysis of terpene-containing furfural:

1 − water ($c_w$); 2 − turpentine in crude furfural $c_t'$; 3 − turpentine in technical grade furfural $\overset{..}{t}$.

The refractive index of the filtrate is determined with the aid of refractometer 10, which should be accurate to at least the fourth decimal figure. The refractometer and the chromatographic column are thermostatted by Vobzer, Heppler or TS-15m water thermostat.

The emergence curve of frontal analysis contains two steps, the difference between which ($\Delta n^{25} \cdot 10^4$) is proportional to the content of water and turpentine in the furfural (Figure 62). These are the major impurities in crude furfural and in technical grade furfural made from autovaporization steam of the hydrolyzate. The furfural content is found by difference. The results of the refractometric analysis of the filtrate are compiled in the form of a table or plotted as a graph, with the values of the refractive indexes along the ordinate and the volume of the filtrate along the abscissa. Calibration curves for the analysis of technical grade furfural and crude furfural are shown in Figure 63. They have been plotted for chromatographic grade alumina, activity II, as sorbent. If other brands of alumina are employed, and also if the adsorbent has been stored for a long time, the calibration graphs must be verified.

Tsirlin /88/ studied the composition of the impurities found in technical grade furfural by gas-liquid chromatography. He detected acetaldehyde, acetone, methanol, methyl formate, methyl acetate, formic and acetic acids and methylfurfural with the aid of genuine standard compounds.

Column chromatography on celite 545 was utilized /93/ to determine furfural in the form of its bisulfite compound in hydrocarbon oils.

## 4. Analysis of the products of the yeast industry

In the yeast industry chromatographic methods are employed to study the substrates on which the yeast is grown and in the analysis of the amino acid composition of the finished product.

Kryuchkova and Vorob'eva /94/ studied the sequence of utilization of pentoses and hexoses by yeast. Sugars in the fermented substrate have been determined by paper chromatography /1/. Kinetic data relating to the consumption of individual sugars by the industrial strains of protein fodder yeast grown on hydrolyzate media have been obtained by paper chromatography /96/.

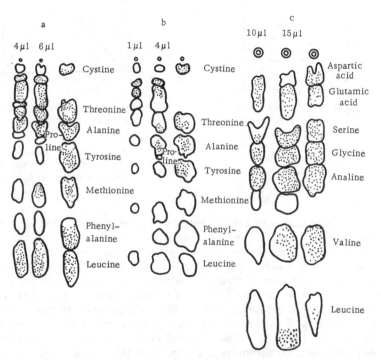

FIGURE 64. Chromatograms of the hydrolyzates of protein fodder yeast:

a — hydrolysis yeast; b and c — sulfite yeast.

The feed value of protein yeasts is determined by their amino acid composition. Nutrition requirements will be met in full by proteins containing valine, leucine, isoleucine, arginine, lysine, threonine, methionine, phenylalanine (or tyrosine), tryptophane and histidine. Lomova /97/ analyzed the amino acid composition of fodder yeast by paper chromatography. To isolate the protein, dry industrial yeast was ground, treated with hot water to remove the carbohydrates, and then with hot alcohol and ether to remove the lipids. The precipitate was separated by centrifugation and the alcohol and ether were suction-filtered through filter paper on a porcelain funnel. The resulting protein was hydrolyzed with

196

6 N HCl for 24 hours in a flask under reflux. The hydrochloric acid was removed from the hydrolyzate by repeated vacuum-distillation at 60°, and the completeness of the removal was checked with Congo Red paper. The hydrolyzate was then dissolved in hot water and the humic substances separated on filter paper.

The amino acids were separated by developing with n-butanol: glacial acetic acid: water = 40:10:50. An 80% aqueous solution of phenol may also be employed. In the former case a 0.002 mg sample is applied to the starting line, in the latter 0.03 mg. The volume of hydrolyzate samples applied to the chromatograms is shown in Figure 64 which shows the results obtained on separating the amino acids of protein hydrolyzates of industrial yeast (Lalsk chromatographic paper) and a sulfite waste alcohol plant (chromatographic paper made of cotton fiber). The solvents used were butanol: acetic acid: water mixture in the former case and phenol in the latter. The components were separated by the descending method. The spots given by the amino acids were detected by spraying the dried chromatograms with a 0.2% solution of ninhydrin in n-butanol saturated with water. The spots appeared after the chromatogram had been held in a drying oven at 80° for 5 minutes. It was found in this way that the protein fodder yeast contained all the indispensable amino acids.

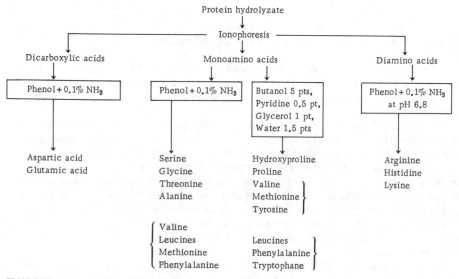

FIGURE 65. Analytical scheme of protein hydrolyzates by one-dimensional chromatography.

Amino acids contained in protein hydrolyzates can be successfully separated /101/ by development in four different solvent systems (Figure 65). Each of these solvents yields discrete spots of a number of amino acids; the acids shown bracketed together give a common spot. If all four solvent systems are used, the spots of all the main amino acids in the proteins can be isolated.

197

In order to improve the qualitative and quantitative analysis of the amino acid composition of protein hydrolyzates it has been recommended /99/ to use phenol containing up to 1.5 — 2% ammonia as solvent. In this way the amino acid composition of the yeast grown on spent ammonium-base sulfite liquors was studied /100/. It was shown that the fodder yeast C a n d i d a u t i l i s contained (%): valine 6.3, leucine 7.0, isoleucine 5.3, threonine 5.5, methionine 1.2, phenylalanine 4.3, tryptophane 1.2, histidine 1.9, lysine 6.7, glycine 4.8, alanine 3.4, serine 5.5, cystine 0.7, proline 3.5, tyrosine 3.3, aspartic acid 4.7, glutamic acid 15.0 and arginine 5.4 on the weight of the protein. The composition of the yeast grown on spent calcium-base liquor does not markedly differ from that just given.

Paper chromatography was utilized /101/ to determine the amino acids in hydrolysis yeast. Chromatography on a diethylaminoethylcellulose column served to isolate and purify the $\beta$-fructofuranosidase from yeast /102/.

Amino acids are frequently analyzed by column chromatography /103/, thin layer chromatography /104/, and by a combination of electrophoresis with paper chromatography /105, 106/. Gas-liquid chromatography has been recently used in the analysis of amino acids /107 — 109/ and their derivatives /110, 111/.

Development of a gas-liquid chromatographic method for the analysis of commercial fodder yeast would be of high practical interest.


## 5. Analysis of products of hydrogenation of sugars

Hydrogenation and hydrogenolysis of sugars yields mixtures of products which are very difficult to analyze by chemical methods. The application of different chromatographic methods, on the other hand, has proved successful.

Mixtures of polyhydric alcohols can be separated on ion exchange resins of the type Dowex-50($\times$12). In this way the products of hydrogenolysis of sorbitol could be separated into four fractions: the glycol fraction, which included ethylene glycol and 1, 2-propylene glycol; a glycerol fraction; an erythritol fraction; and a xylitol and sorbitol fraction /112/. Compounds of polyhydric alcohols with boric acid were studied by paper electrophoresis /113/. Similar complexes with carbohydrates are separated on ion exchange resins /114/ or by electrophoresis /115/. A quantitative determination of glycerol in mixture with other polyhydric alcohols by paper chromatography has been described /116/.

Vasyunina et al. /117/ applied chromatographic methods to the study of the composition of mixtures of polyhydric alcohols formed as a result of catalytic hydrogenolysis of xylitol. These mixtures include ethylene glycol, 1, 2-propylene glycol, glycerol, erythritol and some of the initial xylitol. A complete separation of the mixture of polyhydric alcohols was attained by partition chromatography on cellulose powder column.

Semiquantitative analysis of the mixtures was effected by paper chromatography. The mixtures were developed by the ascending technique on brand M chromatographic paper during 12 — 18 hours and on brand B paper during 6 — 10 hours, using pyridine : ethyl acetate : water = 2 : 7 : 1 as solvent. After drying the spots were revealed by spraying the chromatogram with a saturated solution of potassium periodate; after 6 minutes' holding in the air they were sprayed with a mixture of 10 volumes of 0.1 M benzidine in 50% ethanol, 2 volumes of acetone and 1 volume of 0.2 N HCl /118/. Xylitol, erythritol and glycerol give yellow spots, while ethylene glycol and 1, 2-propylene glycol give white spots against the blue-green background of the chromatogram.

In quantitative evaluation of the chromatogram a visual method /119/ was employed. The method involved the use of a specially prepared calibration scale, which consisted of chromatograms obtained by using standard compounds in known concentrations. The color intensities and spot sizes on the chromatograms given by the sample mixture were compared with those of the scale. The accuracy of the method is low: $0.5 - 1.0$ abs.% for glycerol, erythritol and xylitol and $2.5 - 3.0$ abs.% for ethylene glycol and 1, 2-propylene glycol if the content of the components in the mixture is $20 - 30\%$.

The method was applied /117/ to the analysis of the composition of mixtures of polyhydric alcohols obtained during the hydrogenolysis of xylitol in the laboratory and under industrial conditions.

Belozerova /120/ compared the effectiveness of separation of polyhydric alcohols using eight systems of solvents. A comparison of the mobilities of the different alcohols is given in Table 35. It is seen from the table that most of the components can be separated by the ascending technique in the solvent system butanol: benzene: pyridine: water = 5:1:3:3; the separation of dulcitol and sorbitol by this method is more difficult.

TABLE 35. $R_f$-values of polyhydric alcohols in different solvent systems

| Polyhydric alcohol | n-butanol: ethanol: water = 4:1:5 | n-butanol: ethanol: water = 4:1.1:1.9 | n-butanol: benzene: pyridine: water = 5:1:3:3 | n-butanol: acetic acid: water = 4:1:5 | ethyl acetate: pyridine: water = 7:2:1 | ethyl acetate: pyridine: water = 1:1:1.5 | ethyl acetate: pyridine: water = 1:1:1.5 | n-amyl alcohol: n-propanol: water = 4:1:1.5 | n-propanol: ethyl acetate: water = 7:1:2 |
|---|---|---|---|---|---|---|---|---|---|
| Dulcitol | 0.11 | 0.21 | 0.19 | 0.20 | 0.12 | 0.17 | 0.22 | 0.14 | 0.28 |
| Sorbitol | 0.11 | 0.22 | 0.20 | 0.20 | – | – | – | 0.14 | 0.28 |
| Mannitol | 0.14 | – | – | 0.22 | – | 0.22 | – | 0.14 | 0.33 |
| Xylitol | 0.21 | 0.28 | 0.31 | 0.31 | – | – | – | 0.16 | 0.38 |
| Arabitol | 0.50 | 0.29 | 0.34 | 0.33 | 0.19 | 0.38 | 0.42 | 0.16 | 0.41 |
| Erythritol | 0.32 | – | 0.44 | – | 0.29 | 0.64 | 0.72 | – | 0.46 |
| Glycerol | 0.49 | 0.44 | 0.54 | 0.41 | 0.40 | 0.80 | 0.90 | – | 0.54 |
| Ethylene glycol | – | 0.50 | 0.65 | – | – | – | – | – | 0.65 |
| Chromatographic technique | d (1.5) | a (1) | a (2) | a (1.5) | a (1) | d (1) | d (2) | a (1) | d (1.5) |

Note. d – descending chromatography; a – ascending chromatography; numbers in parentheses indicate the duration of the analysis in days.

For quantitative determination of polyhydric alcohols the components may be eluted from the chromatograms /121/. Paper chromatography has been used /122/ in an investigation of the products of hydrogenation of levoglucosan. After ion exchange purification in solution, a substance was detected in solution which had an $R_f$ corresponding to the $R_f$ of sorbitol

199

monoanhydride (development with butanol: acetic acid: water = 4:1:5; spots revealed with 2% alkaline solution of permanganate).

Paper chromatography was employed /123/ in the determination of sorbitol, xylitol, erythritol, glycerol, ethylene glycol and 1, 2-propylene glycol formed during the catalytic hydrogenolysis of monosaccharides.

Chromatographic analysis makes it possible to study mixtures of alcohols and glycols formed by hydrogenation and fermentation of wood hydrolyzates /124/. Glycerol can be determined /125/ in fermentation solutions on a column of alumina-cellulose mixture.

Gas-liquid chromatography is a promising technique in routine control of monosaccharide processing, in particular, in the production of polyhydric alcohols.

The main product of hydrogenolysis of monosaccharides is glycerol. Since glycerol has a low volatility, a number of workers prepared volatile glycerol derivatives such as glycerol triacetate prior to the chromatographic analysis /126, 127/.

Balakhontseva and Poltinina /128/ developed a method for direct determination of glycerol. The chromatographic column (185×0.6 cm) was filled with 25% of acetylated dextran on celite 545. The acetylated dextran was prepared according to /129/. Temperature of column 214 — 220°, flow rate of carrier gas (helium) 85 — 95 ml/min, pressure 2.1 — 0.2 = 1.9 atm, katharometric detector, current intensity in detector bridge 150 mA, sample volume 0.002 — 0.003 g, sensitivity of potentiometer 1 mV over the scale range, UKh-1 chromatograph.

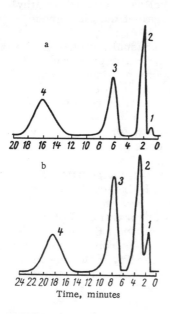

Time, minutes

FIGURE 66. Chromatograms of model mixture (a) and evaporated hydrolyzate (b):

1 — water; 2 — ethylene glycol and 1, 2-propylene glycol; 3 — diethylene glycol; 4 — glycerol.

Figure 66 shows the results of the analysis of an artefact mixture and of the evaporated hydrolyzate. The experimental error is ± 1.5 — 2.4% (absolute), if the average glycerol content in the evaporated hydrogenation product is 20 — 25%. Higher polyhydric alcohols (sorbitol, erythritol) do not interfere with the determination of glycerol and do not cause a deterioration in the performance of the column on repeated use. If there is no need to determine all the components of the hydrolyzate, this technique is to be preferred to paper chromatography.

## 6. Analysis of products of processing of hydrolytic lignin

Chromatographic methods are utilized in the analysis of the products of thermal processing of lignin. Panasyuk /130 — 131/ used paper chromatography to study the composition of phenols obtained by thermal processing of hydrolytic lignin.

TABLE 36. $R_f$ -values of a number of phenols

| Compound | Bp, °C | $R_f$ | Color of spot |
|---|---|---|---|
| Phenol . . . . . . . . | 181 | 0.48 | Yellow orange |
| o–Cresol . . . . . . . . | 191 | 0.54 | Dark orange |
| m–Cresol . . . . . . . . | 203 | 0.48 | Orange |
| p–Cresol . . . . . . . . | 202 | 0.58 | Dark orange |
| Guaiacol . . . . . . . . | 205 | 0.40 | Red violet |
| o–Ethylphenol . . . . . | 207 | 0.54 | Yellow orange |
| 1, 3, 4–Xylenol (m) . . . | 211 | 0.62 | Orange red |
| p–Ethylphenol . . . . . | 214 | 0.58 | The same |
| m–Ethylphenol . . . . . | 219 | 0.66 | Orange pink |
| Methoxycresol . . . . . | 221 | 0.54 | Reddish gray |
| 1, 2, 4–Xylenol (o) . . . | 225 | 0.60 | Yellow orange |

Chromatographic analysis was carried out on phenol fractions obtained in a narrow temperature range by dry-distilling the resins from the lignin of wood or cottonseed hulls. Prior to the analysis the phenols were converted to the ammonium salts by successive treatments with pyridine sulfotrioxide and ammonia. The compounds were separated on Whatman paper No. 2 in the solvent system aqueous ammonia : n-butanol = 1 : 1. The chromatograms were revealed by a solution of 4, 4'-diazoaminotoluene, after which the strips were treated with vapors of hydrochloric acid and ammonia. The color of the spots is unstable, disappears in about half an hour and the spots must be circumscribed in pencil immediately after development. The elution temperature affects the mobility of the phenol ethers. The $R_f$-values of a number of pure phenols at 12° are shown in Table 36.

The ratio between the components in the mixture was determined visually by inspecting the chromatograms.

Nine different phenols and phenol ethers have been identified in the dry-distillation tar from lignin in this manner. The major phenolic component in wood lignin was guaiacol, while cresols were obtained from cottonseed hulls.

Paper chromatography was also applied to the study /132/ of the composition of aldehydes in the oxidation products of hydrolytic lignin from cottonseed hulls. Vanillin and syringin were isolated in this manner.

Morozov /133/ studied the composition of the phenolic components of the bottoms tar obtained by pyrolysis of hydrolytic lignin by column chromatography on silica gel, paper chromatography and gas-liquid chromatography.

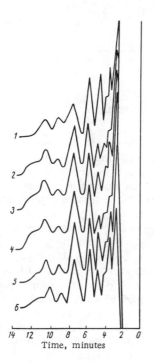

Time, minutes

FIGURE 67. Chromatograms of products of pyrolysis of different samples of hydrolytic lignin (serial numbers of samples are marked on the graphs).

Paper chromatography was applied /134, 135/ to the study of five or six quinone nitropolycarboxylic acids which are obtained as a result of stepwise oxidation by nitric acid of condensed hydrolytic lignin and its hydrolysis in aqueous medium. The ammonium salts of these acids are effective growth stimulators of agricultural plants.

Maleic acid in the reaction mixture obtained by oxidation of model compounds and lignin by nitric acid was also identified by paper chromatography /135, 136/. The solvent used for the development was amyl alcohol : 5 M formic acid = 1:1; the spots were revealed by spraying with a mixture of 0.1 N $AgNO_3$ with 0.1 N $NH_4OH$ (1:1), when the spots appeared after 5 — 6 hours against a brown background.

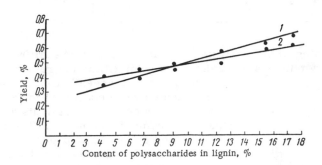

FIGURE 68. The yields of acetaldehyde (1) and acetone (2) as a function of the content of polysaccharides in technical grade lignin.

Polycarboxylic acids may be analyzed by paper chromatography /137 — 139/ as well as by chromatography on celite columns /140/.

Khol'kin and Poletaeva /141/ were the first to employ pyrolytic gas-liquid chromatography to study hydrolytic lignin. The optimum pyrolysis conditions in the modified pyrolytic block of a KhL-7 chromatograph proved to be 11 seconds pyrolysis at 600°.

The following phases in a 200×0.6 cm column were tried out in separating the products of the pyrolysis: 10% poly(ethylene glycol) with dibutyl phthalate (1:2) on Chromosorb P (60 — 80 mesh); 5% poly(ethylene glycol succinate) on celite 545 (60 — 80 mesh); 10% poly(ethylene glycol) 1540 on Chromosorb P (60 — 80 mesh); 10% of a 9:1 mixture of poly(ethylene glycol) and dibutyl phthalate on celite 545 (60 — 80 mesh); and 15% of the nonionic surfactant Provacel W-OF-100 on celite 545 (60 — 80 mesh). The best separation was achieved on the last-named phase; column temperature 100°, flow rate of carrier gas (nitrogen) 30 ml/min, current intensity of detector 90 mA, potentiometer sensitivity 1 mV over the scale range.

The pyrolysis products of technical grade lignin were found to include acetaldehyde, propionic aldehyde, acetone, methyl ethyl ketone and methanol. The contents of individual components were determined with the aid of calibration curves. Examples of chromatographic analyses of different samples of technical grade lignin are shown in Figure 67.

It was found that there is a linear relationship between the yields of acetaldehyde and acetone and the content of polysaccharides in lignin (Figure 68), and also between the yield of formaldehyde and the content of lignin in technical products. The results obtained are of interest in the study of the problems concerning the practical utilization of lignin.

BIBLIOGRAPHY

1. EMEL'YANOVA, I. Z. and T. A. BATRAKOVA. — Gidroliznaya i Lesokhimicheskaya Promyshlennost', No. 3:14—15. 1956.
2. EMEL'YANOVA, I. Z. and T. A. BATRAKOVA. — ZhAKh, 13(1):142. 1958.
3. ZAMANSKAYA, R. I. — Khimicheskaya Pererabotka Drevesiny, No. 9:37—39. 1962.
4. GAILLARD, B. D. E. — Nature, Vol. 171:1166. 1953.
5. EMEL'YANOVA, I. Z., N. V. LEBEDEV, and K. P. VAKHRUSHEVA. — Sbornik Trudov VNIIGS, Vol. 11:66—72. 1963.
6. SHARKOV, V. I. et al. — ZhPKh, 36(7):1576—1583. 1963.
7. ANTONOVSKII, S. D., L. A. BELOZEROVA, and A. F. ZAITSEVA. — Bumazhnaya Promyshlennost', No. 8:6—7. 1964.
8. SULTANOV, A. S., S. R. TULYAGANOV, and R. S. TILLAEV. — DAN UzbSSR, No. 5:27—29. 1955.
9. KRAYANSKII, O. B., D. N. LATAEVA, and I. F. RUDOMANOVA. — Izv. VUZov, Pishchevaya Tekhnologiya, No. 1:149—152. 1963.
10. DUDKIN, M. S. — Izv. VUZov, Pishchevaya Tekhnologiya, No. 2:147—150. 1958.
11. DUDKIN, M. S. and V. E. STARICHKOVA. — Izv. VUZov, Pishchevaya Tekhnologiya, No. 1:41—44. 1962.
12. KHUTORSHCHIKOV, I. S. — Trudy LTA, Vol. 85:31—34. 1960.
13. WITTWER, R. — Faserforsch. und Textiltechnik, 6(2):58—62. 1955.
14. BRID'KO, Yu. I. — Sbornik Studencheskikh Nauchnykh Rabot Kubanskogo Sel'skokhozyaistvennogo Instituta, No. 2:149—152. 1958.
15. SAIKIA, T. C. and P. R. RAO. — Chem. Age India, 15(1):75—77. 1964.
16. MAKOVSKA, A. — Prace Inst. Celul. Papiern., 4(2):47—54. 1955.
17. MININA, V. S. — Author's Summary of Candidate's Thesis. 1963.
18. USMANOV, Kh. U., K. AKMAMEDOV, and V. S. MININA. — Izv. AN TurkmSSR, Seriya fiziko-tekhnicheskikh, khimicheskikh i geologicheskikh nauk, 5(4):38—42. 1963.
19. KOROL'KOV, I. I. — Author's Summary of Doctoral Thesis. 1963.
20. KOROL'KOV, I. I. and E. F. LIKHONOS. — Gidroliznaya i Lesokhimicheskaya Promyshlennost', No. 3:9—12. 1965.
21. MATSIO, I. and A. NAMBA. — J. Ferment. Technol., 39(5):256—262. 1961.
22. BROWER, H. E., J. E. JEFFERY, and M. W. FOLSOM. — Analyt. Chem., 38(2):362—364. 1966.
23. SWEELEY, C. C., R. BENTLEY, M. MAKITA, and W. W. WELLS. — J. Am. Chem. Soc., Vol. 85:2497. 1963.
24. ISHIKAWA, K. — J. Ferment. Technol., 42(3):156—161. 1964.
25. USMANOV, Kh. U., A. M. YAKUBOV, and R. S. TILLAEV. — Doklady AN UzbSSR, No. 6:23—26. 1955.
26. MININA, V. S., A. E. SARUKHANOVA, and Kh. U. USMANOV. — In: Sbornik "Fizika i khimiya prirodnykh i sinteticheskikh polimerov," No. 1:72—77. Tashkent. 1962.
27. DUDKIN, M. S. and N. G. SHKANTOVA. — ZhPKh, 34(6):1337—1342. 1961.
28. VOROB'EVA, G. I. and L. M. BOBYR'. — Sbornik Trudov VNIIGS, Vol. 12:129—137. 1964.
29. FAL'KOVICH, Yu. E. — Gidroliznaya i Khimicheskaya Promyshlennost', No. 8:18—20. 1962.
30. FAL'KOVICH, Yu. E. — Izv. VUZov, Pishchevaya Tekhnologiya, No. 3:33—36. 1962.
31. KHOL'KIN, Yu. I., V. I. MOROZOVA, and G. N. CHERNYAEVA. — Certificate of Authorship No. 47537 of 24. 6. 1964.
32. KHOL'KIN, Yu. I., G. N. CHERKAEVA, and I. A. KRYLOVA. — Gidroliznaya i Lesokhimicheskaya Promyshlennost'. (In press).
33. JENSEN, W., P. RINNE, and M. VAINIO. — Paperi ja Puu, 35(4a):135—138. 1953.
34. KAMIBAYASI, A. et al. — Rept. Felment. Res. Inst., No. 27:35—51. 1965.
35. BRÄNNLAND, R. and B. NYCANDER. — Svensk Papperstidn., 65(7):282. 1962.
36. WAHHAB, A. — J. Am. Chem. Soc., Vol. 70:3580—3583. 1948.
37. STADTMAN, F. H. — J. Am. Chem. Soc., Vol. 70:3583. 1948.
38. BURDE, R., J. E. JARRELL, and A. BAVLEY. — Analyt. Chem., 35(10):1535—1536. 1963.
39. KHOL'KIN, Yu. I. and G. D. PONUROV. — Trudy Sibirskogo Tekhnologicheskogo Instituta, Vol. 23:71—73. 1959.
40. CORTIS-JONES, B. — Nature, 191(4785):272—273. 1961.
41. GABRIELSON, G. and O. SAMUELSON. — Zschr. Analyt. Chem., Vol. 135:291. 1952.
42. ABOT, A. A. et al. — Izv. LatvSSR, Seriya Khimicheskaya No. 5:551. 1966.
43. MIZUGUCHI, J., S. SUZUKI, S. MOTOI, and K. HORIKE. — J. Chem. Soc. Japan, Ind. Chem. Sec., 60(4):445—449. 1957.
44. BIRD, R. F. and S. G. E. STEVENS. — Analyst, 87(1034):362—365. 1962.

45. KEMULA, W., D. SYBILSKA, and K. CHELEBICKA. − Rev. Chim. Acad. RPR, 7(2):1003−1009. 1962.
46. KOLESNIKOV, G. I. and V. I. PODDUBNYI. − Izv. VUZov, Pishchevaya Tekhnologiya, No. 5:40−42. 1962.
47. KHOL'KIN, Yu. I., G. N. CHERNYAEVA, and N. P. SMIRNOVA. − In: Sbornik "Issledovaniya v oblasti khimii i khimicheskoi tekhnologii drevesiny", pp. 53−63. − Izd. AN SSSR, Moskva. 1963.
48. KHOL'KIN, Yu. I. − Izv. VUZov, Lesnoi Zhurnal, No. 4:131−133. 1960.
49. KONONOVA, M. M., N. P. BEL'CHIKOVA, and V. K. NIKIFOROVA. − Pochvovedenie, No. 3:83−88. 1958.
50. KHOL'KIN, Yu. I., V. M. REZNIKOV, A. I. CHASHCHINA, A. S. KHOL'KINA, and G. D. PONUROV. − Certificate of Authorship No. 128457 of 21. 6. 1959. (Bulleten' Izobretenii, No. 10. 1960): Khol'kin, Yu. I., A. I. Karpusheva, and O. A. Antonova. Certificate of Authorship No. 161781 of 3. I. 1963. (Bulleten' Izobretenii, No. 8. 1964).
51. PERYSHKINA, G. I. and Yu. I. KHOL'KIN. − In: Sbornik "Issledovaniya v oblasti khimii i khimicheskoi tekhnologii drevesiny," pp. 101−106. Izd. AN SSSR. 1963.
52. TIMMERMANS, J. Physicochemical Constants of Pure Organic Compounds. − Elsevier Publ. Co., New York., p. 501. 1950.
53. SHIMANSKAYA, M. V. and V. A. SLAVINSKAYA. Analiticheskoe opredelenie furfurola (Analytical Determination of Furfural), pp. 147−153. − Izd. AN LatvSSR. Riga. 1961.
54. BUYSKE, D. A., L. H. OWEN, M. D. WILDER, and M. E. HOBBS. − Analyt. Chem., 28(5):910−913. 1956.
55. SELIGMAN, R. B., M. D. EDMONDS, A. E. O'KEEFFE, and L. A. LEE. − Chem. and Ind., No. 39:1195. 1954.
56. STRUCK, H. − Mikrochim. Acta, Nos. 7−8:1277−1282 1956.
57. SCHULTE, K. E. and C. B. STORP. − Fette und Seifen, No. 1:36−42. 1955.
58. McKIBBINS, S. W., J. F. HARRIS, and J. F. SAEMAN. − J. Chrom., 5(3):207−216. 1961.
59. FRANC, J. − J. Chromatogr., 3(4):317−321. 1960.
60. TANIYAMA, TAKATA. − J. Chem. Soc. Japan. Ind. Chem. Sec., 57(2):149−152. 1954.
61. KREILE, D. R., V. A. SLAVINSKAYA, and M. V. SHIMANSKAYA. − Izv. AN LatvSSR, Seriya Khimicheskaya, No. 4:459−461. 1963.
62. HACHIHAMA, Y. and T. SHONO. − Technol. Repts Osaka Univ., Vol. 7, Oct., pp. 479−483. 1961.
63. MILLER, J. M. and J. G. KIRCHNER. − Anal. Chem., Vol. 25:1107−1109. 1953.
64. REITSEMA, R. H. − Analyt. Chem., 26(6):960−963. 1954.
65. TERULISA, KATAYAMA. − Bull. Japan Soc. Sci. Fisheries, Vol. 21:412−415; 416−419; 425−428. 1955.
66. HANNEMAN, W. W., C. F. SPENCER, and J. F. JOHNSON. − Analyt. Chem., 32(11):1386−1388. 1960.
67. SHUIKIN, N. I., V. V. AN, and V. L. LEBEDEV. − Zavodskaya Laboratoriya, 27(8):976−977. 1961.
68. HANES, A. and D. SANDULESCU. − Rev. Chim. RPR, 12(11):664. 1961.
69. ANDERSONS, A. A. et al. − Izv. AN LatvSSR, Seriya Khimicheskaya, No. 2:168−176. 1963.
70. JAMES, A. T. and A. J. P. MARTIN. − Biochem. J., Vol. 50:679. 1952.
71. ANDERSONS, A. A. et al. − In Sbornik "Molekulyarnaya khromatografiya," pp. 52−57, Izd. Nauka, Moskva. 1964.
72. ANDERSONS, A. A. et al. − Izv. AN LatvSSR, Seriya Khimicheskaya, No. 4:455−457. 1963.
73. GILLER, S. A. et al. − Izv. AN LatvSSR, Seriya Khimicheskaya, No. 5:575−578. 1965.
74. POLYAKOVA, T. A., T. A. SOKOLOVA, and Ya. A. TSARFIN. − Zavodskaya Laboratori̯a, 29(1):18−19. 1963.
75. POLYAKOVA, T. A., T. A. SOKOLOVA, and Ya. A. TSARFIN. − Zavodskaya Laboratoriya, 29(6):664−665. 1963.
76. POLYAKOVA, T. A., T. A. SOKOLOVA, and Ya. A. TSARFIN. − In: Sbornik "Gazovaya khromatografiya," pp. 258−260. Izdatel'stvo Nauka. 1964.
77. JANAK, J., J. JONAS, and M. KRATOCHVIL. − Collect. Czechosl. Chem. Communs, 30(1):265−276. 1965.
78. YAKERSON, V. I., Ya. L. DANYUSHEVSKII, and Ya. L. GOL'FARB. − Khimiya Geterotsiklicheskikh Soedinenii, No. 1:25−30. 1965.
79. KYRUACOS, G. and H. R. MENAPACE. − Analyt. Chem., 31(2):222−225. 1959.
80. FURTH, B. and J. WIEMANN. − Bull. Soc. chim. France, No. 6:1819−1831. 1965.
81. MOYE, C. J. and Z. S. KRZEMINSKI. − Austral. J. Chem., 16(2):258−269. 1963.
82. IVANOVSKII, F. P. et al. − Zavodskaya Laboratoriya, 31(3):296. 1965.
83. PALFRAMAN, J. F. and B. A. ROSE. − Analyst, 89(1061):553−555. 1964.
84. STEVENS, M. P. − Analyt. Chem., 37(1):167−168. 1965.
85. ISHIGAKI, A. − J. Chem. Soc. Japan, Ind. Chem. Sec., 67(3):496−500. 1964.
86. IBRAEV, G. Zh. and M. I. GORYAEV. − Gidroliznaya i Lesokhimicheskaya Promyshlennost', No. 8:25−26. 1962.
87. FEDOTOVA, S. A. and Yu. A. TSIRLIN. − Sbornik Trudov VNIIGS, Vol. 14:117−123. 1965.

88. TSIRLIN, Yu. A. Doklad na Zasedanii Vsesoyuznogo Uchenogo Soveta po probleme ispol'zovaniya pentozansoderzhashchego syr'ya (Paper Read at the Session of the All-Union Scientific Council on the Utilization of Pentosan-Containing Raw Materials). — Rotaprint AN LatvSSR, Riga. 1963.

89. Gidroliznaya i Lesokhimicheskaya Promyshlennost', No. 6: 31. 1965.

90. KHOL'KIN, Yu. I., V. M. REZNIKOV, and A. I. CHASHCHINA. — In: Sbornik "Materialy I nauchnoi konferentsii kompleksnoi problemnoi laboratorii," pp. 43—52. Sibirskii Tekhnologicheskii Institut, Krasnoyarsk. 1961.

91. REZNIKOV, V. M., Yu. I. KHOL'KIN, and V. I. MOROZOVA. — Gidroliznaya i Lesokhimicheskaya Promyshlennost', No. 6: 19—22. 1962.

92. SHIMANSKAYA, M. V. and V. A. SLAVINSKAYA. Analiticheskoe opredelenie furfurola (Analytical Determination of Furfural), p. 144. — Izd. AN LatvSSR, Riga. 1961.

93. HARRISON, R. B. and J. E. PALFRAMAN. — Analyst, 86(1026): 561—565. 1961.

94. KRYUCHKOVA, A. P. and G. I. VOROB'EVA. — Gidroliznaya i Lesokhimicheskaya Promyshlennost', No. 2: 5—7. 1962.

95. RACHINSKII, V. V. and E. I. KNYAZYATOVA. — Doklady AN SSSR, 85(5): 1119—1122. 1952.

96. SEMUSHKINA, T. N. — Sbornik Trudov VNIIGS, Vol. 13: 69—75. 1965.

97. LOMOVA, N. I. — Gidroliznaya Promyshlennost' SSSR, No. 4: 11—12. 1954.

98. SOLOV'EV, L. T. et al. — In: Sbornik "Khromatografiya," pp. 149—156. Izd. LGU. 1956.

99. SADIKOVA, N. V. and V. A. SKVORTSEVICH. — In: Sbornik "Khromatografiya," pp. 157—159. Izd. LGU. 1956.

100. PEPPLER, H. — J. Agric. and Food Chem., 13(1): 34—36. 1965.

101. VÖGELI, H. — Diss. Dokt. techn. Wiss., Eidgenöss. Techn. Hochschule Zürich, Juris-Verl. 1957.

102. KAYA, T. — J. Agric. Chem. Soc. Japan, 38(9): 417—422. 1964.

103. KRAVCHENKO, N. A. and G. V. KLEONINA. Rukovodstvo po khromatograficheskomu analizu aminokislot na kolonkakh (Textbook of Amino Acid Analysis by Column Chromatography). — Izdatel'stvo Nauka. 1964.

104. LLOSA, P., C. TERTRIN, and M. JUTISZ. — J. Chromatogr., 14(1): 136—139. 1964.

105. KAPLAN, J. M. and F. L. SCHNEIDER. — Microchem. J., 6(4): 557—560. 1962.

106. GOLSHMID, V. K. — Laboratornoe Delo, No. 8: 461—464. 1965.

107. Kolichestvennyi gazovokhromatograficheskii analiz aminokislot. Ekspress-informatsiya. Promyshlennyi organicheskii sintez (Quantitative Gas-Chromatographic Analysis of Amino Acids. Rapid Information. Industrial Organic Synthesis). — Izd. VINITI, No. 2: 11—12. 1965.

108. SHLYAPNIKOV, S. V. et al. — Biokhimiya, 30(3): 457—462. 1965.

109. VITT, S. V., M. B. SAPOROVSKAYA, and V. M. BELIKOV. — ZhAKh, 21(2): 227—231. 1966.

110. VITT, S. V., M. B. SAPOROVSKAYA, and V. M. BELIKOV. — Izv. AN SSSR, Seriya khimicheskaya, No. 5: 947—948. 1964.

111. DARBRE, A. and K. BLAU. — J. Chromatogr., 17(1): 31—49. 1965.

112. CLARK, R. M. — Anal. Chem., Vol. 30: 1776. 1958.

113. MICHL, H. — Monatsheft. Chemie, Vol. 83: 737. 1958.

114. KHUM, J. X. and L. P. ZILL. — J. Am. Chem. Soc., Vol. 73: 2399. 1951.

115. JAENICKE, L. — Naturwiss., Vol. 39: 86. 1952.

116. SMULLIN, C. F., L. HARTMANN, and R. S. STRETZLER. — J. Am. Chem. Soc., Vol. 35: 179. 1958.

117. VASYUNINA, N. A. et al. — Gidroliznaya i Lesokhimicheskaya Promyshlennost', No. 1: 13—14. 1962.

118. CIFONELLI and S. SMITH. — Anal. Chem., Vol. 26: 1132. 1954.

119. BLOCK, R., R. LESTRANGE, and G. ZWEIG. Paper Chromatography. [Russian translation. 1954.]

120. BELOZEROVA, L. A. — Author's Summary of Candidate's Thesis. 1966.

121. BALAKHONTSEVA, V. N. and R. M. POLTININA. — Sbornik Trudov NIIGS, Vol. 11: 73—76. 1963.

122. BARYSHEVA, G. S., N. A. BASYUNINA, and S. V. CHEPIGO. — Sbornik trudov NIIGS, Vol. 11: 94—101. 1963.

123. SLUTSKIN, R. L. — Author's Summary of Candidate's Thesis. 1966.

124. MOORE, W. E., M. J. EFFLAND, D. B. JOHUSON, M. A. DAUGHERTY, and E. J. SCHWERDTFEGER. — Appl. Microbiol., 8(3): 169—173. 1960.

125. WILLIAMS, A. F. — Nature, 171(4354): 655. 1953.

126. HORROCKS, L. and D. G. CORNWELL. — J. Lipid Res., Vol. 3: 165. 1962.

127. ANGELE, H. P. — Monatsber. Dtsch. Akad. Wiss., Berlin, Vol. 4: 791. 1962.

128. BALAKHONTSEVA, V. N. and R. M. POLTININA. — ZhAKh, 20(6): 739—742. 1965.

129. SCHLENK, H., Y. L. GELLERMAN, and D. H. SAND. — Analyt. Chem., Vol. 34: 1529. 1962.

130. PANASYUK, V. G. — Trudy LTA, Vol. 75: 133—143. 1956.

131. PANASYUK, V.G. — ZhPKh, Vol. 30: 1049—1056. 1957.
132. PANASYUK, V.G., V.V.DAL', and L.V.PANASYUK. — ZhPKh, 29(1): 144—146. 1956.
133. MOROZOV, E.F. — Author's Summary of Candidate's Thesis. 1966.
134. CHUDAKOV, M.I. et al. — Khimicheskaya Pererabotka Drevesiny, No. 7: 6—9. 1965.
135. CHUDAKOV, M.I. et al. — Sbornik Trudov VNIIGS, Vol. 13: 227—253. 1965.
136. CARLES, J., A.SCHENDER, and A.M.LACOSTE. — Bull. Soc. Chim. Biol., Vol. 40: 221. 1958.
137. GERMAIN, J.-E., J.MONTREUIL, and P.KOUKOS. — Comptes Rendus, 245(6): 683—686. 1957.
138. GERMAIN, J.-E. and F.VALADON. — Bull. Soc. chim. France, Nos. 11—12: 1415—1417. 1958.
139. GERMAIN, J.-E., J.MONTREUIL, and P.KOUKOS. — Bull. Soc. chim. France, No. 1: 115—120. 1959.
140. GERMAIN, J.-E. and F.VALADON. — Bull. Soc. chim. France, No. 1: 11—16. 1960.
141. KHOL'KIN, Yu.I. and A.G.POLETAEVA. — OPKh. (In press).

## C. CHROMATOGRAPHY OF PRODUCTS OF WOOD CHEMICAL INDUSTRIES

Wood chemical industries are distinguished by the variety of the raw materials employed, of the processing methods and of the final products.

Chromatographic methods are widely employed in the analysis of the products of the rosin and turpentine industry. This section will deal mainly with the methods of gas-liquid chromatography as applied to the analysis of rosin, turpentine and the products of their chemical processing. Chromatographic methods have been successfully applied to the analysis of complex multicomponent mixtures formed as a result of pyrolysis of wood. The application of these methods to routine control of the production of acetate solvents and to the analysis of other technical products of the wood chemical industry is very promising.

### 1. Analysis of products of the rosin and turpentine industry

Analysis of turpentine and turpentine-based products

Commercial turpentine can be analyzed by different chromatographic techniques, but gas-liquid chromatography is the most important, since a rapid quantitative determination of all components in the commercial products can be effected in this manner.

Sidorov et al. /1/ studied the effect of different factors (temperature, amount of liquid stationary phase, length of column, etc.) on the effectiveness of separation of terpenes by gas-liquid chromatography and developed a procedure for the quantitative analysis of turpentine. The following proved to be the optimum experimental conditions: U-shaped 400×0.7 cm column filled with 25% castor oil on diatomite fire-proof brick (brand 500, 25 — 45 mesh) as solid support; working temperature 115°, flow rate of carrier gas 70 — 80 ml/min, Scott micro-flame detector, chromatographic apparatus assembled in the laboratory. The experimental accuracy varies between 2 and 4% for the individual components.

Figure 69 shows examples of separation of a model mixture and pinewood turpentine on a 200 cm long column. It is seen from the figure that terpenes, except for $\alpha$-pinene and tricyclene, are successfully separated under the conditions employed.

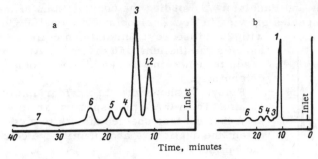

FIGURE 69. Chromatograms of:

a — model mixture; b — pinewood turpentine; 1 — α-pinene; 2 — tricyclene; 3 — camphene; 4 — β-pinene; 5 — $\Delta^3$-carene; 6 — dipentene; 7 —
terpinolene.

This method was applied /2/ in the analysis of pinewood turpentine and
its fractions obtained by rectification on a column. The distillate turpentine
contained (in %): α-pinene 73.7, camphene 1.4, β-pinene 6.3, $\Delta^3$-carene 6.5,
limonene 4.3, and high-boiling compounds 7.8. As an improved variant /3/
it is recommended to analyze turpentine on a column with 25% poly(ethylene
glycol adipate) on INZ-600 brick (25 — 60 mesh); the temperature of the
column should be 50 — 60° below the average boiling point of the components
to be separated; the linear flow rate of carrier gas (hydrogen) should be
4 — 5 cm/sec. The evaporator temperature should be 200 — 250° higher
than that of the column.

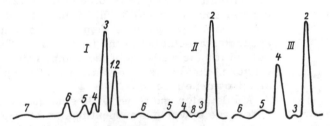

FIGURE 70. Chromatograms of:

I — artefact mixture of terpenes; II — pinewood turpentine; III — sprucewood turpentine; 1 — tricyclene; 2 — α-pinene; 3 — camphene; 4 — β-
pinene; 5 — $\Delta^3$-carene; 6 — limonene; 7 — terpinolene; 8 — not identified.

Examples of chromatographic separation of an artefact mixture of
terpenes, and pinewood and sprucewood turpentine are shown in Figure 70.

This method was also employed /4/ in a study of the isomerization of
α-pinene on acid catalysts supported by silica gels of different brands.

Gas-liquid chromatographic analyses of different kinds of turpentine
form the subject of numerous publications.

Turpentine has been analyzed /5/ at 120° on a U-shaped 182×1 cm
column with 30% silicone E-301 on celite 545 (30 — 80 mesh); flow rate of
carrier gas (nitrogen) 1 liter/hour, katharometric detector, Griffin Mark II
chromatograph.

Williams and Bannister /6/ studied the compositions of the sap turpentine of 22 pine species growing in New Zealand at 80° on a 100×0.4 cm column with 20% diisodecyl phthalate on celite 545; flow rate of carrier gas (helium) 116 ml/min. All components except sesquiterpenes and traces of other compounds were determined.

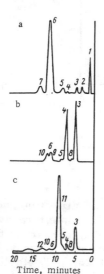

Figure 71 shows the chromatograms of turpentines obtained from three pine species, from which it can be seen that the tree species affects to a considerable extent the qualitative and quantitative composition of the turpentine.

The compositions of sap turpentines of P. n e l s o n i i and P. o c c i d e n t a l i s /7/ have been determined; studies were also carried out on turpentines of P. k h a s y a /8/ and other pine species /9/.

Bardyshev et al. /10/ studied turpentines produced by various industrial plants by gas-liquid chromatography and showed that Soviet turpentines contained terpinolene.

The technique of gas-liquid chromatography may be used not only to analyze the final commercial product — turpentine — but also for routine production control, in particular, for the analysis of the feed mixture /11/.

FIGURE 71. Chroma-
tograms of turpentines
from three species of
pine:

a — Pinus torre-
yana; b — P. rigida;
c — P. muricata; 1 —
n-heptane; 2 — n-no-
nane; 3 — α-pinene;
4 — β-pinene; 5 — β-
myrcene; 6 — limon-
ene; 7 — n-undecane;
8 — camphene; 9 —
α-phellandrene; 10 —
β-phellandrene; 11 —
$\Delta^3$-carene; 12 — p-
cymene.

Chudinov et al. /12/ utilized gas-liquid chromatography in their study of the catalytic liquid phase disproportio-nation of the total monocyclic terpene fraction to p-men-thene and p-cymene. The analysis was effected on a 150×0.4 cm column with 15% polyphenylmethylsilicone-4 on diatomite brick (0.35 — 0.50 mm) at 125°, flow rate of carrier gas (nitrogen) 35 ml/min, katharometric detection following conversion of components to $CO_2$, apparatus assembled in the laboratory. The method served for the analysis of the composition of the initial mixture, that of the catalyzate and of the p-menthene and p-cymene fractions.

Mühlethaler and Giger /13/ studied the alterations undergone by various turpentines on storage. Chroma-tographic determination of the resins formed in turpentine showed that the method is much more sensitive than the refractive index method. The resins formed can be revealed by thin layer chromatography before their presence can affect the refractive index.


Analysis of rosin

Brun and Gasland /14/ published a detailed 265-reference survey on the studies of resin acids in the sap of North European pine and spruce and of the different types of rosin from tall oil by the methods of partition chromatography.

Quantitative determination of the composition of the resin acids in rosins is frequently effected by column chromatography /15/, as described in Chapter V. Bardyshev and Tkachenko /16/ utilized the method in their study of the isomerization of resin acids from sap during the production of rosin. It has been established by chromatographic and spectrophotometric methods that during the processing of tree sap levopimaric acid is almost entirely converted to other compounds, mostly to abietic acid, the amount of which increases by a factor of 2.5. This process is particularly intense during the boiling stage.

The composition of rosin produced by different industrial plants was studied by chromatographic and spectrophotometric methods /17/. The rosin had been first clarified with furfural; the composition of the clarified rosin was (in %): palustric acid 8 — 16, abietic acid 39 — 45, levopimaric acid 0.5 — 2, neoabietic acid 8 — 11, dehydroabietic acid 13 — 16, dextro-pimaric, isodextropimaric and other acids which do not absorb in the ultraviolet 19 — 28.

The analysis of the resin acids contained in rosin and disproportionated rosin is carried out /20/ on columns with silica gel /21/. Methyldehydro-abietate may thus be quantitatively isolated /22/.

For chromatographic analysis of rosin from the sap of common pine see also /18/; for that from the sap of common spruce see /19/.

A recent development in the analysis of industrial rosin is the use of gas-liquid chromatography /23/.

Rosin, tall oil and wood chemical tars also contain higher fatty acids. Kosyukova et al. /24/ developed a method for the detection and determination of higher fatty acids in wood chemical products by paper chromatography. It is recommended to use "slow" chromatographic grade paper, manufactured by Leningrad Paper Mill No. 2; the dimensions of the strips should be $35 \times 2$ cm. Prior to the analysis the paper is washed free from traces of cations with glacial acetic acid, dried, and made hydrophobic by three seconds' immersion in the hydrocarbon kerosine fraction (bp 190 — 220°) saturated with acetic acid. The hydrophobization takes place by the reverse phase mechanism and is made necessary by the fact that the higher fatty acids are insoluble in water.

Mixtures of higher acids are dissolved in a 3 : 7 alcohol-benzene mixture, and $3.0 — 5.0 \mu l$ of the solution, containing 30 — 150 $\gamma$ of each acid is applied to the paper strip 7 — 8 mm from the edge; the diameter of the drop should not exceed 3 — 5 mm. The chromatograms are placed in a chamber and are developed by the descending technique; it is recommended to use 90 or 95% acetic acid saturated with the hydrocarbon kerosine fraction as solvent. The separation takes 12 — 15 hours, after which the strips are dried for 10 — 20 minutes in a fume hood and 2 hours in a drying oven at 120° in order to remove the hydrocarbons which interfere with the detection of the spots.

The spots are revealed by the formation of silver or cadmium salts of the higher fatty acids. To prepare the cadmium salts, the chromatograms are immersed for 30 minutes into a 1% solution of cadmium acetate, the strips are then washed with water and immersed for 2 — 5 seconds into a 1% solution of sodium sulfide. Stable yellow cadmium sulfide spots on white background are obtained.

The acids were identified by determining the $R_f$- and $R_p$-values by the formula

$$R_p = \log \left( \frac{1}{R_f} - 1 \right).$$

It has been shown that, for $C_{10} - C_{18}$ acids, $R_p$ varies linearly with the number of carbon atoms in the molecule.

Quantitative analysis is based on polarographic determination of cadmium salts, which are readily reduced on dropping mercury electrode. To perform the determination, the yellow cadmium sulfide spots are cut out and treated with 1 N HCl. The resulting cadmium chloride passes into solution; HCl is expelled from the solution by evaporation, and the cadmium chloride precipitate is dissolved in 1 ml 1 N HCl and 0.2 ml water. Polarographic determination is carried out on the resulting solution.

Table 37 gives the $R_f$-values of a number of higher fatty acids which may be present in wood chemical products.

TABLE 37. $R_f$-values of higher fatty acids

| Acid | Mobile phase — acetic acid saturated with hydro-carbons | |
|---|---|---|
| | 90% acid | 95% acid |
| Stearic $C_{18}$ . . . . . . | 0.16 | 0.20 |
| Palmitic $C_{16}$ . . . . . | 0.24 | 0.28 |
| Myristic $C_{14}$ . . . . . | 0.35 | 0.37 |
| Lauric $C_{12}$ . . . . . . | 0.47 | 0.48 |
| Capric $C_{10}$ . . . . . . | – | 0.57 |
| Oleic $C_{18}$ . . . . . . . | 0.19 | 0.25 |
| Linoleic $C_{18}$ . . . . . . | 0.25 | 0.33 |
| Linolenic $C_{18}$ . . . . . | – | 0.49 |

Oleic and linoleic acids have been identified in this manner in the fatty acid fraction isolated from extractive rosin and tall oil.

Analysis of the products of the camphor industry

In the synthesis of camphor, the starting material is technical grade $\alpha$-pinene, which is obtained from turpentine. In the first stage of the synthesis, $\alpha$-pinene is catalytically isomerized to camphene; the main products of the reaction are camphene, tricyclene, fenchenes and monocyclic terpenes.

The mixture which is formed in the course of industrial synthesis of camphor is best analyzed by gas-liquid chromatography. Lishtvanova and Goryaev developed appropriate methods for the analysis of the raw material, intermediates, by-products and final products of the camphor industry. These workers used gas-liquid chromatography to analyze turpentine and technical grade $\alpha$-pinene, products of catalytic isomerization of $\alpha$-pinene and technical grade camphor, as well as the waste products, viz., the still residues from the distillation of $\alpha$-pinene from turpentine and camphene from the isomerization product.

It has been recommended /25/ to analyze the raw material (sap turpentine and technical grade $\alpha$-pinene) on a 300×0.4 cm column with 15% medicinal grade lanolin on INZ-600 brick (grain size 0.5 mm) treated with concentrated hydrochloric acid and 5% alkali and washed with water until no longer acid to phenolphthalein. Temperature of determination 100°, flow rate of carrier gas (hydrogen) 30 ml/min, inlet pressure 1.35 atm, sample volume 0.5 — 2 μl, micro-flame detector, Shandon chromatograph.

The components were identified by comparing the relative retention times of the components of turpentine with those of genuine pure compounds, and by chromatogramming mixtures of turpentine with pure compounds. The contents of the components in the sample are found from the areas under the peaks. The method may also be used to analyze the still residue and thus to monitor the completeness of the removal of α-pinene from turpentine as a result of the distillation.

The isomerizate, technical camphene and the still residue were analyzed by the same technique, with certain modifications /26, 27/. In particular, the isomerizate was analyzed at 140° on a column with lanolin; technical grade camphene and still residue were analyzed (after separation of camphene from the isomerizate) at 135° on a column with 15% castor oil.

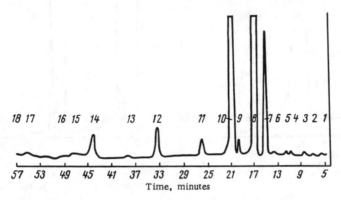

FIGURE 72. Chromatogram of terpenes formed in the initial stages of isomerization:

1, 2 — not identified; 3 — δ-fenchene (identified by retention time); 4 — cyclofenchene; 5 — γ-fenchene; 6 — bornylene; 7 — tricyclene; 8 — α-pinene; 9 — α-fenchene; 10 — camphene; 11 — β-pinene; 12 — $\Delta^3$-caren 13 — α-terpinene; 14 — dipentene; 15 — p-cymene; 16 — γ-terpinene; 17 — terpinolene; 18 — 2,4-p-menthadiene.

Successful separation of the components was also achieved at 70° on a 15 m long capillary column, 0.15 mm in diameter, filled with tricresyl phosphate applied in a 5 μ thick layer on the walls of the column. Figure 72 shows the results of the analysis in the capillary column of terpenes formed in the initial stages of the isomerization. The use of capillary columns proved to be more effective /28/. In particular, the separation of camphene from α-fenchene, tricyclene from α-pinene and dipentene from p-cymene could be accomplished only on capillary columns. It was shown by gas-liquid chromatographic analysis that technical grade camphene contained groups of bicyclic terpenes and ketones, including fenchone and isofenchone.

211

In view of the large potentialities in the application of gas-liquid chromatography in the production control of camphor, it would be desirable that the quality specifications for the raw material and for the final product be based not on physical constants, but on the actual content of the main component.

Gas-liquid chromatography was also utilized /29/ in the determination of the composition of synthetic camphor, camphor oil and a number of essential oils. The experimental conditions were: a copper W-shaped 300×0.4 cm column with 15% medicinal grade lanolin on INZ-600 brick (0.3 — 0.4 mm) which had been treated with concentrated HCl, 5% alkali and water, column temperature 165°, flow rate of carrier hydrogen 30 ml/min, inlet pressure 1.4 atm, flame ionization detector.

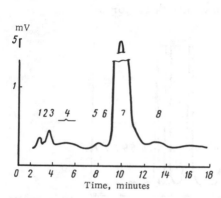

FIGURE 73. Chromatogram of synthetic camphor:

1 — tricyclene; 2 — α-pinene; 3 — camphene; 4 — traces of esters; 5 — fenchone; 6 — isofenchone; 7 — camphor; 8 — not identified.

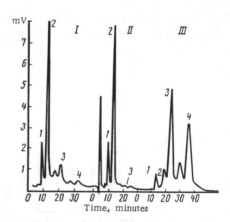

FIGURE 74. Chromatograms of industrial products of rosin and turpentine industry:

I — still residue from the rectification of camphene; II — technical grade camphene; III — isomerization product; 1 — tricyclene; 2 — camphene; 3 — dipentene; 4 — terpinolene.

Figure 73 gives the chromatogram of synthetic camphor with a crystallization point of 155.2° and a camphor content of 88.5%. It is seen that the main impurities present in the industrial product are terpenic hydrocarbons (α-pinene, camphene, tricyclene), bicyclic ketones, fenchone and isofenchone. The method is recommended for routine control of camphor production.

Bardyshev and Vedeneev /30/ developed a method for the analysis of the technical products obtained in the manufacture of camphor. The following conditions were found to be optimal in gas-liquid chromatography of camphene-containing products: 150×0.4 cm stainless steel column, tricresyl phosphate as the liquid stationary phase (20 wt.% on deactivated diatomite brick with 0.25 — 0.5 mm grain size), carrier gas technical grade nitrogen (flow rate 25 ml/min). The brick was deactivated by heating with 2% aqueous sodium carbonate, after which the brick was washed with distilled water until neutral.

The column temperature was 120± 1°; katharometric detection with tungsten spirals, with conversion of products to $CO_2$. Furnace temperature for the catalytic combustion of the components was 700± 10°. When working with products containing camphor, the stationary liquid phase in gas-liquid chromatographic analysis was polyphenylmethylsilicone-4 (18% on the weight of the brick), column temperature 155± 1°, nitrogen flow rate 27 ml/min, other parameters the same as for products containing camphene. Quantitative determination of all industrial samples was conducted by the method of internal normalization; the experimental error was ± 10 rel.%.

This method was used to analyze the product of isomerization of technical grade camphene, still residue from the distillation of camphene, technical grade and recrystallized camphor and camphor mixtures, as well as artefact mixtures of camphor with fenchone.

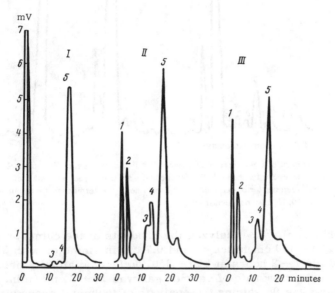

FIGURE 75. Chromatograms of technical grade camphor and camphor oils:

I – camphor oils; II – camphor oil with 4% added fenchone; III – technical grade camphor with 1.5% added fenchone; 1 – ethanol; 2 – toluene; 3 – fenchone; 4 – isofenchone; 5 – camphor.

Figures 74 and 75 show the chromatograms of samples of different technical products of the camphor industry. It is seen from the data given that a satisfactory separation of the components is attained under these experimental conditions. A number of peaks remained unidentified.

Quantitative interpretation of the chromatogram showed that the composition of camphene obtained in different industrial plants differs as regards the contents of the main components and impurities. The major impurities in technical grade camphor are fenchone, isofenchone and an unidentified substance.

213

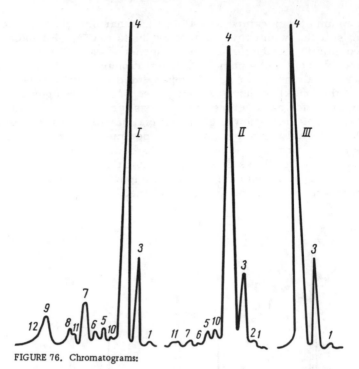

FIGURE 76. Chromatograms:

I — product of isomerization of pinene; II — liquid camphene; III — crystalline
camphene; 1 — fenchene-1; 2 — fenchene-2; 3 — tricyclene; 4 — camphene;
5 — $\Delta^3$-carene; 6 — α-terpinene; 7 — limonene; 8 — γ-terpinene; 9 — terpinolene; 10, 11, 12 — not identified.

Baboshin et al. /31/ analyzed the products of the camphor industry on
columns 200 — 400 cm in length and 0.7 cm in diameter with 25% castor oil,
preheated for 1 — 2 hours at 300 — 350° on Inzen diatomite brick- 600
(25 — 60 mesh); flow rate of carrier gas was 19 — 24 ml/min. The column
temperature was 96° during the analysis of technical grade pinene and
liquid and crystalline camphene; 115° during the analysis of the isomerization
product of pinene; 28° during the analysis of the still residue from the
rectification of turpentine and camphene; 145° in the determination of
isobornyl formate; 150° in the determination of isoborneol and 155° in the
determination of camphor. In addition, artefact mixtures of α-pinene,
tricyclene and camphene, and of borneol with isoborneol were also analyzed.

Figure 76 shows examples of chromatographic separation of the
components of the isomerization mixture of pinene and of liquid and
crystalline camphene.

It was found that the analysis of the products of the camphor industry by
gas-liquid chromatography is most rapid and least laborious and for this
reason the results of the analysis can be utilized to correct the processing
parameters. This technique also allowed a quantitative determination of
the components whose identity is unknown (technical grade pinene contains
camphene and one unidentified component). Certain technological
conclusions have been arrived at on the strength of the results of
chromatographic analysis.

Gas-liquid chromatography was employed /32/ in a study of the composition of purified and unpurified native camphor and camphor oil. Traces of α-pinene, camphene, dipentene, cineole and safrole were found as impurities.

## 2. Analysis of products of thermal processing of wood

The pyrolysis of wood results in the formation of complex mixtures of reaction products which comprise phenols, organic acids, furfural and its homologs, neutral oils and other products. Some of the reaction products are gaseous, but most of the industrially valuable compounds are contained in the liquid, which consists of two phases — an aqueous layer and tar. The tar constituents of practical interest are mono- and polyhydric phenols.

Kosyukova et al. /33/ analyzed the phenols contained in the products of the wood chemical industry by gas-liquid chromatography.

The most satisfactory separation of monohydric phenols was obtained /34/ under the following conditions: $400 \times 0.4$ cm chromatographic column with 35% polyphenylmethylsilicone-4 on diatomite brick $(0.3 - 0.5$ mm) treated with hydrochloric acid; column temperature $200 \pm 0.5°$; flow rate of carrier gas (hydrogen) 48 ml/min, inlet pressure 1.5 atm, outlet pressure atmospheric, katharometric detector, current intensity in bridge 175 mA; sensitivity of potentiometer scale 1.5 and 2.5 mV. In quantitative analysis m-cresol was used as the internal standard; experimental error up to 4.3 rel.%.

The degree of separation of the components was calculated from the well known /35/ formula for the criterion $K_1$

$$K_1 = \frac{1}{4} \frac{m-1}{m+1} \sqrt{2n} ,$$

where $m = \frac{V_{R_1}}{V_{R_2}}$ ; $V_{R_1}$ and $V_{R_2}$ are the respective retention volumes of compounds 1 and 2, and $n$ is the number of theoretical plates found from the equation

$$n = 5.54 \left( \frac{l}{\mu_{0.5}} \right),$$

where $l$ is the retention volume, $cm^3$ and $\mu_{0.5}$ is the width of the peak at mid-height.

The components were identified using the corrected retention volumes, according to the formula /36/:

$$V_{Rj} = V_R \frac{3}{2} \frac{\left( \frac{p_1}{p_0} \right)^2 - 1}{\left( \frac{p_1}{p_0} \right)^3 - 1} ,$$

where $j$ is the pressure drop factor and $p_0$ and $p_1$ are the pressure at the inlet and the issue of the column, respectively.

In quantitative analysis of mixtures the correction coefficients were not introduced, since the sensitivity of the detector with respect to the different

monohydric phenols showed only insignificant variations. The average
sensitivity, as calculated from the formula /37/

$$S_r = \frac{\Pi C_1 C_2 v}{q} ,$$

was 130 units; in the formula $\Pi$ is the surface area under the peak, $C_1$ is the
sensitivity of the potentiometer, mV/cm, $C_2$ is the reciprocal rate of
motion of potentiometer band, min/cm, $v$ is the flow rate of carrier gas,
ml/min and $q$ is the sample weight, mg.

Phenols in the creosote fraction (180 — 240°) of the distillate of wood
chemical tar, and the phenol fraction extracted from waste waters with
ethyl acetate have been analyzed in this manner. Figure 77 shows
chromatograms of a model mixture of phenols and the results of the analysis
of the creosote fraction which indicate that its composition is complex. The
main components of the fraction were (in %): 2,4-dimethylphenol + methyl-
guaiacol 20.8, guaiacol 18.5, 3- and 4-methylguaiacol 15.3, phenol 10.3 and
other components. Phenol, cresols, xylenols and guaiacols were identified
in the phenol fraction extracted with ethyl acetate from waste waters.

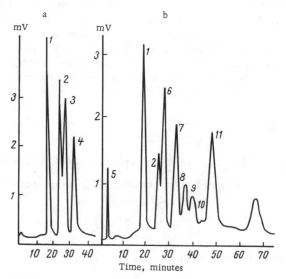

FIGURE 77. Chromatograms of:

a — model mixture; b — mixture of phenols from the creosote
tar fraction of wood chemical industry; 1 — phenol; 2 — o-
cresol; 3 — m-cresol; 4 — guaiacol; 5 — solvent; 6 — m- and
p-cresols; 7 — guaiacol + 2,6-xylenol; 8 — 2,4- and 2,5-
xylenols; 9 — 3,5-xylenols; 10 — 2,3-xylenol; 11 — 3,4-xylenol.

Pyrolysis at 500 — 600° of incompletely methylated pyrocatechol and
pyrogallol contained in the crude phenols isolated from the bottom tar
enhances the reactivity of the crude phenols. The pyrolysis process results
in an increase in the content of phenols and catechol derivatives and at the
same time reduces the content of phenols with methoxyl groups.

Shaposhnikov and Kosyukova /38/ studied the process of pyrolysis of a number of methyl ethers of phenols; in particular they investigated the pyrolysis at 500 — 600° of the vapors of anisole, veratrole, guaiacol, p-methylguaiacol and pyrogallol dimethyl ether.

The composition of the pyrolyzates was studied by gas-liquid chromatography under the following conditions: a $200 \times 0.4$ cm column with 20% PFMS-4 silicone oil and 1% poly(ethylene glycol succinate) on diatomite brick (0.25 — 0.5 mm) at 200°, flow rate of carrier gas (helium) 40 ml/min, katharometric detector, UKh-1 chromatograph.

The results of the gas chromatographic analysis served to determine the quantitative composition of the pyrolyzates and the yields of the reaction products as percentage of the pyrolyzed material. It was found, for example, that the main products of pyrolysis of guaiacol are pyrocatechol, phenol, o- and m-cresols, 2,6- and 2,4-xylenols and certain other compounds. Thus, pyrolysis involves mainly demethylation and demethoxylation reactions.

Fedorova /39/ described a chromatographic method for the determination of pyrocatechol in pyrocatechol concentrate obtained from the products of thermal processing of solid fuel. The analysis is conducted by the method of paper chromatography using butanol: glacial acetic acid: water = 40:12:29 as solvent. The pyrocatechol spot, $R_f = 0.83$, is visible directly and need not be detected by special reagents. For quantitative determination the spot is cut out, extracted with distilled water and the pyrocatechol in the extract is determined spectrophotometrically at 272 m$\mu$.

Pyrocatechols in industrial products may also be quantitatively determined by column chromatography /40/.

The dry-distilled tar fraction (bp 180 — 240°) of hardwood was examined /41/ by three chromatographic techniques. Initial phenols and their conversion products (aromatic acids) were identified by chromatography on paper. The results were compared with the data of chromatographic analysis on alumina column. The fraction was found in this manner to contain 13 phenols, including major amounts of guaiacol. Phenols separated from wood tar are suitable for the synthesis of phenol-formaldehyde resins. Gas chromatography served to study the composition of the guaiacol fraction of crude phenols from dry-distilled wood tar /42/, to analyze carbolic oil from coke, gas and generator tars of coking industry /43/ and other industrial products.

Processing of tar yields, in addition to phenols, also neutral substances in a yield of up to 35% on the total initial amount of wood tar oils. Prior to the development of chromatographic methods of analysis, the composition of the neutral substances was practically unknown, with consequent serious difficulties in their utilization.

Column chromatography of alumina and IR spectroscopy served to identify neoabietate in the hydrocarbon fraction of the neutral oils /44/. It was also shown that the neutral oils can be successfully separated into a hydrocarbon and an oxygenated fraction by this technique.

Even less is known about the composition of the neutral compounds formed as a result of pyrolysis of bottom tars which is effected in order to enhance the reactivity of the phenolic fraction in the tar. The resulting pyrolyzates contain up to 45% of neutral substances. The constitution of neutral compounds in the pyrolyzate of wood tar oils was studied by Krutov and Kovalev /45, 46/, who worked on wood oils obtained as a result of continuous distillation of the bottom tar in a softwood-processing gas works.  The neutral oils were extracted from the alkali-treated pyrolyzate with ether, washed with a solution of alkali, vacuum-distilled and rectified. The resulting fractions were investigated by gas-liquid chromatography.

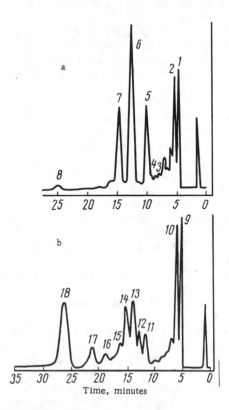

FIGURE 78.  Chromatograms of two fractions (a, b) of neutral compounds isolated from the pyrolyzate of wood tar oils:

1 — nonene-1; 2 — isomeric nonenes; 3 — allyl-acetone; 4 — ethylbenzene; 5 — m-xylene; 6 — o-xylene; 7 — styrene; 8 — cyclohexanone; 9 — decene-1; 10 — isomeric decenes; 11 — mesitylene; 13 — o-ethyltoluene; 14 — pseudo-cumene; 15 — p-cymene; 16 — o-vinyltoluene; 18 — coumarone; 12, 17 — not identified.

Figure 78 gives the results of chromatographic analysis of two fractions of the neutral substances in the pyrolyzate.  The low-boiling (45 — 47° / 20 mm Hg) fraction was analyzed at 132° on a 600×0.6 cm column containing 12% tricresyl phosphate on diatomite brick, flow rate of carrier gas (hydrogen) 50 ml/minute, inlet pressure 2.5 atm, outlet pressure atmospheric, current intensity of detector 130 mA, sensitivity of recorder scale 2 mV.

The second fraction (bp 59° / 16 — 20 mm Hg) was analyzed under similar conditions except that the flow rate of carrier gas was 83 ml/min, column temperature 148°, length of column 300 mm and the current intensity of the detector was 148 mA.

The components were identified by the tag method and also by UV and IR spectroscopy.  It is seen from Figure 78 that the main oxygenated components of neutral oils are cyclic ketones and coumarone (benzofurane).  Allylacetone was the first compound to be identified in the products of wood thermolysis.

Nikandrov /47/ used gas-liquid chromatography to determine the content of furfural and acetic acid in the distillate obtained as a result of prepyrolysis of wood in a liquid heat transfer medium (Diesel oil).  The components of the reaction mixture were separated on a column 200 cm in length and 0.3 — 0.4 cm in diameter with 10 parts of silicone grease on 100 parts of Teflon (grain size 0.1 mm) at 150°; flow rate of carrier gas (helium) 43 ml/min; sample volume 5 μl; Perkin-Elmer chromatograph.  Methanol, water and volatile acids were detected in addition to furfural in the pyrolyzate.

Piyalkin /48/ effected a qualitative and quantitative analysis of the volatile products formed during continuous high-temperature pyrolysis of wood in the laboratory by the gas-liquid chromatographic technique.

The composition of noncondensing gases was studied in two steps: nonhydrocarbon gases and methane were determined on a column with molecular sieve 5A, whereas $C_2 — C_5$ hydrocarbons were determined on a column with 24% diisoamyl phthalate on INZ-600 brick. Column temperature 22°, length of column 2.5 meters, katharometric detector, UKh-1 chromatograph. The gas phase was found to contain 28 components, $H_2$, CO, $CH_4$, and $CO_2$ being the major species. Dimethyl ether, methyl ethyl ether and formaldehyde were present in small amounts.

Gaseous products of thermal processing of wood may be carried out by way of chromatographic determination of carbon monoxide and oxygen in the combustion products /49/.

Low-boiling components of the pyroligneous distillate were analyzed /48/ at 70° on a 300 cm long column with 15% of $\beta, \beta'$-oxydipropionitrile on INZ-600, KhL-4 chromatograph, katharometric detector. Twenty-six components were detected in the fraction, the major ones being methylal, acetaldehyde, $\alpha$-methylfurane, methyl acetate, methanol, acetone, methyl ethyl ketone, allyl alcohol, methyl isopropyl ketone, methyl vinyl ketone, methyl propyl ketone, diacetyl, crotonaldehyde, etc.

Lower fatty acids up to $C_7$ were determined on a 250 cm column with 33% of a mixture of dioctyl sebacate with sebacic acid on celite 503 at 154°, using a UKh-1 chromatograph. The acids thus isolated contained 17 identified components, mainly formic, acetic, propionic, acrylic, isobutyric, n-butyric, $\alpha$-crotonic, n-valeric, caproic and other acids.

Phenols with bp up to 285° were determined at 185° on a 250-cm column with 15% silicone oil OE-4011 on celite 503. The 20 components which were detected included derivatives of pyrogallol, guaiacol, o-, m- and p-cresols, phenol, xylenols, etc. as the major compounds.

Mixtures of lower fatty acids or their slats were determined /50/ by partition chromatography on a column. Mixtures of organic acids in water or in organic solvents (benzene, chloroform) were separated on silica gel columns and eluted with benzene or with benzene-butanol mixtures containing 2 — 30 vol.% butanol. The individual acids can thus be determined to within ± 3.5 rel.%; the determination takes 3 hours.

The method has been utilized in studying the composition of some products of pyrogenetic processing of wood — acetate powders, gas generator condensates, pyroligneous distillate. The method may be utilized in the analysis of wood chemicals which do not contain a large proportion of tars.

## 3. Analysis of products of manufacture of acetate solvents

A number of wood chemical plants carry out secondary chemical processing of organic acids and alcohols to acid esters. The chemical produced in largest quantities is ethyl acetate. The starting materials are technical grade acetic acid and ethanol, which contain a number of impurities. In particular, wood chemical acetic acid contains formic, propionic and butyric acids as impurities, whereas hydrolytic ethanol contains methanol, various esters, fusel oil, aldehydes, etc.

Owing to the presence of these impurities, the corresponding esters are formed in the course of esterification. In the control of esterification processes and especially in the quality control of the final product it is necessary to determine the content of these impurities, which cause a deterioration in the quality of the commercial ethyl acetate.

In the ethyl acetate industry, as in the analysis of most commercial products, this was done until recently by chemical methods which, as a rule, give only approximate contents of individual components or groups of similar components and are in addition very time-consuming.

Mixtures of esters are best analyzed by gas-liquid chromatography which makes it possible to separate various multicomponent mixtures of esters, acids, alcohols and other compounds.

Druskina et al. /51/ developed a method for the separation of mixtures containing the following products of the ethyl acetate industry: ethyl acetate, ethyl propionate, ethyl butyrate, acetic, propionic and butyric acids. The experimental conditions are as follows: $150 \times 0.4$ cm chromatographic column with the stationary phase prepared by applying 18 g silicone oil PFMC-4 (polyphenylmethylsilicone) and 3.5 g stearic acid onto 100 g diatomite brick $(0.4 - 0.5$ mm); column temperature 95°; flow rate of carrier gas (nitrogen) 45 ml/min; sample volume $0.005 - 0.015$ ml; duration of the separation 33 minutes; experimental error ± 6 rel. %. Chromatograph assembled in laboratory.

The method was utilized in the analysis of a still residue of the ethyl acetate industry, which was found to contain (in %): acetic acid $78.3 - 84.6$, water $3.9 - 10.3$, propionic acid $5.6 - 6.8$, as well as formic and butyric acids, ethyl acetate, ethyl propionate, ethyl butyrate. It was found that the chromatographic method yields more accurate results than the azeotropic method of TsNILKhI.

The method was also applied /52/ in the analysis of technical grade ethyl acetate. The analysis of the product was conducted on a KhL-3 chromatograph, $200 \times 0.6$ cm column with 30% poly(ethylene glycol adipate) on diatomite brick $(0.25 - 0.5$ cm). The flow rate of carrier gas (nitrogen) is 43 ml/min, and the duration of one determination is 25 minutes. Sample volume $10 - 20 \mu l$; experimental error less than 5 rel. %.

Gas-liquid chromatography was also utilized /53, 54/ in the analysis of other products of the ethyl acetate industry — head fraction, still residue, crude ethyl acetate and technical grade ethyl acetate. In developing the method, the separation efficiencies of model and industrial mixtures (Figure 79) were compared on the following stationary phases: tricresyl phosphate, dibutyl phthalate, dinonyl phthalate, poly(ethylene glycol)-400 (PEG-400), poly(ethylene glycol succinate) (PEGS), polyphenylmethyl-silicone (PFMS-4), poly(ethylene glycol adipate) (PEGA), triethanolamine and triethylene glycol.

The following optimum parameters were chosen: the chromatographic column $(200 \times 0.6$ or $150 \times 0.4$ cm) is filled with $15 - 30\%$ PEGA on diatomite brick $(0.25 - 0.5$ mm), column temperature 70 or 80°, flow rate of carrier gas (nitrogen) 20 or 43 ml/min, inlet pressure 1.2 atm, outlet pressure atmospheric; KhL-3 chromatograph or apparatus assembled in the laboratory, katharometric detection after conversion of components to carbon dioxide.

Quantitative analysis is effected by the method of internal normalization, using correction coefficients for individual components of the mixture. The following values were found for the correction coefficients (with ethyl acetate as standard):

| | | | |
|---|---|---|---|
| ethyl propionate | 0.70 | ethyl butyrate | 1.09 |
| methyl acetate | 0.85 | ethyl formate | 1.37 |
| ethyl acetate | 1.00 | ethanol | 1.43 |

The average experimental error does not exceed ± 4.5 rel.%.

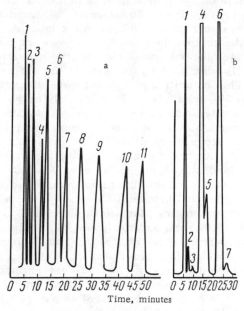

FIGURE 79. Chromatograms:

a − artefact mixture of substances present in the products of the ethyl acetate industry; b − head fraction of
the rectificate of crude ethyl acetate. 1 − diethyl
ether; 2 − acetaldehyde; 3 − methyl formate; 4 −
ethyl formate; 5 − methyl acetate; 6 − ethyl acetate;
7 − ethanol; 8 − ethyl propionate; 9 − propyl acetate;
10 − methyl isovalerate; 11 − ethyl butyrate.

The method has been employed in a comparison of the composition of
technical products samples in different wood chemical plants. Industrial
grade ethyl acetate contained (in %): ethanol 5 − 6, ethyl propionate 5 − 6,
ethyl formate up to 1 and methyl acetate up to 1.

Trofimov et al. /55/ used gas-liquid chromatography to analyze the
ethyl formate fraction in the wastes of the ethyl acetate industry. The
composition of fractions sampled in a narrow temperature range during
the rectification of the ethyl formate fraction was also studied. The
analytical parameters were: 25% poly(ethylene glycol adipate) on diatomite
brick (0.25 mm), temperature 50°, flow rate of carrier gas (nitrogen)
110 ml/min, pressure 220 mm Hg, chromatograph Khrom-1.

The presence of impurities in technical grade acetic acid is responsible
for the formation of the corresponding esters during the manufacture of
butyl acetate which is utilized as solvent. During the esterification of
acetic acid with butanol butyl formate, butyl propionate, butyl valerate and
other compounds are formed along with butyl acetate. The method of
gas-liquid chromatography was employed /56/ in the investigation of the
composition of products and semi-products of the butyl acetate industry.

221

The composition of the impurities in technical grade acetic acid was determined on a $150 \times 0.4$ cm column with 18 g polyphenylmethylsilicone-4 and 3.5 g stearic acid on 100 g of diatomite brick; the flow rate of carrier gas (nitrogen) was 40 ml/min; katharometric detector; chromatograph assembled in the laboratory. After separation on the column the components were ignited at 700° in a quartz tube with copper oxide; the water was absorbed in a $CaCl_2$ tube; the $CO_2$ was sent to the katharometer.

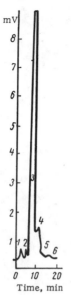

FIGURE 80.
Chromatogram of crude butyl acetate:

1 – dibutyl ether; 2 – butyl formate; 3 – butyl acetate; 4 – butyl propionate; 5 – butyl butyrate; 6 – butyl valerate.

The impurities in butanol were determined on a column with 30% triethylene glycol or poly(ethylene glycol)-400 on diatomite brick (0.4 – 0.5 mm), flow rate of carrier gas (air) 38 ml/min, temperature of column and detector 90°, KhT-2M chromatograph modified by the presence of an air thermostat for column and detector. Ethanol served as the internal standard; the experimental error did not exceed ± 7 rel. %.

It was found that the main impurities in acetic acid are aldehydes and ketones (0.5 – 1.0%), while calcium acetate powders contained formic (0.48 – 1.92%), propionic (4.4 – 6.4%) and butyric (about 1%) acids. Butanol contained n-propanol, isobutanol, allyl alcohol, isoamyl alcohol, crotyl alcohol, n-amyl alcohol.

Shaposhnikov et al. /57,58/ determined impurities in technical grade butyl acetate at 85° on a $150 \times 0.4$ cm column with 30% poly(ethylene glycol) adipate) on fireproof diatomite brick (0.025 – 0.050 cm); flow rate of carrier gas (nitrogen or air) 35 ml/min, inlet pressure 1.3 atm, outlet pressure atmospheric, sample volume 0.005 – 0.015 ml; katharometric detection. The impurities which were determined in butyl acetate included dibutyl ether, n-butanol and butyl esters of $C_1 - C_5$ normal fatty acids. The duration of a determination is 20 minutes and the experimental error does not exceed 6%.

Shaposhnikov et al. /59/ analyzed a number of model mixtures and also crude butyl acetate (Figure 80). Quantitative analysis of a number of industrial products was effected by the method of internal normalization. It was found that crude butyl acetate (75.0 – 89.7% $CH_3COOBu$) also contains butyl propionate (2.4 – 11.8%), butyl butyrate (5.2 – 5.3%), butyl formate (2.8 – 2.9%) and dibutyl ether (0.8 – 2.0%).

The retention volumes of the esters thus separated are given in Table 38, with butyl acetate as standard. The experimental error does not exceed 6 rel. %.

Shaposhnikov et al. /56/ determined the composition of low-boiling esters obtained during the rectification of head and tail fractions of commercial grade butyl acetate of different wood chemical plants. The composition of the esterification products will depend on the structure and on the contents of the impurities in the crude material. Propyl formate, isopropyl formate, propyl acetate, butyl formate and butanol were determined in the low-boiling fraction. The composition of commercial grade fractions and still residue of different industrial plants were also studied.

TABLE 38. Relative retention volumes of esters and other compounds

| Compound | Bp, °C | Retention time, min | Relative retention volume |
|---|---|---|---|
| Dibutyl ether . . . . . | 142.4 | 4.0 | 0.5 |
| Butyl formate . . . . . | 106.9 | 5.5 | 0.7 |
| Butyl acetate . . . . . | 125.5 | 8.0 | 1.0 |
| Butyl propionate. . . . | 146.0 | 11.5 | 1.4 |
| Butanol . . . . . . . . | 117.0 | 13.9 | 1.8 |
| Butyl butyrate . . . . . | 165.7 | 16.0 | 2.0 |
| Butyl valerate . . . . . | 186.0 | 20.0 | 2.5 |

The composition of crude vinyl acetate was determined /60/ by gas-liquid chromatography. Gas chromatography was used in a study of the trans-esterification of acetoacetic ester by methanol /61/ and in a study of chlorinated acetoacetic ester /62/. The method may also be used in the determination of the impurities present in technical methyl acetoacetate /63/, and to analyze the derivatives of different fatty acids /64/.


## 4. Chromatographic analysis of preparations employed for the protection of wood

Chromatographic methods are employed in the analysis of both the initial preparations used in the protective impregnation of wood and in the determination of the antiseptics in the treated wood. Ion exchange chromatography is used in the determination of pentachlorophenol /65/ and of copper and chromium compounds in pentachlorophenol-impregnated wood /66/.

Paper chromatography is a suitable method for the determination of the composition of different preparations employed in wood impregnation for antiseptic purposes; the solvent is butanol saturated with 30% acetic acid /67/. Butanol saturated with 20% acetic acid or with 1 N HCl can be used /68/ in the quantitative determination of the protective salts such as $H_3BO_3$, $Ag^{3+}$, $Cr_2O_7^{2-}$, $Cu^{2+}$, $AsO_4^{3-}$, $Cr^{3+}$, $F^-$. Paper chromatography is also employed to determine the content of pentachlorophenol /69/ and other products /70/.

The composition of coal tar used for the protection of wood was determined by thin layer chromatography on silica gel /71/. Gas-liquid chromatography was employed /72/ in the study of the variations of the composition of the oils of coal tar in beechwood and pinewood.


It should be again stressed, in conclusion, that chromatography is one of the most important methods in modern scientific research. The scope of application of chromatographic methods in industrial production and quality control becomes more extensive every year. The data presented in this book show that extremely varied chromatographic techniques are applied in the chemistry and chemical technology of wood. The main task in the near future is to develop and to introduce rapid methods of analysis for control and monitoring of technological processes in pulp and paper, hydrolysis and wood chemical industries; the applications of chromatography in scientific research concerned with the chemistry of wood are even more extensive.

BIBLIOGRAPHY

1. SIDOROV, R. I., B. K. BABOSHIN, and G. A. RUDAKOV. — Gidroliznaya i Lesokhimicheskaya Promyshlennost', No. 2:12—14. 1963.
2. BABOSHIN, B. K. et al. — Gidroliznaya i Lesokhimicheskaya Promyshlennost', No. 4:14—15. 1963.
3. BABOSHIN, B. K. et al. — In: Sbornik "Sinteticheskie produkty iz kanifoli i skipidara," pp. 283—287. Izdatel'stvo Nauka i tekhnika, Minsk. 1964.
4. IVANOVA, L. S. and G. A. RUDAKOV. — In: Sbornik "Sinteticheskie produkty iz kanifoli i skipidara," pp. 223—227. Izdatel'stvo Nauka i tekhnika, Minsk. 1964.
5. BRUS, G., P. LEGENDRE, and G. NIOLLE. — Ann. falsific. et expert. chem., 54(627):142—150. 1966.
6. WILLIAMS, A. L. and M. H. BANNISTER. — J. Pharmac. Sci., 51(10):970—975. 1962.
7. MIROV, N. T., E. ZAVARIN, and J. G. BICHO. — J. Pharmac. Sci., 51(12):1131—1135. 1962.
8. FISHER, G. S. — Chem. and Ind., No. 44:1761. 1963.
9. MANJARREZ, A. and A. GUZMAN. — Bol. Inst. Quim. Univ. Nac. Autonoma de Mexico, Vol. 16:20—24. 1964.
10. BARDYSHEV, I. I., G. V. MOLCHAN, and V. I. KULIKOV. — ZhPKh, 39(3):172—176. 1966.
11. ERMOLOV, B. V. — Gidroliznaya i Lesokhimicheskaya Promyshlennost', No. 7:17. 1965.
12. CHUDINOV, S. V., K. P. VEDENEEV, and Yu. K. SHAPOSHNIKOV. — Gidroliznaya i Lesokhimicheskaya Promyshlennost', No. 1:13—14. 1963.
13. MÜHLETHALER, B. and S. GIGER. — Farbe und Lack, 70(2):116—120. 1964.
14. BRUN, H. H. and S. GASLAND. — Acta Acad. Aboensis, Math. et phys., 22(1):122. 1960.
15. BARDYSHEV, I. I., Kh. A. CHERCHES, and L. A. MEERSON. — ZhAKh, Vol. 18:901. 1963.
16. BARDYSHEV, I. I. and O. T. TKACHENKO. — Gidroliznaya i Lesokhimicheskaya Promyshlennost', No. 8: 6—9. 1963.
17. BARDYSHEV, I. I., O. T. TKACHENKO, and Kh. A. CHERCHES. — ZhPKh, 38(9):2049—2053. 1965.
18. BARDYSHEV, I. I., O. T. TKACHENKO, and Kh. A. CHERCHES. — ZhOKh, 32(3):999—1001. 1962.
19. CHERCHES, Kh. A., I. I. BARDYSHEV, and Zh. F. KOKHANSKAYA. — ZhPKh, 34(4):938—941. 1961.
20. LOEBLICH, W. M. and R. V. LAWRENCE. — J. Am. Oil. Chemists Soc., 33(7):320—322. 1956.
21. RAMSEY, L. L. and W. I. PATTERSON. — J. Assoc. Offic. Agric. Chemists, Vol. 31:441—452. 1948.
22. LEHTINEN, T. — Suomen Kem., 39(2) B38 — B39. 1966.
23. EFREMOV, A. I., V. I. LISOV, and A. I. SEDEL'NIKOV. — Khimicheskaya Pererabotka Drevesiny, No. 7: 10—12. 1966.
24. KOSYUKOVA, L. V., Yu. V. VODZINSKII, and Yu. K. SHAPOSHNIKOV. — Gidroliznaya i Lesokhimicheskaya Promyshlennost', No. 7:9—11. 1963.
25. LISHTVANOVA, L. N. and M. I. GORYAEV. — Gidroliznaya i Lesokhimicheskaya Promyshlennost', No. 5:18—19. 1963.
26. GORYAEV, M. I. and I. PLIVA. Metody issledovaniya efirnykh masel (Investigation of Essential Oils). — Izd. AN KazSSR, Alma-Ata. 1962.
27. LISHTVANOVA, L. N. and M. I. GORYAEV. — Gidroliznaya i Lesokhimicheskaya Promyshlennost', No. 7:19—22. 1964.
28. GORYAEV, M. I. and L. N. LISHTVANOVA. — In: Sbornik "Sinteticheskie produkty iz kanifoli i skipidara," pp. 304—309. Izdatel'stvo Nauka i tekhnika, Minsk. 1964.
29. LISHTVANOVA, L. N. and M. I. GORYAEV. — Gidroliznaya i Lesokhimicheskaya Promyshlennost', No. 1: 19—20. 1966.
30. BARDYSHEV, I. I. and K. P. VEDENEEV. — In: Sbornik "Sinteticheskie produkty iz kanifoli i skipidara," pp. 288—298. Izdatel'stvo Nauka i tekhnika, Minsk. 1964.
31. BABOSHIN, B. K. et al. — In: Sbornik "Sinteticheskie produkty iz kanifoli i skipidara," pp. 299—304. Izdatel'stvo Nauka i tekhnika, Minsk. 1964.
32. HANADA, V. and M. KITAJIMA. — J. Chem. Soc. Japan, Pure Chem., Sec., 80(11):1272—1274. 1959.
33. KOSYUKOVA, L. V., Yu. K. SHAPOSHNIKOV, and Yu. V. VODZINSKII. — In: Sbornik "Gazovaya khromatografiya," No. 2:101—106. 1964.

34. SHAPOSHNIKOV, Yu. K., L. V. KOSYUKOVA, and Yu. V. VODZINSKII. — Gidroliznaya i Lesokhimicheskaya
    Promyshlennost', No. 1 : 21 — 24. 1966.
35. ZHUKOVITSKII, A. A. and N. M. TURKEL'TAUB. Gazovaya khromatografiya (Gas Chromatography),
    p. 45. — Gostoptekhizdat. 1962.
36. GOL'BERT, K. A. and M. S. VIGDERGAUZ. — Neftekhimiya, No. 6. 1962.
37. DIMBAT, M., PORTER, and F. H. STROSS. — Analyt. Chem., Vol. 28 : 290. 1956.
38. SHAPOSHNIKOV, Yu. K. and L. V. KOSYUKOVA. — Khimicheskaya Pererabotka Drevesiny, No. 3 : 6 — 9.
    1966.
39. FEDOROVA, G. A. — Gidroliznaya i Lesokhimicheskaya Promyshlennost', No. 5 : 17 — 18. 1965.
40. LEIBNITZ, E., U. BEHRENS, and H. CZECH. — J. prakt. Chem., 11(1—2) : 73 — 78. 1960.
41. WIACKOWSKI, J. — Prace Inst. Technol. Drewna, 11(1) : 93 — 116. 1964.
42. McGINESS, J. D., J. A. WHITTENBAUGH, and C. A. LUCCHESI. — Tappi, 43(12) : 1027 — 1029. 1960.
43. SZEWCZYK, J. and R. DESOL. — Koks, Smola, Gaz, 10(2) : 53 — 60. 1965.
44. KOVALEV, V. E. and O. M. GOS. — Izv. VUZov, Lesnoi Zhurnal, No. 5 : 137 — 143. 1963.
45. KRUTOV, S. M. and V. E. KOVALEV. (In press).
46. KRUTOV, S. M. and V. E. KOVALEV. — Trudy LTA. (In press).
47. NIKANDROV, B. F. — Gidroliznaya i Lesokhimicheskaya Promyshlennost', No. 3 : 19 — 20. 1963.
48. PIYALKIN, V. N. — Author's Summary of Candidate's Thesis. Leningrad. 1966.
49. LIKHACHEV, A. D. — Zavodskaya Laboratoriya, 29(11) : 1302 — 1304. 1963.
50. TURGEL', E. O. and T. V. KASHANOVA. — Gidroliznaya i Lesokhimicheskaya Promyshlennost', No. 1 : 16 —
    18. 1961.
51. DRUSKINA, E. Z. et al. — Gidroliznaya i Lesokhimicheskaya Promyshlennost', No. 3 : 15 — 17. 1964.
52. DRUSKINA, E. Z., Yu. K. SHAPOSHNIKOV, and Yu. V. VODZINSKII. — Zavodskaya Laboratoriya,
    30(11) : 1333. 1964.
53. DRUSKINA, E. Z. and Yu. K. SHAPOSHNIKOV. — In: Sbornik "Gazovaya khromatografiya," No. 3 : 146 — 149.
    1965.
54. DRUSKINA, E. Z. and Yu. K. SHAPOSHNIKOV. — Khimicheskaya Pererabotka Drevesiny, No. 16 : 8 — 10.
    1965.
55. TROFIMOV, A. N. et al. — Khimicheskaya Pererabotka Drevesiny, No. 20 : 6 — 9. 1965.
56. SHAPOSHNIKOV, Yu. K. et al. — Gidroliznaya i Lesokhimicheskaya Promyshlennost', No. 6 : 5 — 7. 1964.
57. SHAPOSHNIKOV, Yu. K., K. P. VEDENEEV, Yu. V. VODZINSKII, and N. K. LAZAREVA. — Gidroliznaya
    i Lesokhimicheskaya Promyshlennost', No. 6. 1962.
58. SHAPOSHNIKOV, Yu. K. et al. — In: Sbornik "Gazovaya khromatografiya," pp. 265 — 269. Izdatel'stvo
    Nauka. 1964.
59. SHAPOSHNIKOV, Yu. K., K. P. VEDENEEV, and Yu. V. VODZINSKII. — Gidroliznaya i Lesokhimicheskaya
    Promyshlennost', No. 6 : 20 — 22. 1963.
60. BALANDINA, V. A. et al. — In: Sbornik "Gazovaya khromatografiya," pp. 229 — 231. Izdatel'stvo Nauka.
    1964.
61. HRIVŇÁK, J., Z. VESELÁ, E. SOHLER, and J. DRÁBEK. — Chem. Průmysl., 15(1) : 7 — 9. 1965.
62. HRIVŇÁK, J. and Z. VESELÁ. — Chem. Zvesti, 19(9) : 711 — 714. 1965.
63. MOMODA, Ts. and I. IOSHIE. — J. Chem. Soc. Japan, Ind. Chem., Sec., 68(9) : 1699 — 1674. [sic]. 1965.
64. SIVARAMA, K. R., L. A. WITTING, and M. K. HORWITT. — J. Chromatogr., 13(1) : 22 — 25. 1964.
65. KABAU, C. — Japan Analyst, 12(12) : 1191 — 1192. 1963.
66. YSHIDA, H. and M. HATTORI. — J. Japan Wood Res. Soc., 11(4) : 171 — 174. 1965.
67. DRAGUTIN, M. — Drvna Ind., 15(8) : 129 — 133. 1964.
68. MURKO, D. and S. RAMIC. — Glasnik Hem. i Tehnol., pp. 13 — 14, 95 — 98. 1964 — 1965.
69. KRATZL, K., H. SILBERNAGEL, and E. ANTON. — Holzforsch. und Holzverwert., 13(3) : 49 — 52. 1961.
70. DIETRICHS, H.-H. and W. SANDERMANN. — Holz Roh- und Werkstoff, 16(9) : 340 — 346. 1958.
71. PETROWITZ, H.-J. — Materialprüfung, 2(8) : 309 — 310. 1960.
72. BECKER, G. and H.-J. PETROWITZ. — Materialprüfung, 7(9) : 325 — 330. 1965.

# EXPLANATORY LIST OF ABBREVIATIONS OF USSR INSTITUTIONS
## AND JOURNALS APPEARING IN THIS TEXT

| Abbreviation | Full name (transliterated) | Translation |
|---|---|---|
| DAN | Doklady Akademii Nauk | Proceedings of the Academy of Sciences |
| Izd. AN SSSR | Izdatel'stvo Akademii Nauk SSSR | Publishing House of the Academy of Sciences of the USSR |
| Izv. VUZov | Izvestiya Vysshikh Uchebnykh Zavedenii | Bulletin of the Higher Educational Institutions |
| LGU | Leningradskii Gosudarstvennyi Universitet | Leningrad State University |
| LTA | Lesotekhnicheskaya Akademiya | Forestry Academy |
| LTI | Leningradskii Tekhnologicheskii Institut imeni Lensoveta | Lensovet Leningrad Technological Institute |
| OKhN | Otdelenie Khimicheskikh Nauk (Akademii Nauk SSSR) | Department of Chemical Sciences (of the Academy of Sciences of the USSR) |
| SO AN SSSR | Sibirskoe otdelenie Akademii Nauk SSSR | Siberian Department of the Academy of Sciences of the USSR |
| TsBP | Tsentral'noe Byuro Pogody | Central Weather Bureau |
| TsBTI | Tsentral'noe Byuro Tekhnicheskoi Informatsii | Central Office of Technical Information |
| TsINTI | Tsentral'nyi Institut Nauchno-Tekhnicheskoi Informatsii | Central Institute of Scientific and Technical Information |
| VINITI | Vsesoyuznyi Institut Nauchnoi i Tekhnicheskoi Informatsii | All-Union Institute for Scientific and Technical Information |
| VNII | Vsesoyuznyi Neftegazovyi Nauchno-Issledovatel'skii Institut | All-Union Petroleum and Gas Scientific Research Institute |
| VNIIGS | Vsesoyuznyi Nauchno-Issledovatel'skii Institut Gidroliznoi i Sul'fitno-Spirtovoi Promyshlennosti | All-Union Scientific Research Institute of the Hydrolysis and Sulfite Alcohol Industries |
| ZhAKh | Zhurnal Analiticheskoi Khimii | Journal of Analytical Chemistry |
| ZhPKh | Zhurnal Prikladnoi Khimii | Journal of Applied Chemistry |